CONTENTS

BUILT BY TEACHERS

A shared effort to make language accessible for all students

It is anticipated that the shared efforts of good teachers who understand their students, their content areas, and the standards, supported with high-quality coaching, will make a difference for adolescent English Language Learners in science classes.

Bonnie Baer-Simahk, M.Ed., & Patricia Aube, M.Ed.
Fitchburg Public Schools

Fitchburg Public Schools

The Fitchburg Public School System, located in a culturally diverse community in Central Massachusetts, serves approximately 5,000 students in Pre K–12. In Fitchburg, 12 percent of the students are identified as limited English proficient, with Spanish and English as the two most high-frequency home languages, which is reflective of the national average. Science is one of the district's concerns, as ELLs struggle to pass the state testing in that area.

Fitchburg Public School Authors

Bonnie Baer-Simahk serves as Fitchburg's Director for the Office of English Language Acquisition. Patricia Aube is the Science/ESL Curriculum Integration Specialist. They worked with a team of ESL and science teachers to create the curriculum for *Language Central for Science*.

From the Teaching Team

Language Central for Science was designed by the Fitchburg Public School authors to serve as an introduction to the language of science, boosting science learning and reducing the performance gap between ELL and native English speaking students. Using a collaborative teaching model, involving both science and ESL teachers along with this book, gives students a greater opportunity to understand core science lessons.

The strategies and solutions offered in this book are to help ELL students develop fluency as readers, writers, listeners, and speakers of academic English, while previewing science concepts. In addition, this book offers activities to help scaffold and support ELL instruction so that students learn in comprehensible and meaningful ways that promote academic success and achievement.

IMPLEMENTING THE PROGRAM

Features and Components

- Lessons that develop students' academic language through visual support, hands-on activities, and opportunities for talking and writing
- Systematic and predictable instruction in language development across the grades
- Modules organized according to the vocabulary and language associated with specific science strands
- Lessons that can be used in conjunction with any science curriculum

Teacher's Edition Grades 6–8

Earth Science, Life Science, and Physical Science Student Editions

Flexible Implementation Options

DAY 1
60-minute class

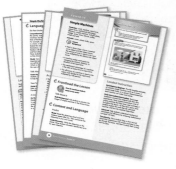

OR

DAYS 1, 2, 3, and 4
15-minute classes

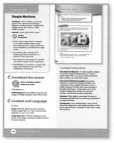   

TEACHING ENGLISH LANGUAGE LEARNERS IN THE SCIENCE CLASSROOM

By JIM CUMMINS
The University of Toronto

Language and the School Curriculum

Language is central to the teaching of virtually every school subject. The concepts embedded in the curriculum are inseparable from the language we use to teach these concepts to our students. For example, science concepts such as *nutrition, ecosystem,* and *astronomy* are not just ideas that belong in the realm of science; they also belong in the realm of language and are encoded linguistically.

The Challenges of Academic Language

The intersection of language and content entails both challenges and opportunities in teaching English language learners (ELLs). It is clearly challenging to teach science content to students whose knowledge of English academic language may be considerably below the level assumed by the curriculum and textbooks. In a typical elementary science lesson, for example, several difficult words may be explained. However, there may be many more words in each lesson that are new to ELL students. These gaps in their knowledge of academic language are likely to seriously impede their understanding of the text.

Students may also be unfamiliar with grammatical constructions and typical conventions of academic writing that are present in the text. For example, academic texts frequently use passive voice, whereas we rarely use this construction in everyday conversation. Also, students are often given writing assignments to demonstrate their understanding. Without strong writing skills in English, ELL students will find it difficult to demonstrate content knowledge.

Obviously, teachers focus their instruction on explaining concepts to students, but ELL students may not yet have acquired the English proficiency to understand explanations that are accessible to native speakers of the language. Thus, a major challenge for teachers is to teach content effectively to *all* students, particularly those who are not yet fully proficient in English. Although this challenge is formidable, teachers can draw on a knowledge base of recent research findings in order to implement instructional approaches that have proved highly effective in enabling ELL students to gain access to academic content.

Students who are learning science are also learning the language of science.

Vocabulary Activities
Language Central
FOR SCIENCE

Teacher's Edition

Author: Fitchburg Public School District, *Fitchburg, Massachusetts*
Consulting Author: Dr. Jim Cummins, *University of Toronto*

Glenview, Illinois • Boston, Massachusetts • Chandler, Arizona • Upper Saddle River, New Jersey

PEARSON

Language Central for Science: Grades 6–8

Fitchburg Public Schools Curriculum Project Team

Principal Author
Patricia Page Aube

Contributing Authors Grades 6–8
Bonnie Baer-Simahk
Suzanne DiGeronimo
Christine DiMauro
Glenn Johnson
Christopher G. Landry
Viviana Martinez
Shilpa Pujari
Evelyn Santana

Project Director
Bonnie Baer-Simahk, *Director*

Sponsor
Massachusetts Department of Elementary and Secondary Education's (ESE) Office of English Language Acquisition

Cover Art:
"Snowflakes" designed and folded by Brian Chan, in handmade Origamido® paper by Michael G. LaFosse and Richard L. Alexander. "Grasshopper" designed and folded by Brian Chan, in handmade Origamido® paper by Michael G. LaFosse and Richard L. Alexander. "Helicopter" designed and folded by Brian Chan, in handmade Origamido® paper by Michael G. LaFosse and Richard L. Alexander.

PEARSON
Longman

ISBN-13: 978-0-13-318368-9
ISBN-10: 0-13-318368-8

5 6 7 8 9 10   V011   18 17 16 15 14

Opportunities for Extending Language

Teachers are usually acutely aware of the challenges of teaching ELL students within the elementary classroom. However, they may be less aware of the opportunities that exist for extending students' knowledge of academic English. Students who are learning science are also learning the language of science. They are learning, for example, words that are specific to the subject area such as *experiment, reaction, hypothesis,* etc. and how to apply them.

Similarly, when students share with the class on their observations of a hands-on activity or project, teachers have the opportunity to model the kinds of explicit formal language that is required to talk and write about scientific phenomena. The feedback they provide to students on their oral or written assignments clarifies not only the scientific concepts that students are learning but also the language forms, functions, and conventions that are required to discuss these concepts. Thus, elementary science teachers are also language teachers and have significant opportunities to extend students' ability to understand and use academic language.

The Knowledge Base

There is considerable agreement among researchers about the general patterns of academic development among ELL students and the factors that support students in catching up academically. The following findings are well-established:

The language of academic success in school is very different from the language we use in everyday conversational interactions. Face-to-face conversational interactions are supported by facial expressions, eye contact, gestures, intonation, and the immediate concrete context. Conversational interactions among native-speakers draw on a core set of high-frequency words (approximately 2000) and use a limited set of grammatical constructions and discourse conventions. Academic language, by contrast, draws on a much larger set of low-frequency words, including both general academic words and the specific technical vocabulary of a particular content area (e.g., *nucleus, habitat,* etc.). This language is found predominantly in two places—classrooms and texts (both printed and electronic).

%

The number of ELLs has grown rapidly in the last 15 years, to about **5 million** *students. Estimates project this number will increase 100%, to* **10 million,** *by 2015 (NEA, 2008).*

TEACHING ENGLISH LANGUAGE LEARNERS IN THE SCIENCE CLASSROOM, *cont.*

ELL students typically require at least five years to catch up academically to native speakers; by contrast, basic conversational fluency is usually acquired within 1–2 years. These trajectories reflect both the increased linguistic complexity of academic language and the fact that ELL students are attempting to catch up to a moving target. Students whose first language is English are not standing still waiting for ELL students to catch up. Every year, they make gains in reading, writing, and vocabulary abilities. So, ELL students have to learn faster to bridge the gap. The fact that at least five years is typically required for ELL students to catch up academically highlights the urgency of providing academic and linguistic support to students *across the curriculum.* Ideally, ELL teachers and subject-matter teachers will work together to enable ELL students to develop the academic language skills they need to access subject-matter content and succeed academically.

Sustained growth in reading and writing skills is strongly related to students' level of literacy engagement. If academic language is found predominantly in classrooms and texts, then it is not surprising that active classroom participation and engaged reading of texts across a range of genres is strongly related to the development of academic language proficiency. When teaching science in the elementary classroom, literacy engagement can be interpreted as the extent to which students actively explore science concepts orally, in writing, and during engaged reading and classroom instruction.

All learning builds on a foundation of preexisting knowledge and skills. For ELL students in the early stages of learning English, this conceptual foundation is likely to be encoded predominantly in their home language (L1). This finding implies that students' L1 is potentially relevant to learning English academic skills and concepts. Students' L1 is the cognitive tool they have used to interact with the world and learn academic content. Thus, rather than ignoring students' L1, we should consider teaching for transfer across languages and encourage students to use their L1 as a stepping stone to higher performance in English academic tasks.

The Pearson ELL Curriculum Framework

The core principles of teaching ELL students across the curriculum are outlined in The Pearson ELL Curriculum Framework. (See page T10.) This framework was designed to assist teachers in addressing the needs of ELL students. The five principles in the outer circle of the framework represent the ways in which the teacher plans and organizes the delivery of instruction. The three processes in the inner circle highlight what teachers attempt to do in direct interaction with their students. As depicted in the diagram on the next page, these principles and processes flow into each other and represent components or phases of a dynamic whole.

1 **Identify and Communicate Content and Language Objectives** In planning and organizing a lesson, teachers must first identify what content and language objectives they will attempt to communicate to students. For example, an early focus in a science lesson might be on the scope of the field itself—what phenomena are encompassed within the field of science? These issues might be explored by challenging students to investigate the definition of the word *science* and the ways in which it is present in their everyday lives. This basic language objective might be extended by asking students, working in small groups, to list words that they associate with science and share their reasoning with the class.

2 **Frontload the Lesson** Frontloading refers to the use of prereading or preinstructional strategies that prepare English language learners to understand new academic content. It involves strategies such as activating prior knowledge, building background, previewing text, preteaching vocabulary, and making connections.

3 **Provide Comprehensible Input** Language and content that students can understand is referred to as comprehensible input. Teachers make use of nonlinguistic supports to enable students to understand language and content that would otherwise have been beyond their comprehension. Typical supports or "scaffolds" include graphic organizers, photographs, illustrations, models, demonstrations, outlines, etc. Language clarification and use of paraphrasing also contribute to making the input comprehensible.

4 **Enable Language Production** Language production complements comprehensible input and is an essential element in developing expertise in academic language. Use of both oral and written language enables students to solve problems, generate insights, express their ideas and identities, and obtain feedback from teachers and peers.

5 **Assess for Content and Language Understanding** Finally, the instructional cycle flows into assessing what students have learned and then spiraling upwards into further development of students' content knowledge and language expertise.

TEACHING ENGLISH LANGUAGE LEARNERS IN THE SCIENCE CLASSROOM, *cont.*

The Pearson ELL Curriculum Framework

The Pearson ELL Curriculum Framework was designed to assist teachers address the needs of the growing and diverse English language learner population. The framework incorporates five research-based essential principles and establishes an effective instructional environment that leads to academic success.

Classroom Interactions

When we shift into the actual classroom interactions that this lesson cycle generates, a primary focus is on the extent to which teachers' interactions with students motivate them to engage academically. Promotion of motivation and engagement represents a process of negotiating identities between teachers and students. Students who feel their culture and personal identity validated in the classroom are much more likely to engage with academic content than those who perceive that their culture and identity are ignored or devalued. An excellent way of enabling ELL students to take pride in their academic accomplishments is to encourage (or require) them to undertake challenging project work while providing the support to enable them to complete the task successfully.

Differentiation of instruction is widely accepted as necessary to address the learning needs of a diverse school population. One-size-fits-all programs typically exclude ELL students from meaningful participation. When applied to ELL students, differentiation involves scaffolding of input to students and output from students. Activating prior knowledge and building background knowledge is one example of a differentiation/scaffolding strategy.

Assessment and intervention are fused into the cycle of motivating students and providing differentiated instruction that addresses the background knowledge and learning needs of individual students. It is essential that teachers regularly assess the extent to which ELL students understand the content presented through classroom instruction and in the textbook. If not, many students who are still in the process of learning academic English may grasp only a fraction of this content. This formative assessment represents an ongoing process in the classroom and, in comparison to most standardized tests, gives the teacher information that is immediately relevant to intervention and further scaffolding of instruction.

Conclusion

The knowledge base that research has generated about ELL students' academic trajectories shows clearly that ELL students must be understanding instruction and learning English across the curriculum if they are to catch up in time to meet academic requirements. Teaching science at the elementary level affords opportunities for extending ELL students' academic language proficiency. The Pearson ELL Curriculum Framework incorporates the essential elements that teachers need to implement effective instruction for all students—English-language and native English-speaking learners alike.

%

Of teachers with ELLs, only 29.5% have been trained to teach English language learners effectively. And, 57% of teachers think they need additional training to teach ELLs effectively (NCELA, 2008).

RESOURCES

References

Anthony, A. R. Beckman (2008) "Output strategies for English language learners: Theory to practice." *The Reading Teacher, 61*(6), 472–482.

August, D., and T. Shanahan, (Eds.). *Developing Literacy in Second-Language Learners: Report of the National Literacy Panel on Language-Minority Children and Youth.* Executive Summary, 2006.

Barrera, R. B., and R. T. Jiménez. *Literacy Instruction for Bilingual Latino Students: Teachers' Experiences and Knowledge.* Office for Bilingual Education and Minority Language Affairs, Washington D.C. 2000.

Beilenberg, B., and Lily Wong Fillmore. "The English They Need for the Test." *Educational Leadership, Vol. 64, No. 4,* December 2004/January 2005.

Collier, V., and Thomas, W. (2002). *A National study of school effectiveness for language minority students' long-term academic achievement.* Santa Cruz, CA, and Washington, DC: Center for Research on Education, Diversity & Excellence. www.crede.org

Cummins, J. "Affirming Identity in Multilingual Classrooms." *Educational Leadership, (63)*1, 38–43, 2005.

Cummins, J. "A Proposal for Action: Strategies for Recognizing Heritage Language Competence as a Learning Resource within the Mainstream Classroom." *The Modern Language Journal, 89,* 585–592, 2005.

Cummins, J. "BICS and CALP: Clarifying the Distinction." *Working Papers on Bilingualism, No. 20, 1999.*

Cummins, J. (1981). The role of primary language development in promoting educational success for language minority students. In *Schooling and Language Minority Students: A Theoretical Framework.* Sacramento, CA: California Department of Education.

Fillmore, L. Wong. "English Learners and Mathematics Learning: Language Issues to Consider," in *Assessing Mathematical Proficiency.* MSRI Publications, Volume 53, 2007.

Fillmore, L. Wong, and Catherine E. Snow. "What Teachers Need to Know About Language." ERIC Special Report, 2000.

Garcia, Georgia Earnest. "The Literacy Assessment of Second-Language Learners." Center for the Study of Reading, September 1992.

Garcia, G. E. "Supporting Second Language Literacy: Enhancing the English Literacy Development of Students Who Are Learning English-as-a-second-language." *Illinois Reading Council Journal, 22*(1) Special Supplement.

Garcia, Georgia Earnest, and Eurydice Bouchereau Bauer. "Lessons from a Classroom Teacher's Use of Alternative Literacy Assessment." *Research in the Teaching of English,* Volume 36, May 2002.

Garcia, Georgia Earnest, and Heriberto Godina. "Bilingual Preschool Children's Participation in Classroom Literacy Activities: 'Once Upon a Time' and Its Alternatives." *Paper presented at the Annual Meeting of the National Reading Conference,* 1994.

Garcia, Georgia Earnest, and Sarah J. McCarthey. "English Language Learners Writing Practices and Attitudes." *Written Communication, Vol. 22 No. 1,* January 2005.

Garcia, Georgia Earnest, and P. David Pearson. "Modifying Reading Instruction to Maximize Its Effectiveness for All Students." Technical Report #489, Urbana Center for the Study of Reading, Illinois University, 1990.

Jiménez, R. T. "Key Research, Policy, and Practice Issues for fostering the Literacy Development of Latino Students." *Focus on Exceptional Children, 34*(6), 1–10, 2002.

Jiménez, R.T., G. E. Garcia, and P. D. Pearson. "The Reading Strategies of Bilingual Latino/a Students Who Are Successful English Readers: Opportunities and Obstacles." *Reading Research Quarterly, 31*(1), 90–106, 1996.

Kieffer, M. J., and N. K. Lesaux. "Breaking Down Words to Build Meaning: Morphology, Vocabulary, and Reading Comprehension in the Urban Classroom." *The Reading Teacher, 61,* 134–144, 2007.

Leos, K., (2004). *No Child Left Behind.* Paper presented at the annual conference of the National Association for Bilingual Education, Albuquerque, NM.

Massachusetts Department of Elementary and Secondary Education's (ESE) Office of English as a Second Language Acquisition, *Guide for Developing a Content-Based English as a Second Language Curriculum,* 2009. www.doe.mass.edu

National Clearinghouse for English Language Acquisition (NCELA). (2008). *Educating English language learners: Building teacher capacity.* Washington, DC. www.ncela.gwu.edu

National Clearinghouse for English Language Acquisition (NCELA). (2008). *How many school-aged limited English proficient (LEP) students are there in the U.S.?* Washington, DC. www.ncela.gwu.edu

National Education Association (NEA). (2008). *NEA 2008 Campaign Briefing Book.* Washington, DC. http://educationvotes.nea.org

NCTE Position Paper on the Role of English Teachers in Educating English Language Learners (ELLs).

Schleppegrell, M. J., M. Achugar, and T. Oteiza. "The grammar of history: Enhancing content-based instruction through a functional focus on language." *TESOL Quarterly, 38*(1), 67–93, 2004.

Short, D., J. Crandall, and D. Christian. *How to Integrate Language and Content Instruction: A Training Manual.* The Center for Applied Linguistics, 1989.

Short, D., and J. Echevarria. "Teacher Skills to Support English Language Learners." *Educational Leadership 62*(4), 2004–5.

Science-Specific Resources

Amaral, O., Garrison, L., & Klentschy, M. (2002). Helping English learners increase achievement through inquiry-based science instruction. *Bilingual Research Journal, 26*(2), 213–239.

Barton, M.L., & Jordan, D. (2001). *Teaching reading in science,* Alexandria, VA: ASCD.

Bernhardt, E. (1995) *Science Education and the Second Language Learner.* Columbus, OH: National Center for Science Teaching and Learning.

Carr, J., Sexton, U., & Lagunoff, R. (2006). *Making science accessible to English language learners: A guidebook for teachers.* San Francisco: West Ed.

Dobb, F. (2004). *Essential elements of effective science instruction for English learners.* Los Angeles, CA: California Science Project. Available from http://csmp.ucop.edu

Fathman, A., and Crowther, D. (Eds.). (2006). *Science for English language learners: K–12 classroom strategies.* Arlington, VA: NSTA Press

Jarrett, D. (1999). *The inclusive classroom: Teaching mathematics and science to English language learners.* Portland, OR: Northwest Regional Educational Laboratory. Available from www.nwrel.org

Lee, O. (2005). Science education and English language learners: Synthesis and research agenda. *Review of Educational Research, 75*(4), 491–530.

Medina-Jerez, W., Clark, D., Medina, A, & Ramirez-Marin, F. (2007). Science for ELLS: Rethinking Our Approach. *Science Teacher,* March 1, 2007, Arlington, VA: NSTA Press.

Olson, J., Levis, J., Vann, R., & Bruna, K. Methods and Strategies: Enhancing Science for ELLS. *Science & Children,* Jan. 2009. Arlington, VA: NSTA Press.

Nutta, J., Bautista, N., & Butler, M. (2010) Teaching Science to English Language Learners. NY, NY: Routledge.

Rosebery, A., and Warren, B. (Eds.) (2008). *Teaching science to English language learners: Building on students' strengths.* Arlington, VA: NSTA Press.

Schleppegrell, M. (2002). Challenges of the science register for ESL students: Errors and meaning-making. *In Developing advanced literacy in first and second languages,* pp. 119–142. Mahway, NJ: Lawrence Erlbaum Press.

Siegel, H. (2002). Multiculturalism, universalism, and science education: In search of common ground. *Science Education, 86,* 803–820.

LANGUAGE PROFICIENCY CHART

Use this chart to understand language proficiency levels in the four skill areas of listening, speaking, reading, and writing. Note that an English language learner will not necessarily be at the same proficiency level in all four skill areas.

		Level 1 Early Beginner **Entering/Starting**	Level 2 Beginner **Beginning/Emerging**
		BEGINNING	
CHARACTERISTICS OF THE ENGLISH LANGUAGE LEARNER	**Listening Skills**	• Minimal comprehension • One-step directions • Comprehends oral facts accompanied by pictures	• Limited comprehension • Two-step directions • Oral descriptions
	Speaking Skills	• Minimal speaking production • Individual words or two- to three-word phrases • Gestures and actions to communicate	• Two- or three-word phrases to some simple sentences • Simple information questions • Simple descriptions
	Reading Skills	• High-frequency words • Slowly, word-by-word • Concrete words represented by pictures • Environmental print • Sound/symbol/word relations • Picture dictionaries and glossaries	• Dependence on visuals and prior knowledge • Multi-step directions • Able to follow text that is being read aloud • Locate specific information • Bilingual dictionaries and glossaries
	Writing Skills	• Little or no ability • Express ideas through pictures and graphics • Label pictures using word bank	• List, label, and copy • Phrases and simple, short sentences • Present tense • Complete graphic organizers • Respond to questions

Level 3 Early Intermediate **Developing**	Level 4 Intermediate **Expanding**	Level 5 Advanced **Bridging**	Level 6 Transitioning **Reaching**
INTERMEDIATE		**ADVANCED**	
• Good comprehension • Simple sentences • Multi-step directions • Oral questions and descriptions	• Very good comprehension • Complex sentences • Understanding and application of oral information	• Comprehension of complex directions and discussions with processing time • Ability to draw conclusions and make connections from oral information	• Comprehension of elaborate directions and discussions • Nearly comparable to native English speakers
• Simple sentences • Simple content-based questions • Description of processes • Retell stories and events • Statement of opinion	• Complex sentences • Discussions of stories, events, and concepts • Speeches and reports • Statement of opinion and defense of point of view	• Nearly proficient • Academic discussions with minimal hesitation • Detailed explanations • Multimedia oral presentations	• Near native ability • Full participation in academic discussions and debates • Effective communication using abstract language
• Use of context clues to determine meaning of words • Sequence pictures, events, processes • Identify main idea • Interpret charts and graphs • Make predictions • English dictionaries and glossaries	• Use of reading strategies • Identify word families • Interpret information • Locate details to support main idea • Match cause to effect • Differentiate between fact and opinion	• A variety of grade-level academic texts with support • Able to use strategies and higher-order comprehension skills with support • Conduct research • Synthesize information from multiple sources	• A variety of grade-level academic texts, nearly comparable to native peers • Application of higher-order comprehension skills with minimal support • Able to critique material and support arguments
• Compound sentences • Paragraphs with main idea and details • Describe events, people, processes, procedures • Give opinions	• Multiple paragraphs • Summarize • Take notes using graphic organizers • Express original ideas • Explain problem-solving strategies • Able to edit/revise	• Expression of ideas at grade level with support • Grasp of basic grammar features • Content-related reports from multiple sources • Multiple genres • Ability to peer edit	• Expression of ideas at grade level with minimal support • Rare grammatical errors • Occasional difficulty with natural phrasing • Grade-level reports • Ability to peer edit with recommendations

FIVE ESSENTIAL PRINCIPLES FOR BUILDING ELL LESSONS

PRINCIPLE 1
Identify and Communicate Content and Language Objectives

Content Objectives

Effective educational practices, as well as state and federal mandates, require that English language learners meet grade-level standards. The first step in reaching these standards is clearly targeting and communicating the content objectives of a lesson. While the content objectives for English language learners are the same as for mainstream learners, the objectives must be presented in language that suits the students' levels of language proficiency. This involves using simpler sentence structures and vocabulary, paraphrasing, repeating, and avoiding idioms and slang.

Language Objectives

Language objectives focus on promoting English language development while learning content. They can be thought of as a scaffold to help students learn content objectives. Language objectives include: content vocabulary, academic vocabulary, and language form and function.

Content vocabulary These terms are the specialized vocabulary of a subject area. Content vocabulary can be particularly challenging for English language learners who come from a variety of school backgrounds. ELLs should receive explicit instruction of key vocabulary words. Studies show that with this instruction, students are more likely to understand new words encountered during reading.

Academic vocabulary These terms can be described as "school language," or the language that students encounter across all subjects—in discussions, in textbooks, and in tests—as opposed to the informal English words and structures used in conversation. Academic vocabulary includes words such as *summarize, similar, demonstrate, conclude,* and

survey. Research indicates that acquiring a strong grasp of academic vocabulary is perhaps the most vital factor distinguishing successful students from those who struggle in school. Becoming fluent in academic language will enable English language learners to understand and analyze texts, write clearly about their ideas, and comprehend subject-area material.

Language form and function Language forms include sentence structure and grammar, while language functions involve the purpose of language (such as classifying or comparing). The language forms and functions students need to complete academic tasks should be taught within the context of the lesson. To develop appropriate form and function objectives, teachers can use local and state standards developed for ELLs or coordinate with staff members who specialize in language development. For example, when teaching the concept of relative dating, the language objective might be the structures for comparison (*older* and *younger*) and the function of how to make comparisons.

Teaching Strategies and Support for Principle 1

There are a number of basic strategies teachers can implement to meet the needs of their English language learners. Many are commonsense, everyday strategies that teachers in all content areas already know and use. These strategies lay the foundation for a positive learning relationship between student and teacher.

☐ **Previous lesson objectives** Begin each lesson with a review of the previous lesson's objectives.

☐ **Content objectives** Present the content objectives using visual aids, graphic organizers, and paraphrasing. Write the objectives on the board.

☐ **Prior knowledge** Ask students to talk about the content based on their prior knowledge. Document the results of the discussion with a graphic organizer, such as a KWL chart.

☐ **Content and academic vocabulary** Present content and academic vocabulary.

- Pronounce the word and have students repeat.

- Provide examples, descriptions, visuals, and explanations.

- Clarify the part of speech and discuss cognates, synonyms, and antonyms.

- Ask students to provide examples, descriptions, visuals, and explanations of their own to determine comprehension.

☐ **Vocabulary notebooks** Have students keep a vocabulary notebook. Suggest that they use their own words to define the terms and incorporate visuals whenever possible.

☐ **Word-analysis strategies** Teach students word-analysis strategies so that new words can be attacked independently. For example, teach the prefix and the root of a vocabulary word. Write the meaning of the prefix and the root word on the board and have students do the same in their vocabulary notebooks.

☐ **Academic vocabulary practice** Provide flashcards or flashcard frames for key academic vocabulary. Have students use them for paired or independent practice, both during the week and for subsequent reviews. Encourage students to add personal notes and pictures to their flashcards.

☐ **Vocabulary practice** Design writing assignments so that students practice using the new words.

☐ **Language objectives** With the cooperation of an ELL teacher, provide language objectives at different proficiency levels.

☐ **Opportunities for language objectives** If the lesson's content includes idioms, colloquialisms, or slang, use these as opportunities to teach language objectives.

☐ **Lesson objectives review** End each lesson with a review of the lesson's content and language objectives and a preview of the next lesson's objectives.

FIVE ESSENTIAL PRINCIPLES FOR BUILDING ELL LESSONS, *cont.*

PRINCIPLE 2
Frontload the Lesson

Frontloading is the use of prereading strategies that prepare English language learners to read new texts. The goal of frontloading is to reach all ELLs by lessening the cognitive and language loads, thereby allowing them to take control of their learning process.

Frontloading involves the use of the following strategies:

Activating prior knowledge Instruction is most effective when it links knowledge and experiences students already have to new concepts. Experiences can be academic, cultural, and personal. Teachers can help students see the relationships between their prior knowledge and the new lesson through direct questioning techniques, the use of visuals and graphic organizers, dramatization, and discussion. The more students know about the topic of a lesson, the more they will understand.

Building background knowledge In order to make a lesson's content accessible to ELLs, teachers may need to familiarize them with social, cultural, or historical facts and concepts of which mainstream learners are already aware. These facts and concepts may be brought out during the activating prior knowledge phase or through direct questioning and instruction.

Previewing text Previewing text serves the purpose of familiarizing students with what is to come in a lesson and putting them at ease. To preview text, teachers focus more closely on using visual supports such as taking a "picture walk" through a lesson. In addition, English language learners should be taught discrete skills that are required for successfully reading content-area texts, such as how to read and interpret charts, tables, graphs, and maps.

Setting a purpose for reading Teachers should help students realize that good readers focus on the message of the text. Teaching ELLs in the content areas also includes explicit instruction in the kinds of text structures they will encounter in content-area readings. In addition, it includes teaching reading strategies such as identifying the main idea and details, summarizing, and comparing and contrasting.

Making connections Teachers can extend the lesson by helping students see relationships between the lesson and other aspects of their lives. Connections can be made to other academic subjects, to current events, or to cultural traditions. By incorporating aspects of students' primary language and culture, teachers can ease the transition toward learning the content and language.

Integral to these frontloading strategies is the need for teachers to learn about the backgrounds of the English language learners. Learning about an ELL's experiences validates the student's sense of identity, increases the teacher's knowledge, and broadens the horizons of the English-speaking students in the class.

Teaching Strategies and Support for Principle 2

☐ **Prior knowledge** Determine English language learners' prior knowledge of a topic through a variety of activities. For example, have students

- use a KWL chart.
- brainstorm aspects of the topic.
- construct a concept map.
- relate the topic to their personal lives through the use of examples.
- discuss a series of true-or-false statements.
- put steps of a process in a sequence chart.
- complete information in a chart.

☐ **Cultural background** Because there may be cultural, historic, or societal factors with which English language learners are unfamiliar, teachers should learn about the background of these students. Teachers can then use this knowledge to determine what additional background knowledge (facts and concepts) needs to be presented.

☐ **Lesson feature preview** Preview the lesson by calling attention to key features: titles, visuals, captions, charts, bold or italicized words, and any special features.

☐ **Self-questioning strategies** When previewing the text, students should be taught to ask themselves questions such as:

- What do I think this text is about?
- What do I already know about this topic?
- What do the features tell me?

☐ **Predicting strategies** Have students use predicting strategies. They can predict what a text is going to be about by looking at its title and the features. They can also read the first line of a paragraph and predict the theme. Students should always confirm any predictions after reading.

☐ **Note-taking organizers** Present a graphic organizer that students can use for taking notes. Show students how to use headings and subheadings to create an outline framework.

☐ **Set a purpose for reading** Have students set a purpose for reading so they take active control of their learning. After previewing a passage, students should ask themselves questions such as:

- What is this passage about?
- What is my purpose for reading the passage?
- How does this passage relate to the topic?

☐ **Make connections** At the end of a lesson, have students make a connection between what they have learned with (a) an aspect of their academic lives, and (b) an aspect of their personal lives. This activity can be done as a Think-Pair-Share exercise or in small groups.

FIVE ESSENTIAL PRINCIPLES FOR BUILDING ELL LESSONS, *cont.*

PRINCIPLE 3
Provide Comprehensible Input

Providing comprehensible input refers to making written and oral content accessible to English language learners, especially through the use of nonlinguistic supports.

Because English language learners are frequently overwhelmed by extraneous information and large blocks of text, they need help focusing on the most important concepts. With comprehensible input strategies, teachers make information and tasks clear by using step-by-step instructions, by making modifications to their speech, and by clearly defining objectives and expectations of the students.

Nonlinguistic supports teachers can use to accompany student reading include:

- photographs
- illustrations
- models
- graphs, charts, tables
- graphic organizers, such as flowcharts and KWL charts
- outlines

Graphic organizers and outlines provide essential visual aids by showing at a glance the hierarchy and relationship of concepts.

Nonlinguistic supports teachers can use during class presentations include:

- gestures
- facial expressions
- dramatization
- props
- tone of voice
- realia (real-life visuals and objects)
- models
- demonstrations
- hands-on activities, such as short labs

Another effective form of comprehensible input is the "think-aloud," especially as modeled by the teacher. In a think-aloud, the teacher stops periodically and shares how to make sense out of a text or question by talking about his/her thought processes. The think-aloud shows how thinkers comprehend texts or answer difficult questions. ELLs can practice think-alouds, thereby learning to reflect and comprehend. Teachers can use the student's think-aloud to assess strengths and challenges.

A variety of comprehensible input techniques should be incorporated into lesson plans for English language learners as well as multiple exposures to new terms and concepts. Hands-on activities are particularly helpful to ELLs. The use of multimedia and other technologies will also enhance instruction.

Teaching Strategies and Support for Principle 3

☐ **Visuals** Provide meaningful visuals for English language learners. These may include pictures, images, diagrams, standard graphic organizers (e.g., Venn diagrams, charts, and concept maps), and outlines (filled-in or cloze).

☐ **Multimedia** Use a variety of media to reduce the reliance on language and place the information in a context that is more comprehensible.

- Bring realia (real-life objects) into the lessons. Have visual displays (graphs, charts, photos), objects, visitors, and authentic materials (newspaper and magazine clippings, etc.).
- Use video, audio, and CD/online interactive activities.

☐ **The five senses** Use teaching techniques that involve the senses. For example:

- When teaching about polymers, have students touch a chain of paper clips to learn how the monomers link together.
- When teaching factors that attract insect pollinators to flowers, give students opportunities to smell flowers and examine their bright colors.

☐ **Hands-on learning** Provide hands-on experiences when appropriate to help students contextualize or personalize abstract concepts.

☐ **Demonstrations** Provide demonstrations of how something works. For example, to demonstrate how a rocket works, blow up a balloon and then release the opening.

☐ **Role-playing** Concepts can also be presented through role-playing or debates.

☐ **Think-alouds** Use think-alouds to model the kinds of question-asking strategies that students should use to construct meaning from text. Write the 5 Ws (Who? What? When? Where? Why?) on a wall chart, and remind students to use these questions as they read to help them understand the text.

☐ **Delivery of instruction** Providing comprehensible input also refers to the delivery of instruction. For example:

- Face students when speaking.
- Speak clearly and slowly.
- Pause frequently.
- Use gestures, tone of voice, facial expressions, and emphasis as appropriate.
- Avoid the use of idioms and slang.
- Say and write instructions.

PRINCIPLE 4

Enable Language Production

Enabling language production for English language learners encompasses the four skills of listening, speaking, reading, and writing.

Because the language used by teachers and in content-area textbooks and assessment is sufficiently different from everyday spoken language, English language learners find themselves at a disadvantage in the classroom. Acquiring academic language in all four skill areas is challenging and requires at least five years of exposure to academic English to catch up with native-speaker norms. Therefore, particular attention should be paid to expanding ELLs' academic language so that they can access the learning materials and achieve success.

Brain research has ascertained that people under stress have difficulty learning and retaining new concepts. Students with limited language are naturally highly stressed. By promoting interaction among students where all contribute to a group effort, practice language, and develop relationships with one another, anxieties are reduced, thereby enabling more effective learning. See ideas for peer learning strategies beginning on page T28.

While the four language skills are intertwined, English language learners will likely not be at the same proficiency level in all four skills. Teachers will need to modify their instruction in response to students' strengths and needs in each area, keeping in mind the following concepts:

- When providing listening input to ELLs, the language must be understandable and should contain grammatical structures and vocabulary that are just beyond the current level of English language development.

- Teachers should provide appropriate "wait time" for students to respond to questions. ELLs need time to process the question and formulate an answer.

1 Identify and Communicate Content and Language Objectives

2 Frontload the Lesson

3 Provide Comprehensible Input

4 Enable Language Production

5 Assess for Content and Language Understanding

Motivate ENGAGE

Assess INTERVENE

Differentiate SCAFFOLD

SUCCESS

- For cultural reasons and/or due to lack of oral language skills, ELLs may not express themselves openly or may consider it disrespectful to disagree with authority figures.

- Teachers should encourage students to verbalize their understanding of the content.

- Think-alouds and recordings of oral reading increase oral language production.

- In addition to frontloading and comprehensible input from the teacher, ELLs need to practice effective reading strategies, such as asking questions, taking notes, predicting, and summarizing.

- There is a direct correlation between speaking and writing; by increasing oral language production, writing skills can be increased. For example, teachers can have ELLs say and write vocabulary to connect oral and written language.

- Opportunities for students to write in English in a variety of writing activities should be built into the lessons. For example, reading-response logs and journaling are activities that increase written language production.

Teaching Strategies and Support for Principle 4

☐ **Listening skills** Use audio recordings to develop English language learners' listening skills as well as fluency and accuracy.

☐ **Idioms, colloquialisms, and slang** Give explanations of any idioms, colloquialisms, or slang that arise in content.

☐ **Oral communication activities** Present specific oral communication activities. For example:

- telling or retelling stories

- role-playing

- giving instructions

- giving oral reports

- debating

- brainstorming

☐ **Speaking skills** Model summarizing information and reporting on projects or experiences. Then have students summarize and report.

☐ **Reading comprehension skills** Provide explicit teaching of reading comprehension skills. These are particularly important for expository reading. For example, teach or review summarizing, sequencing, inferring, comparing and contrasting, asking questions, drawing conclusions, distinguishing between fact and opinion, or finding main idea and details.

☐ **Reading strategies practice** Have students practice using reading strategies. For example, ask them to

- record the main ideas and details for certain paragraphs.

- develop their own questions.

- write the facts and opinions for certain paragraphs.

☐ **Paraphrase** Provide ELL-appropriate paraphrases of text questions.

☐ **Writing skills** Suggest dialogue journals for note taking and responses to writing prompts.

☐ **Writing process** Review or teach the steps of the writing process (prewrite/draft/revise/edit/publish).

☐ **Note-taking support** Provide note-taking supports, such as writing templates, fill-in-the-blank guides, or other graphic organizers.

☐ **Self-monitoring** Provide students with checklists for monitoring their own writing, such as checklists for revising, editing, and peer editing.

☐ **Partner writing** Pair ELLs with writing partners for peer feedback.

☐ **Scoring rubrics** Provide scoring rubrics for oral and written assignments and assessments. For example, students' writing can be evaluated for focus, ideas, order, writer's voice, word choice, and sentence structure. Students should be evaluated according to their proficiency levels.

PRINCIPLE 5
Assess for Content and Language Understanding

An ever-increasing emphasis on assessment requires that all students—including English language learners—achieve the same high standards. Yet below-level language proficiency can have a negative impact on an ELL's success in the content areas. It is, therefore, essential to use assessment results as a way to identify an ELL's strengths and challenges.

Three types of assessments are key to instruction for all students, including ELLs: diagnostic assessment, formative assessment, and summative assessment.

Diagnostic assessment Diagnostic assessment is used for placing English language learners into the appropriate class, as well as for providing a diagnosis of strengths and challenges.

Formative assessment Formative assessment is part of the instructional process. It includes ongoing informal and formal assessment, reviews, and classroom observations. Informal assessments include class discussions, teacher observations, self- and peer-assessment, and teacher-student conversations. Formal assessments include essays, quizzes, tests, and presentations.

Formative assessment is used to improve the teaching and learning process—which is particularly important in regards to English language learners. By using formative assessments, teachers can target an ELL's specific problem areas, adapt instruction, and intervene earlier rather than later.

Summative assessment Summative assessment occurs at the end of a specific period and evaluates student competency and the effectiveness of instruction. Examples are mid-year and final exams, state tests, and national tests.

Federal and state law requires that all students, including English language learners, be assessed in reading, math, and science.

Assessment accommodations Assessment accommodations for ELLs can minimize the negative impact of the lack of language proficiency when assessing in the content areas. These accommodations can be used for formal and informal assessments.

Possible assessment accommodations include: time extensions, use of bilingual dictionaries and glossaries, repeated readings of listening passages, use of dual-language assessments, allowing written responses in the native language, and separate testing locations.

Teaching Strategies and Support for Principle 5

☐ **Informal assessment** Use a variety of informal assessments for ELLs including acting, singing, retelling, demonstrating, and illustrating.

☐ **Content area log** Have students keep a "content area log." Use a two-column format with the headings What I Understand and What I Don't Understand. Follow up with students on the What I Don't Understand items so that they can move those items into the other column.

☐ **Portfolios** Portfolios are a practical way to assess student progress. Provide specific examples of what to include in a portfolio, including examples of speaking and writing. Some portfolio items might be:
- written assignments
- recordings of speaking samples, oral presentations, or role-playing
- exercise sheets
- scoring rubrics and written evaluations by the teacher
- tests and quizzes

☐ **Formal assessments** Use a variety of formal assessments such as practice tests, real tests, and oral and written assessments.

☐ **Assessment format** Create tests with a variety of assessment formats, including dictation, multiple choice, cloze, and open-response formats.

☐ **Standardized tests** Have students practice taking standardized tests by using released test items. These are often available online from your state department of education or district website.

☐ **Academic vocabulary** Explicitly teach the academic English words, phrases, and constructions that often appear in standardized test items. This might include *best, both, except,* and *probably*.

☐ **Restate directions** When giving directions, restate the directions in simplified English, repeat the directions, and emphasize key words.

☐ **Repeat directions** Verify a student's understanding of the directions by having the student repeat the directions in his/her own words.

☐ **Bilingual glossaries** Provide students with bilingual glossaries of academic vocabulary.

☐ **Written assessments** Writing portions of assessments are generally the most difficult for English language learners. Therefore, the writing process should be practiced. Teachers should carefully guide students through the prewriting step with examples of brainstorming, outlining, using a graphic organizer, etc.

STRATEGIES FOR TEACHING ENGLISH LANGUAGE LEARNERS

Teaching Strategies

The following list of teaching strategies can help you differentiate the content for your English language learners. While the Teacher's Edition has identified places where these strategies may be particularly useful, you will likely find many other opportunities to apply them in your class.

There are five basic types of strategies:

- **Reading Support Strategies** provide support for students as they interact with the text and lesson concepts.

- **Vocabulary Strategies** help students who are struggling to learn and comprehend lesson vocabulary terms.

- **Peer Learning Strategies** promote cooperative learning. Beginning and intermediate speakers are able to hear and see concepts presented in different ways, while more advanced speakers benefit by teaching lesson concepts.

- **Organizing Information Strategies** provide students with a scaffolded way to organize lesson information. Often the strategies involve using a graphic organizer.

- **Comprehension Check Strategies** allow teachers to monitor student understanding in an ongoing manner. At a glance teachers can see how many students understand and how many do not.

Reading Support Strategies

Anticipation/Reaction Guide

Before starting a lesson, ask the class questions that focus on lesson topics. While the questions can address topics that have not yet been covered, make sure they require students to access some prior knowledge. After the lesson, have students re-answer the questions and compare how their answers have changed.

Language Proficiency Adaptation Accept relevant terms or short phrases from beginning speakers. Require intermediate and advanced speakers to write full-sentence responses. Encourage all ELLs to read their answers aloud so that they can practice speaking in English.

Cloze Prompts

Provide the class with sentences in which key words or phrases have been replaced with blanks. As students work through the lesson, they should fill in the blanks with the correct terms or phrases.

Language Proficiency Adaptation Provide beginning speakers with word banks to help them complete the cloze prompts. Challenge advanced speakers to create their own cloze prompt sentences and then trade with a partner to help them review lesson concepts.

Directed Reading-Thinking Activity (DR-TA)

This strategy teaches students to make predictions, read to acquire lesson concepts, and then follow up with a review. Have students follow these steps:

- Skim the headings, images, and vocabulary in the text.

- Make a prediction of what the reading is about.

- Read the text.

- At teacher-defined stopping points, compare predictions with concepts and information learned in the lesson.

- Revise predictions.

Language Proficiency Adaptation For beginning speakers, stop more frequently to compare predictions with what students have learned. Give them additional time to respond to what they have read.

Know/Want to know/Learned

KWL charts help students activate prior knowledge, gather information, and check for understanding.

To fill in a KWL chart:

- Before the lesson, have students fill in the K and W columns.

- K column: Students write what they **Know** about the topic.

- W column: Students write what they **Want** to know about the topic.

- After the lesson, have students fill in the L column.

- L column: Students write what they **Learned** about the topic.

KWL charts can be modified to include a **Background** section at the beginning—these are BKWL charts. Use a BKWL chart when you provide students with background information about the lesson. Students can take notes in this column. You may also wish to add an R column after the L column for students to list topics for future **Research.**

Background	Know	Want to know	Learned

Language Proficiency Adaptation Accept drawings and relevant terms or phrases from beginning speakers. For intermediate speakers, encourage them to write in full sentences. Require advanced speakers to write in full sentences. Check their questions for correct sentence structure.

STRATEGIES FOR TEACHING ENGLISH LANGUAGE LEARNERS, *cont.*

Lesson Preview

Have students preview the lesson by skimming topic headings, diagrams, pictures, vocabulary, and key concepts. Then, have students write down or discuss what they think the lesson will be about.

Language Proficiency Adaptation Give English language learners additional time to discuss their predictions with one another. If desired, pair beginning and intermediate speakers with advanced or native English speakers.

Question-Answer Relationships (QAR)

Students learn to recognize four different types of questions so that they can better answer them. After working through a lesson, have students answer and/or write questions of each type.

- *Right There:* Answers are found directly in the text.
- *Think and Search:* Answers come from finding information in different parts of the text and fitting these ideas together.
- *Author and You:* Answers are inferred—they are a mix of students' own knowledge and the author's writing.
- *On My Own:* Answers are composed of students' own knowledge.

Language Proficiency Adaptation Have beginning and intermediate speakers work together to answer questions of each type. Suggest they break the activity into steps. First, have them read the question and confirm what it is asking. Then, have them label the question with its type. Finally, suggest they write the answer. For advanced speakers, have them both answer and write questions of each type.

Quick Write

Give students a short period of time (one, five, or ten minutes) to write everything they know about a topic. Encourage them to write continuously about the topic for the entire time, even if they have to repeat a fact several times.

Language Proficiency Adaptation Accept drawings and/or lists from beginning speakers.

Stop and Answer

Write a list of sequential questions on the board. Next to the question, indicate when each question should be answered. As students read the lesson or discuss a concept, stop them at the specified points and have them answer the questions.

Language Proficiency Adaptation Encourage all English language learners to discuss the questions with one another. These discussions will give them extra opportunities to practice their speaking and listening skills.

Vocabulary Strategies

Frayer Model

The Frayer model helps students understand a vocabulary term by having them examine its definition, characteristics, examples, and nonexamples.

To fill in a Frayer model:

- Write the vocabulary term in the center oval.

- Write the definition, brainstorm characteristics, and provide examples of the term in the appropriate boxes.

- In the nonexample box, list things that are not examples of the term, but are similar in some way.

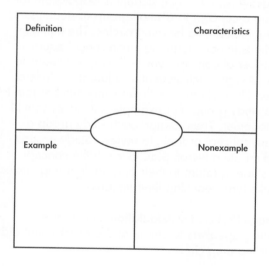

Language Proficiency Adaptation For English language learners who are proficient in writing in their native language, have them use the bottom right box (nonexamples) to define the term in their native language. You may also choose to permit drawings in the "characteristics" box.

Vocabulary Word Map

This graphic organizer helps students learn vocabulary by associating the terms with related words and images.

To fill in a vocabulary word map:

- Write the vocabulary term in the top box.

- Fill in the bottom boxes with terms, phrases, or images that are associated with the vocabulary term.

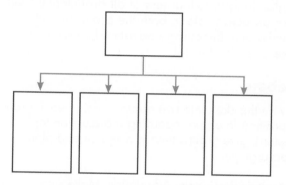

Language Proficiency Adaptation If possible, pair beginning speakers with intermediate and advanced speakers that have the same native language. Suggest that the more-proficient English speakers describe the vocabulary terms in the students' native language, then work with the beginning speakers to complete the word map.

Word Wall

Designate a wall in your classroom to be used as a word wall. Add key vocabulary and difficult words, along with their definitions, for the entire class to reference. Encourage students to contribute to the word wall.

Language Proficiency Adaptation Support beginning and intermediate speakers by suggesting they write down words for you to define and post. Encourage students to add definitions in their native languages.

Peer Learning Strategies

Key Concept Discussion

Divide the class into small groups. Have each student identify a key concept—a main idea or lesson topic—to discuss within his or her group. After small-group discussions, have the class talk about at least one key concept from each group.

Language Proficiency Adaptation Make sure English language learners at all proficiency levels take an active role in both the group and class discussions. Encourage advanced speakers to take a leadership role.

Debate

Divide the class into two groups. Assign each group a position to argue regarding a discussion topic. If desired, give groups time to research and plan their arguments.

Language Proficiency Adaptation Make sure groups contain a mix of students at different language proficiency levels. Encourage all English language learners to take an active role in the debate.

Gallery Walk

In a gallery walk, small groups of students work together to respond to posted prompts and review the responses of other groups.

- Post chart-paper stations around the classroom, each displaying a concept or question for groups to respond to.

- Divide the class into groups and assign each group a different color to write with. The number of groups should equal the number of stations.

- Have each group walk to a station and respond to the posted question or prompt.

- Groups should then circulate through the stations, or "gallery." At each station, have them evaluate the previous groups' answers, making any necessary corrections or comments, and adding any relevant information.

- When groups return to their original stations, have them work together to summarize the information on their charts.

Language Proficiency Adaptation Arrange students so that each group contains a mix of students at different language proficiency levels. Encourage beginning speakers to contribute both orally and, if appropriate, in writing.

Jigsaw Review

In a jigsaw review, each student is responsible for teaching a concept to a small group of students. Divide the class into learning circles. The number of students in each learning circle should equal the number of concepts you will assign students to review. Assign each student in a learning circle a number. Have students with the same number join to form a study group. For example, all the 2s should work together. Then, assign each study group a different concept or topic to review. Study groups should create a lesson plan to teach the concept. Have students return to their original learning circles and take turns teaching their lessons.

Language Proficiency Adaptation Encourage beginning speakers to create and present visual aids to their learning circles.

Problem and Solution

Present students with a problem. Have small groups discuss the problem and propose a solution. Each group should share their solution with the class. Have the class compare and contrast the different solutions.

Language Proficiency Adaptation Make sure groups contain a mix of students at different language proficiency levels. Encourage all English language learners to take an active role in both group and class discussions.

Reader-Writer-Speaker Response

In this strategy, students discuss a question or topic in groups of three. Each group member plays a different role. The *Reader* reads about the topic, the *Writer* records the discussion, and the *Speaker* shares the group's comments with the class.

Language Proficiency Adaptation Make sure groups contain a mix of students at different language proficiency levels. Suggest advanced speakers assume the role that will challenge them most. For example, if a student is a more proficient English writer than speaker, encourage him or her to be the group *Speaker*.

Think-Pair-Share

Give students a question or topic to think about individually. Next, have pairs of students discuss the topic. Pairs should then share their comments with the class or with another pair.

Language Proficiency Adaptation If possible, pair beginning and intermediate speakers with more advanced or native English speakers.

Topic Circles

Arrange the class in small-group circles. Introduce a topic or idea. Then, have one member of each circle give a fact or detail about the topic being discussed. The student to his or her right should then provide a different fact or detail. The cycle should continue until there is no more new information to share.

Language Proficiency Adaptation Allow beginning and intermediate speakers extra time to share their facts and details. You may also wish to permit beginning speakers to refer to their books or notes during the discussion.

Organizing Information Strategies

Timeline

Have students create a timeline to display events that have occurred in a sequential order. Suggest they show the passage of time as a straight line with important events and discoveries marked along the way.

Language Proficiency Adaptation For the timeline descriptions, accept relevant terms or short phrases from beginning speakers.

Cause-and-Effect Diagram

To visually represent cause-and-effect relationships, suggest students make and fill out cause-and-effect diagrams. Reinforce that a single cause can have multiple effects, just as several causes can contribute to a single effect.

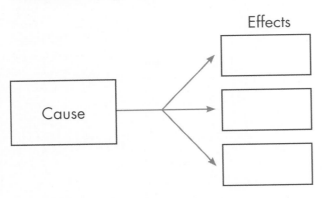

Language Proficiency Adaptation Provide support for beginning speakers by supplying word/phrase banks.

Cluster Diagram

Have students show how concepts are related by making a cluster diagram.

To create a cluster diagram:

- Write the main idea or topic on a sheet of paper. Circle it.
- Draw lines branching off the main idea, connected to circles that contain concepts or characteristics related to the main topic.
- Continue adding facts and details in a branching pattern, connecting related ideas and facts.

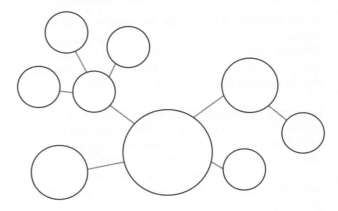

Language Proficiency Adaptation If possible, pair beginning and advanced speakers with the same native language. Allow them to brainstorm in their native language and then work together on their diagrams.

Compare-and-Contrast Table

A compare-and-contrast table helps students organize the similarities and differences between two or more concepts, objects, or processes.

To create a compare-and-contrast table:

- Draw a table.
- Label the columns with the items being compared.
- Label the rows with the characteristics being examined.
- Fill in the boxes with the characteristics of each item.

	Item 1	Item 2	Item 3
Characteristic 1			
Characteristic 2			

Language Proficiency Adaptation Provide beginning speakers with a partially filled-in table and/or a word bank to help them complete their tables.

Concept Map

A concept map helps students organize concepts using visual relationships and linking words. Mapping out these connections helps students think about how information fits together.

To create a concept map:

- Draw a box and write the main concept inside it.
- Draw arrows to additional boxes. Use linking words along the arrow lines to describe the relationships between connected boxes.
- In the second set of boxes, write details that support the main concept.
- Continue to add boxes and linking words as necessary to further organize details and facts.

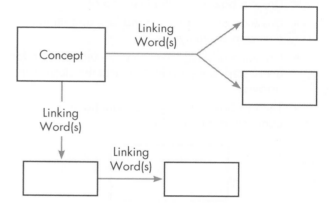

Language Proficiency Adaptation If possible, pair beginning and advanced speakers with the same native language. Allow them to brainstorm in their native language and then work together on their concept maps.

STRATEGIES FOR TEACHING ENGLISH LANGUAGE LEARNERS, *cont.*

Cornell Notes

Cornell notes are a note taking-strategy for outlining lesson concepts. The Cornell notes strategy helps students identify and list key words. Additionally, it requires students to summarize lesson concepts.

Language Proficiency Adaptation Encourage English language learners to list any terms that they are unfamiliar with in one column. Suggest they write a definition for each listed term in another column.

Cycle Diagram

Have students use a cycle diagram to show the steps involved in a repeating process.

To create a cycle diagram:

- Draw a box. Fill in the first step of the cycle.
- Draw an arrow to a second box and fill in the next step of the cycle.
- Continue adding boxes in a circular pattern for every step of the cycle. Connect the steps with arrows.
- The last box of the cycle should have an arrow connecting it to the first.

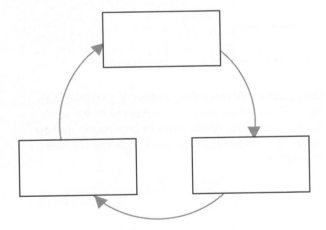

Language Proficiency Adaptation Allow beginning speakers to use drawings and other visual aids in their cycle diagrams.

Fishbone Map

A fishbone map helps students organize complex topics into main ideas and supporting details.

To create a fishbone map:

- Draw a "backbone," or set of horizontal lines, and fill them in with a topic.
- Draw diagonal lines that extend off of this backbone. Label each of these diagonals with a main idea related to the topic.
- Draw several lines branching off each diagonal. Write details that support each main idea on these lines.

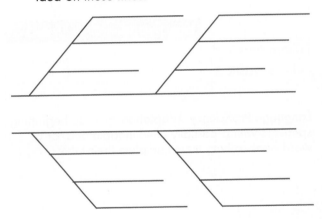

Language Proficiency Adaptation Allow beginning speakers to work in pairs. Encourage intermediate speakers to work independently at first, and then share their work with another student, revising their fishbone map as necessary.

Flowchart

Students can use a flowchart to show a sequence of steps or events in a process. Make sure students understand that a flowchart can have one or more paths.

To create a flowchart:

- Write the first step of a process inside a box.
- Use an arrow to connect this first box with a second box that contains the next step in the process.
- Continue connecting boxes until all steps of the process are represented.

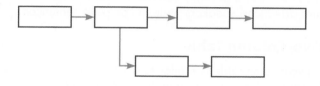

Language Proficiency Adaptation Encourage beginning speakers to use drawings and other visual aids in their flowcharts.

Main Ideas and Details Chart

Students can use this chart to organize lesson concepts by main ideas and supporting details. Advise them to use clues from the text such as headings and topic sentences to determine main ideas.

To create a main ideas and details chart:

- Draw a line down the center of a sheet of paper to divide it into two columns.
- In the left column, write the main ideas of the topic or reading.
- In the right column, write the supporting details for each main idea.

Main Ideas	Details

Language Proficiency Adaptation Accept short phrases or drawings for main ideas and details from beginning speakers. Encourage intermediate speakers, and require advanced speakers, to write in full sentences.

STRATEGIES FOR TEACHING ENGLISH LANGUAGE LEARNERS, *cont.*

Spider Map

A spider map is a way to review and organize information that stems from a central topic.

To create a spider map:

- Write the main topic in a circle.
- Draw diagonal lines branching off the topic and label these with the topic's key concepts.
- From the branches, draw horizontal lines that group facts, details, and examples to support each key concept.

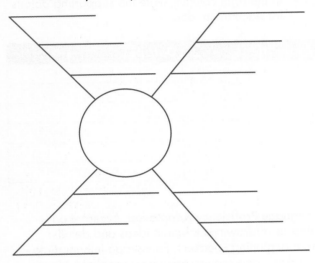

Language Proficiency Adaptation Allow beginning speakers to work in small groups to complete their spider maps. Encourage intermediate speakers to work independently at first, and then share their work with another student, completing and revising their maps as necessary.

T-Chart

A T-chart helps students organize lesson information including concepts, vocabulary, questions, and facts.

To create a T-chart:

- Divide a sheet of paper into two columns. Write a heading for each column based on the information being organized. For example, you might use the headings Key Term and Definition.
- List information.

Language Proficiency Adaptation Provide beginning speakers with a partially completed chart. Make sure advanced speakers write in complete sentences.

Two-Column Table

A two-column table is similar to a T-chart in that it organizes lesson information. It can also be modified to include additional columns as necessary.

Language Proficiency Adaptation Accept short phrases or drawings from beginning speakers. You may also wish to provide partially completed tables to beginning speakers. Encourage intermediate speakers, and require advanced speakers, to write in full sentences.

Venn Diagram

Students can use a Venn diagram to help them compare and contrast items.

To make a Venn diagram:

- Draw two (or more) overlapping circles.
- Write the unique characteristics for each topic in its own circle.
- In the center overlap, write characteristics that the topics share.

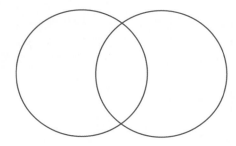

Language Proficiency Adaptation Provide banks of short phrases for beginning speakers to place in the diagram.

Comprehension Check Strategies

It is critical to check for student understanding as you proceed with a lesson. If you move forward and most of the class is not with you, you will lose the students. Each of the following strategies allows teachers to poll a class and see at a glance who is understanding a concept and who is not.

Card Responses

Have each student prepare a set of cards, each card with one answer. Ask questions and have students hold up the appropriate card to indicate their answer to the question. For example, when studying cell structure, students could create cards with the names of cell structures—*cell wall, nucleus, cell membrane, mitochondria,* and so forth. Describe the function of a cell structure, and have students hold up the card that names the structure.

Signals

Create a set of true-or-false statements or multiple-choice questions with numbered answers to check student understanding of the material being taught.

- True or False: Make a statement and have students indicate with a thumbs up gesture if they agree or a thumbs down if they don't agree. Have students indicate their gestures in front of their chests to minimize others imitating their answers.
- Multiple Choice: Provide answers written on the board that are numbered 1–4. Ask questions for which one of the answers is appropriate. Ask students to hold up one, two, three, or four fingers to indicate which of the four answers is the correct one after each question.

Slates

Have each student create an erasable slate by stapling a clear transparency to sturdy cardboard (staple a sheet of white paper between the two if a clearer writing surface is required). Provide students with erasable markers. Ask questions for which short answers are sufficient and have students provide answers by writing on their erasable slates and holding up their slates in front of them (three or four words should be the maximum length). Slates can be wiped clean with tissues to be used for subsequent questions.

SCOPE AND SEQUENCE

Grade	3	4	5	6–8
Nature of Science and Technology				
Doing Science	•	•	•	•
Technology and Design	•	•	•	•
Measurement				•
Mathematics				•
Life Science Topics				
Living and Nonliving Things	•	•	•	•
Classifying Plants and Animals		•	•	•
Classifying Living Things			•	•
Viruses, Bacteria, Protists, and Fungi				•
Cells: Structure and Function				•
Cells: Chemistry and Transport				•
Cells: Processes and Energy				•
Plants	•			•
Plant Processes	•	•	•	
Plant Reproduction	•			
Animals	•			•
Animal Life Cycles	•	•	•	
Ecosystem Basics	•	•	•	
Ecosystems Interactions			•	•
Ecosystems and Biomes				•
Resources and Biodiversity				•
Populations and Communities				•
Change Over Time				•
Heredity and Traits		•		
Animal Adaptations		•		
Adaptation and Survival		•	•	
Genetics				•
DNA: The Code of Life				•
Human Genetics and Gene Technologies				•
The Human Body				•
The Circulatory and Respiratory Systems			•	•
The Skeletal and Muscular Systems			•	•
The Nervous, Digestive, and the Excretory Systems			•	•
Fighting Disease				•

Grade	3	4	5	6–8
Earth and Space Science Topics				
The Earth System and Earth's Interior				•
Earth's Water and the Water Cycle	•	•	•	•
The Oceans			•	•
The Atmosphere and Energy in the Atmosphere				•
Weather and Precipitation	•		•	•
Climate			•	•
Earth's Surface	•			•
Fossils and Earth's History		•		•
Classifying Rocks and Properties of Minerals	•	•	•	•
Soil	•			•
Weathering and Erosion		•		•
Earth's Moving Plates (Plate Tectonics)			•	•
Earthquakes and Volcanoes				•
Resources and Pollution			•	
Earth in Space	•	•	•	•
Phases of the Moon		•		
Gravity, Earth, and the Moon				•
The Solar System	•	•		•
Exploring Space				•
Telescopes, Stars, and the Universe				•
Physical Science Topics				
Matter and Its Properties	•	•	•	•
Changes in Matter		•		
Physical and Chemical Changes			•	
Elements and the Periodic Table				•
Metals, Nonmetals, and Radioactive Elements				•
Atoms and Ions				•
Covalent Bonds and Metallic Bonds				•
Acids, Bases, Solutions, and Chemical Reactions				•
Forms of Energy	•	•	•	
Forces, Motion, and Speed	•	•	•	
Newton's Laws of Motion and Momentum				•
Simple Machines			•	•
Waves				•
Sound Energy	•			•
Heat and Light Energy	•	•		
Light, Color, Reflection, and Refraction				•
Electrical Energy	•	•	•	•
Magnetism and Magnetic Force		•	•	•
Electricity from Magnetism		•	•	•
Electromagnetic Waves				•

TEACHER'S EDITION FEATURES

Science Background
Summary of key grade-level science concepts.

Frontload the Lesson
Activities build background and connect to students' prior knowledge.

Content and Language
Modeling and discussion support content and language objectives.

Lesson 14

Simple Machines

Vocabulary work, machine, input force, output force, mechanical advantage, efficiency, simple machine, inclined plane, wedge, screw, lever, fulcrum, pulley, wheel and axle

materials screw, plastic knife, spoon

 Science Background

- Work is done when a force is exerted on an object and that object moves. The amount of work is equal to the input force multiplied by the distance the object moves.
- A machine makes work easier by changing the amount, distance, or direction of the input force.
- The mechanical advantage of a machine is the ratio of output force to input force.
- The efficiency of a machine is equal to the output work divided by the input work, multiplied by 100 percent.

↻ Frontload the Lesson

 How do machines make it easier to do work?

Talk About It

Build Background Ask students to preview the images of simple machines in the Picture It box.

↻ Content and Language

Predict

Model Read the objectives aloud and have students repeat after you. Then summarize the objectives in your own words.

Guide Discussion Write the objectives on the board. Have student volunteers identify key terms for each objective.

Simple Machines

 **Big Question** How do machines make it easier to do work?

You will . . .
- Identify and describe the different types of simple machines.
- Explain ways that a machine can make work easier.
- Use the scientific definition of the word work.

Talk About It

Imagine that you just won a new television. It is too heavy for you to lift, and there is no one around to help you carry it. How can you get the television into your house?

Talk with a partner. Discuss some tools and machines that might help you move the television.

Predict
Look at the Big Question and the "You will . . ." statements at the top of the page. Describe what you think you are going to learn in this lesson.

I think I am going to learn about . . .

Leveled Instruction

Early Beginner/Beginner Provide tangible examples of common simple machines (such as a screw, a plastic butter knife, or a spoon). Demonstrate how each machine can make work easier.

Early Intermediate/Intermediate Encourage students to connect this material with their own experiences. Have students brainstorm a list of simple machines that they have used and keep it throughout the lesson. As they learn more, have students explain the work they do with each machine, and how the machine helps them.

Advanced Help students understand *mechanical advantage* and *efficiency* by reviewing mathematical concepts with them.

Transitioning Have students keep a short journal about their experiences with simple machines as they go through the lesson. Ask them to share their writing with the class.

Leveled Instruction
Teaching strategies accommodate all levels of English language proficiency.

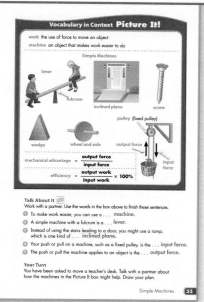

Comprehensible Input

Vocabulary in Context: Picture It!

1. **Say the Term** Say each term slowly, artificially stressing each syllable. Have students repeat. Then say the term more naturally and have students repeat.

2. **Introduce Word Meaning** Connect each term to the visual that illustrates it.

3. **Demonstrate** Use gestures and visuals to demonstrate.

   - Hold up items such as a screw, a knife, or a spoon, and demonstrate how they are used to do work—that is, how they help apply force to move an object or objects.

   - As you demonstrate, remind students that machines are used to change force, distance, or direction. Describe these changes as you model the use of each object.

   - Help students distinguish a wedge from an inclined plane by pointing out that a wedge often has two sloped surfaces, while an inclined plane has just one.

4. **Apply** After all the terms have been discussed, have students demonstrate understanding with Talk About It.

Talk About It

Guide Discussion Read the sentence starters for students. Point out that they will use words from the Picture it box to complete each sentence.

RTI Response to Intervention

If students have difficulty pronouncing the different *ch* sounds of *machine* and *mechanical* . . .

Then remind students that *-e* and *-i* after a consonant often result in a soft sound, while other vowels tend to create a hard sound.

Your Turn

Guide Discussion As a class, brainstorm words that describe a change in force, direction, or distance for students to use as they describe how to move the desk. (Useful words include *turn, up, down, push, pull,* and *under.*)

Comprehensible Input

Visuals, demonstrations, and hands-on experiences improve understanding.

Intervention

"If/Then" statements help monitor language progress and provide reteaching suggestions.

Academic Vocabulary

- The word *exert* is frequently used when talking about force. Explain that *exert* means "to use or apply force." Demonstrate by pushing or pulling an object, and saying, *I am exerting force on this object. I am applying a force to the object. I am using force to push or to pull the object.*

- The mechanical advantage and the efficiency of machines both use ratios. Write the word *ratio* on the board and pronounce it, pointing out the *sh* sound. Explain that a ratio is a way to compare numbers. Demonstrate by writing ratios to compare items in the classroom. For example, write a desk-to-student ratio, a window-to-room ratio, or a coat-to-sleeve ratio.

- Remind students that an *advantage* is a benefit or a gain. Point out common examples, such as, *Studying hard gives you an advantage when you take a test.*

- Cognates are words that have the same or similar roots and meanings in two languages. Have students share any vocabulary terms they recognize as cognates to words in their first languages. For example, in Spanish *máquina* is a cognate for *machine* and *eficacia* is a cognate for *efficiency.*

Academic Vocabulary

Provides clarification to help ELL students understand teachers, lessons, and science language.

TEACHER'S EDITION FEATURES, *cont.*

Comprehension Support

Modeling and hands-on activities target potential problem areas.

Language Production

Pair and group work provide ample opportunities to use language in conversations.

Word-Study Features

Extra practice reinforces high-frequency academic words and word parts.

Simple Machines

↻ Language Production

Do You Understand?

Comprehension Support Before students start the activity, review the different types of simple machines and their parts. Encourage students to think of familiar examples of simple machines. For example, an axe is a wedge; a wheelbarrow is a lever; a doorknob is a wheel and axle. Extend the search into magazines and textbook illustrations, such that students become more familiar with the six types of simple machines and find references for drawing these types. Have students consider how each machine works as they draw.

Model Ask questions to help students label the important parts of the machines. Say, *What do we call the part around which a lever rotates? Which is the wheel? Which is the axle? What is the rope of the pulley wrapped around?*

Talk About It

Guide Discussion Read the sentences aloud with students. Have them use their pictures and labels to help them complete the sentences.

Your Turn

Guide Discussion Circulate around the room to listen as students tell how the machines work. Provide help as needed.

A Closer Look

On Their Own Have students work in pairs. Model by giving examples of how the word *work* is used with its everyday meaning and with its scientific meaning. For sample sentences, using the scientific meaning, students may want to look in a classroom science book to find ideas.

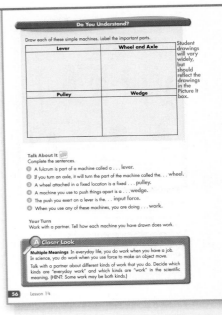

Leveled Language Proficiency

Students at each proficiency level should be able to perform the following tasks.

Listening/Speaking

Early Beginner/Beginner Point to each type of simple machine after hearing an oral description. State the name of each simple machine in response to a picture of it.

Early Intermediate Respond with hand gestures or short phrases to questions about simple machines. Give examples of everyday uses of simple machines.

Intermediate Follow directions for using simple machines. Explain in complete sentences how various simple machines make work easier.

Advanced/Transitioning Respond to complex oral directions for calculating mechanical advantage and efficiency. Use details to explain to a partner how to calculate mechanical advantage and efficiency.

Listening/Speaking Levels

Target goals for listening and speaking are provided for each proficiency level.

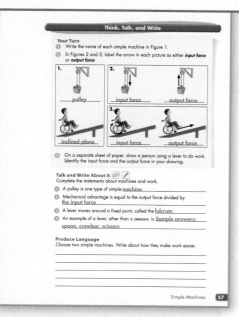

Think, Talk, and Write

Your Turn
1. Write the name of each simple machine in Figure 1.
2. In Figures 2 and 3, label the arrow in each picture as either **input force** or **output force**.

1.
pulley

2.
input force   output force

3.
inclined plane   input force   output force

3. On a separate sheet of paper, draw a person using a lever to do work. Identify the input force and the output force in your drawing.

Talk and Write About It
Complete the statements about machines and work.
1. A pulley is one type of simple <u>machine</u>
2. Mechanical advantage is equal to the output force divided by <u>the input force</u>
3. A lever moves around a fixed point, called the <u>fulcrum</u>
4. An example of a lever, other than a seesaw, is <u>Sample answers: spoon, crowbar, scissors</u>

Produce Language
Choose two simple machines. Write about how they make work easier.
_____
_____
_____
_____
_____

Simple Machines   57

Leveled Language Proficiency

Students at each proficiency level should be able to perform the following tasks.

Reading/Writing

Early Beginner/Beginner Match pictures of simple machines with written names. Label input force and output force on simple machines.

Early Intermediate Identify how simple machines make work easier by reading descriptions with illustrations. Write short paragraphs describing how simple machines make work easier.

Intermediate Interpret written information about work and machines with few visuals. Write explanations of how simple machines can be used to solve practical problems.

Advanced/Transitioning Infer details about work and simple machines from written descriptions. Write several paragraphs that compare and contrast various simple machines.

⟳ Assess Understanding

Your Turn

Model Before students start the activity, review the academic vocabulary term *figure*, as "any picture or diagram, appearing in text." Explain that the word *text,* is an academic way of saying "writing in print," such as a book or magazine. Introduce the abbreviation *Fig.* Explain that calling graphics *Figure 1, 2,* etc., allows readers to quickly find them. Have students brainstorm different types of figures and share any other meanings they know for this word. Then read the directions aloud. Remind students that they will be identifying input and output force for simple machines. If necessary, review the meanings of these vocabulary terms.

Talk and Write About It

On Their Own Have students work with a partner to complete the sentences. If they have difficulty thinking of an example of a lever, suggest that they think about everyday things that move around a fixed point. Give students examples of common levers—such as a spoon, a shovel, a paint-can opener—that they might draw for the second part of the activity.

Produce Language

On Their Own Read aloud the Big Question on the first page of the lesson. Point out that machines make work easier by changing the amount, distance, or direction of the input force. Have students discuss each machine with a partner. Then have them choose two machines and write about how they make work easier. Have students use specific examples from everyday life in their responses.

Wrap Up

Table Talk Have students reflect on what they learned. Encourage students to build fluency by reading their writing in groups or to the class.

✔ **Learned** ways that simple machines make work easier

✔ **Spoken** names of different types of simple machines

✔ **Read** definitions of *mechanical advantage* and *efficiency* of a machine, written as ratios

Simple Machines   57

Writing Support

Activities promote understanding through writing and conversations.

Assess Understanding

Informal assessments and written responses build fluency with language.

Reading/Writing Levels

Target goals for reading and writing are provided for each proficiency level.

CONTENTS

Appendix: STEM Topics

STEM lessons appear, following the Physical Science lessons.

Doing Science

Vocabulary quantitative observation, qualitative observation, objective, subjective, investigate, hypothesis, variable, experiment, data

Materials at least four different types of dried beans; a magnet and small objects, such as yarn, button, pencil, and eraser, always including a metal paperclip

Science Background

- Scientists study the natural world and propose explanations based on evidence.

- An experiment or inquiry must follow scientific principles for its results to be valid.

- A controlled experiment is an experiment in which only one variable is manipulated at a time.

Frontload the Lesson

 How do scientists study the natural world?

Talk About It

Build Background Explain that scientists make observations by gathering information using one or more senses—sight, touch, and so on. Ask students to study the picture. Say, *Suppose you had never seen beans before. How would you describe them?* Read the questions aloud with students. Demonstrate with real beans to help engage students. **CAUTION:** Tell students not to taste or eat the beans.

Content and Language

Predict

Model Read the objectives aloud and have students repeat them.

Guide Discussion Have students use the sentence starter and vocabulary terms to predict what they will learn.

Doing Science

 Big Question How do scientists study the natural world?

You will . . .
- Identify how scientists study and explain the natural world.
- Describe how to follow scientific methods.
- Use terms related to scientific inquiry.

Talk About It

Look at the picture of beans. How many are there?
What colors are they? What else can you say to describe them?

Talk with a partner. Take turns completing the following sentence.
One question a scientist might ask about these beans is, . . .

Predict
Look at the Big Question and the "You will . . ." statements at the top of the page. Describe what you think you are going to learn in this lesson.

I am going to learn about . . .

2   Lesson 1

Leveled Instruction

Early Beginner Partner beginners with students of higher level language proficiency. Expect answers that are single words or phrases, or perhaps in the native language.

Beginner Provide sentence frames to help students construct answers. Expect short and simple sentences as answers to activities. Point out that some of the words in this lesson are similar in several languages.

Early Intermediate/Intermediate Offer students the opportunity to work independently. Full sentences with some details can be expected from intermediate students.

Advanced/Transitioning Partner advanced learners with students of lower level language proficiency. Have the advanced/transitioning students model for their peers how to structure more detailed answers. Offer them opportunities to summarize key concepts for their classmates.

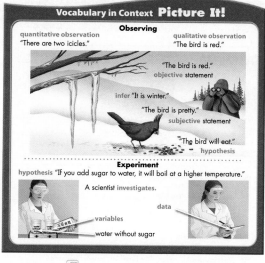

Vocabulary in Context Picture It!

Observing

quantitative observation
"There are two icicles."

qualitative observation
"The bird is red."

"The bird is red."
objective statement

infer "It is winter."

"The bird is pretty."
subjective statement

"The bird will eat."
hypothesis

Experiment
hypothesis "If you add sugar to water, it will boil at a higher temperature."

A scientist **investigates**.

data

variables

water without sugar

Talk About It
Work with a partner. Use the words in the box above to finish the sentences.

1. An observation that uses numbers is a . . . **quantitative observation.**
2. An observation that describes without numbers or amounts is a . . . **qualitative observation.**
3. Using only facts to explain or describe is being . . . **objective.**
4. Using personal feelings to explain or describe is being . . . **subjective.**
5. Information you get from an experiment is called . . . **data.**
6. In this experiment, the amount of sugar in the water is one . . . **variable.**

Your Turn
With a partner, look around your classroom. Take turns making observations. Tell what you see. For each observation, decide: Is it quantitative or qualitative? Is it objective or subjective?

Doing Science **3**

Academic Vocabulary

- Explain to students that the words *quantitative* and *qualitative* come from *quantity* and *quality*. Ask students what *quantity* and *quality* mean ("amount" or *number* and "what something is like").

- Start with the base word *science*. Demonstrate changing the ending to form the related words *scientist* (someone who works in science) and *scientific* (something that is based on science or relates to science).

- Cognates are words that have the same or similar roots and meanings in two languages. Have students share words they recognize as cognates to words in their first languages. The word *investigate*, for example, has a cognate in Spanish, *investigar*.

- Be sure that students understand the academic word *term*. They will see and hear this word in every lesson. Give a few examples, such as, *The term for information gathered in an experiment is data.*

⟳ Comprehensible Input

Vocabulary in Context: Picture It!

1. **Say the Term** Say each term slowly, artificially stressing each syllable. Have students repeat. Then say the term more naturally and have students repeat.

2. **Introduce Word Meaning** Connect each term to the visual that illustrates it.

3. **Demonstrate** Use gestures and visuals to demonstrate. For example:

   - Point to the two icicles. Hold up two fingers. Say *How many icicles are there? A quantitative observation tells how many.*

   - Point to the bird. Say, *What color is the bird? (red)* Say, *This is a qualitative statement. A qualitative observation does not use numbers or amounts.*

   - Hold up a book. Describe the book in objective terms and in subjective terms. Say, *This book was written by [name of author]. This book is very interesting.* Ask students to identify which statement is *objective (the first)* and which statement is subjective *(the second).* Point out to students that scientists rely on objective data from experiments to draw conclusions.

4. **Apply** Have students demonstrate understanding with Talk About It.

Talk About It

Guide Discussion Read the sentences for students first, and then have them repeat. Remind students to use the vocabulary terms from the Picture It box to complete each sentence.

R T I Response to Intervention

If students have difficulty pronouncing *hypothesis* . . .

Then have them practice the sounds that form each syllable. Point out that the first syllable ends with a long *i* sound, while the other three syllables have short vowel sounds.

Your Turn

Guide Discussion Ask student volunteers to share their observations with the class.

Doing Science

↻ Language Production

Do You Understand?

Comprehension Support Pass out a variety of beans to each student. Caution students not to eat the beans or put them in their mouths. Read each prompt below and have volunteers offer possible responses. Demonstrate each direction physically as you say it. When students have finished the activity, tell them to wash their hands.

1. Quantitative observation: Say, *Grab a handful of beans. Count how many you have.*

2. Qualitative observation: Say, *Look at one bean. Describe its color and shape and texture, or how it feels.*

3. Objective observation: Ask, *What is one fact about the bean that you can see or prove? How do you know?*

4. Subjective observation: Say, *Do you like or dislike this type of bean? Why?*

Model Record students' answers in a class chart to show the range and diversity of observations in each category.

Talk About It

Guide Discussion Read the sentences aloud with students as they work together to complete each one.

Your Turn

Guide Discussion Listen to student discussions as they use dried beans to talk about the vocabulary terms. Ask questions to check for comprehension as you circulate through the class.

Do You Understand?

Label each type of observation about the beans. Use the words from the word box.

| subjective | objective | qualitative | quantitative |

1. There are eight beans. quantitative observation, objective observation
2. The pinto beans are pink. qualitative observation, objective observation
3. The pinto beans are larger than the black-eyed peas. quantitative observation, objective observation
4. I like black-eyed peas best. subjective observation

Talk About It
Complete the sentences.

1. When you count the beans, you make an observation that is . . . quantitative/objective.
2. When you describe the size of the beans, you make an observation that is . . . quantitative/objective.
3. When you tell which beans you like the best, your observation is . . . subjective.
4. When you tell what color the beans are, you give data that is . . . objective/qualitative.
5. Testing each bean to see how long it takes to cook is an . . . experiment.
6. The different bean in each cooking test is one of the experiment's . . . variables.
7. When you predict that smaller beans will cook faster, you have made a . . . hypothesis.
8. When you write the amount of time it took each bean to cook, you are recording . . . data.

Your Turn
Work with a partner. Use your dried beans to talk about the vocabulary terms. Then think of other examples for each term that do not use beans.

4 Lesson 1

Leveled Language Proficiency

Students at each proficiency level should be able to perform the following tasks.

Listening/Speaking

Early Beginner/Beginner Match an individual spoken word with an image depicting its meaning. Answer questions about scientific inquiry with one-word oral responses or short spoken phrases.

Early Intermediate Demonstrate understanding of spoken questions by responding with short phrases. Describe aspects of scientific inquiry, using short, spoken phrases or sentences.

Intermediate Follow oral directions with little to no help. Explain aloud, in complete sentences, different ways that scientists observe the natural world.

Advanced/Transitioning Follow oral directions independently. Explain in conversation how to conduct a scientific investigation, using complete, and some complex and compound, sentences.

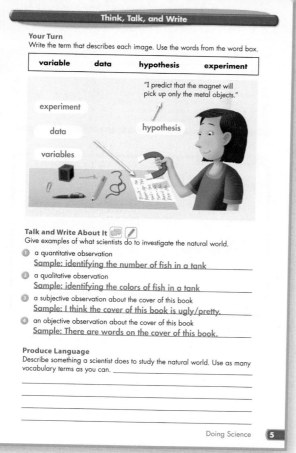

Think, Talk, and Write

Your Turn

Write the term that describes each image. Use the words from the word box.

| variable | data | hypothesis | experiment |

experiment

data

hypothesis

variables

"I predict that the magnet will pick up only the metal objects."

Talk and Write About It

Give examples of what scientists do to investigate the natural world.

1. a quantitative observation
   Sample: identifying the number of fish in a tank

2. a qualitative observation
   Sample: identifying the colors of fish in a tank

3. a subjective observation about the cover of this book
   Sample: I think the cover of this book is ugly/pretty.

4. an objective observation about the cover of this book
   Sample: There are words on the cover of this book.

Produce Language

Describe something a scientist does to study the natural world. Use as many vocabulary terms as you can. _____

_____

_____

_____

Doing Science   **5**

Leveled Language Proficiency

Students at each proficiency level should be able to perform the following tasks.

Reading/Writing

Early Beginner/Beginner Locate words that describe the types of scientific observations. Write one-word answers or short phrases as examples of quantitative and qualitative observations.

Early Intermediate Read to find examples of different types of observations. Write short phrases to describe the types of observations scientists make as they investigate.

Intermediate Comprehend phrases that describe different aspects of of a scientific investigation. Write an explanation of how a scientist conducts a scientific investigation.

Advanced/Transitioning Read aloud sentences that describe objective and subjective observations. Write complete sentences describing the differences between objective and subjective observations.

↻ Assess Understanding

Your Turn

Model As students complete the activity, have them first figure out which label goes at the top of each image. Remind them that this label describes what is happening. Then have them recall what might be recorded in a table or chart when observing the results of different tests, such as this experiment. *(data)* What is a possible answer to a scientific question? *(hypothesis)* What are the things that can change in an experiment? *(variables)*

Talk and Write About It

On Their Own Encourage student groups to reread the Big Question at the start of the lesson and talk about ways scientists study, or investigate, the natural world. Then ask them what questions they would investigate if they could.

Produce Language

On Their Own Have student pairs talk, then write, about ways scientists study the natural world. Encourage them to provide examples.

Wrap Up

Table Talk Have students reflect on what they learned. Encourage students to build fluency by reading their writing in groups or to the class.

✔ **Learned** and applied vocabulary related to scientific investigations

✔ **Spoken** statements about how scientists observe the natural world

✔ **Written** statements about how to conduct a scientific investigation

Lesson 2

The Earth System

Vocabulary system, energy, atmosphere, geosphere, hydrosphere, biosphere, constructive, destructive, landmass, sphere

Science Background

- The Earth is a system in which four main spheres—the atmosphere, hydrosphere, geosphere, and biosphere—interact.

- Lands are constantly being built up and broken down by different Earth processes.

- Energy is the ability to do work. Energy cycles matter through the Earth system.

↻ Frontload the Lesson

What is the structure of Earth?

Talk About It

Build Background Ask students to talk about what forces can make a sand castle fall down, such as wind and water, or living things. Tell students that these same forces can wear down mountains and other parts of the land on Earth. Be sure that students understand the expressions "build up" and "wear down," which are necessary to understand concepts in this lesson.

↻ Content and Language

Predict

Model Read the objectives aloud. As students repeat after you, correct any mispronunciations. Repeat the word *sphere* and have students practice making the /sf/ sound. Point out that the /f/ sound is made by the letters *ph*.

Guide Discussion Ask students to choose one of the objectives and ask a question about it.

The Earth System

Big Question What is the structure of Earth?

You will . . .
- Identify the four main spheres of Earth.
- Describe the processes by which land is built up and broken down.
- Use key terms that describe the structure of Earth.

Talk About It

Look at the pictures. Which picture shows some sand that is built up? Which shows a structure being broken down?

Talk about things that might build up or break down natural features such as hills, cliffs, sand dunes, or mesas.

Predict

Look at the Big Question and the "You will . . ." statements at the top of the page. Describe what you think you are going to learn in this lesson.

I think I am going to learn about . . .

Leveled Instruction

Early Beginner Ask students to point to the word *sphere* in the lesson. Then ask them to point to pictures that illustrate different Earth spheres.

Beginner Write sentence frames to help students provide definitions for vocabulary terms in the lesson.

Early Intermediate/Intermediate Have students work independently. Ask them to give examples of constructive and destructive forces that they have seen in real life or on television.

Advanced/Transitioning Have students use complete and complex sentences to define, describe, and compare each of the Earth's four spheres.

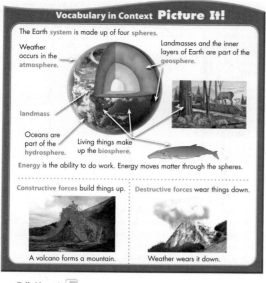

Vocabulary in Context **Picture It!**

The Earth system is made up of four spheres.

Weather occurs in the atmosphere.

Landmasses and the inner layers of Earth are part of the geosphere.

landmass

Oceans are part of the hydrosphere.

Living things make up the biosphere.

Energy is the ability to do work. Energy moves matter through the spheres.

Constructive forces build things up.

A volcano forms a mountain.

Destructive forces wear things down.

Weather wears it down.

Talk About It

Work with a partner. Use the pictures above to finish the sentences.

1. Earth's four spheres make up the Earth . . . system.
2. Weather happens in the sphere called the . . . atmosphere.
3. Plants and animals are part of the sphere called the . . . biosphere.
4. Oceans and rivers are part of the sphere called the . . . hydrosphere.
5. Landmasses are built up by . . . constructive forces.
6. Landmasses are worn down by . . . destructive forces.

Your Turn

Talk with a partner about the pictures in the Picture It box. Describe some examples of things found in each sphere of the Earth.

The Earth System **7**

Academic Vocabulary

- Discuss the parts and processes involved in a familiar system, such as those in a school system or on a sports team. Explain that the Earth is a system, too. Discuss how water, for example, flows through all of the parts of the system and returns to where it started.

- As students read and talk about the lesson, they may come across the word *process*. Explain that a process is a method of doing something or the way in which something happens. Point out that a process usually involves a number of steps or a series of events.

- Ask students to give examples of processes they go through, such as the process of getting dressed, going through the school day, or making dinner. Talk about the steps in each process. Give the example of a process of a constructive or destructive force and have students point out the separate stages or events that take place during the process.

- Draw and label a *sphere* and a *circle* on the board. Explain that these words describe shapes, but can also be used figuratively to discuss connected groups, ideas, or elements. Brainstorm some examples, such as: *circle of friends, sphere of influence, academic spheres,* and *social circles*.

↻ Comprehensible Input

Vocabulary in Context: Picture It!

1. **Say the Term** Say each term slowly, artificially stressing each syllable. Have students repeat. Then say the term more naturally and have students repeat.

2. **Introduce Word Meaning** Connect each term to the visual that illustrates it.

3. **Demonstrate** Use gestures and visuals to demonstrate.

   - Say *hydrosphere*, and point to the water. Explain that *hydro-* means "water" and *sphere* means "the shape of a ball." Ask, *What do you see in the hydrosphere?*

   - Repeat with the words *geosphere* and *atmosphere*. Explain that *geo-* means "land," and that *atmo-* means "vapor" or "air." Ask students to describe things they can see in the geosphere and atmosphere.

   - Point to the picture of the whale. Say, *Bio-* means "life" or "living." What other living things are in the biosphere?

4. **Apply** After all of the terms have been discussed, have students demonstrate understanding with Talk About It.

Talk About It

Guide Discussion Ask students to look back at the pictures in Talk About It. Ask them to use the Picture It terms to describe each picture.

RTI Response to Intervention

If students have difficulty pronouncing the words *destructive* and *constructive* . . .

Then have students repeat the word after you, stressing the second syllable, so students can hear the accent: *de STRUCT ive*. Relate the word part *struct* to the word *structure*.

Your Turn

Guide Discussion Encourage students to discuss the terms one at a time and then clarify them using sentence frames such as *Some constructive forces are . . .*

Language Production

Do You Understand?

Comprehension Support Before students begin, point to each picture and have students talk about what they see. Ask them to describe or point to the thing in each picture that is most noticeable, such as the animals, the water, the sky, or the land. Explain that this will be a hint about which Earth sphere they are looking at.

Model Demonstrate how students can ask themselves questions to help do the activity. Ask, *Which sphere of Earth is made up of living things? Which sphere makes up the oceans and water on Earth?*

Talk About It

Guide Discussion Read the sentence starters aloud with students as they work together to provide the last word in each one.

Your Turn

Guide Discussion Listen to students explain how the Earth spheres work together in the Earth system. Guide them if they mix up the names of spheres or cannot think of the correct name of one of Earth's spheres.

A Closer Look

On Their Own After pointing out each prefix, point out that the word *sphere* is the base of each word on the list. Explain that this is a hint that the words are related. Talk about the meaning of the word *sphere*, both as a solid shape and as a group of connected elements. Then discuss how the words are related.

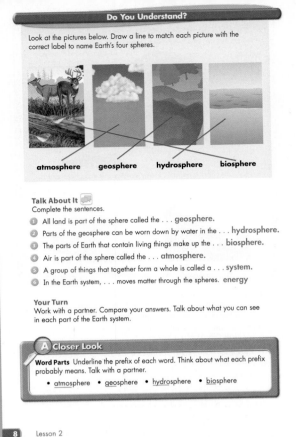

Do You Understand?

Look at the pictures below. Draw a line to match each picture with the correct label to name Earth's four spheres.

atmosphere   geosphere   hydrosphere   biosphere

Talk About It
Complete the sentences.

1. All land is part of the sphere called the . . . geosphere.
2. Parts of the geosphere can be worn down by water in the . . . hydrosphere.
3. The parts of Earth that contain living things make up the . . . biosphere.
4. Air is part of the sphere called the . . . atmosphere.
5. A group of things that together form a whole is called a . . . system.
6. In the Earth system, . . . moves matter through the spheres. energy

Your Turn
Work with a partner. Compare your answers. Talk about what you can see in each part of the Earth system.

A Closer Look

Word Parts Underline the prefix of each word. Think about what each prefix probably means. Talk with a partner.
- atmosphere
- geosphere
- hydrosphere
- biosphere

Leveled Language Proficiency

Students at each proficiency level should be able to perform the following tasks.

Listening/Speaking

Early Beginner/Beginner Gesture or point to respond to oral directions. Name Earth's spheres and point to a picture that represents each one.

Early Intermediate Use hand gestures or short phrases to respond to questions. Tell how constructive and destructive forces change Earth's surface.

Intermediate Follow oral directions with little to no help. Explain in complete sentences what makes up each sphere of Earth's system.

Advanced/Transitioning Follow oral directions independently. Explain, using complete and complex sentences, the difference between constructive and destructive forces. Orally describe how each sphere interacts with other spheres.

Your Turn

Write *constructive force* or *destructive force* below each picture.

glacier

destructive force

river

destructive force

volcano

constructive force

Talk and Write About It

Complete the statements about Earth systems.

1. A constructive force changes Earth by <u>building up land masses</u>.
2. A destructive force changes Earth by <u>wearing down land masses</u>.
3. A mountain is part of the sphere called the <u>geosphere</u>.
4. Rocks can be broken down by <u>weather</u>.
5. The four main parts of the Earth system are <u>the biosphere, the atmosphere, the geosphere, and the hydrosphere</u>.

Produce Language

Write about how a volcano can be a constructive force. Use as many vocabulary terms as you can.

_____

_____

_____

_____

_____

The Earth System   **9**

Leveled Language Proficiency

Students at each proficiency level should be able to perform the following tasks.

Reading/Writing

Early Beginner/Beginner Locate words that describe Earth's spheres. Draw pictures to show examples of each sphere.

Early Intermediate Read to find references to constructive and destructive forces. Write short phrases to describe what each term means.

Intermediate Comprehend phrases that describe the atmosphere. Write a complete sentence to tell how the atmosphere interacts with another one of Earth's spheres.

Advanced/Transitioning Read aloud sentences that describe how Earth's systems interact with each other. Write a complete and original paragraph that gives a real-world example of one of these interactions.

↻ Assess Understanding

Your Turn

Model As students complete the activity, have them discuss what is constructive or destructive about the process shown in each picture. Then ask, *What are other examples of constructive and destructive forces?*

Talk and Write About It

On Their Own Encourage students to use the questions to help them think of new questions about constructive and destructive forces and how energy moves through Earth's spheres.

Produce Language

On Their Own Have students work in pairs or small groups. Encourage students to share what they know about volcanoes.

Wrap Up

Table Talk Direct students to reread the Big Question. Then have them reflect on what they learned. Encourage students to build fluency by reading their writing in groups or to the class.

✔ **Learned** and applied vocabulary related to Earth's systems

✔ **Spoken** statements about how Earth's systems work together

✔ **Written** statements about constructive and destructive forces in each of Earth's systems

Lesson 3

Earth's Interior

Vocabulary seismic waves, crust, mantle, lithosphere, asthenosphere, outer core, inner core, radiation, convection, conduction, convection current

Materials photo or drawing of a pie, a globe, an orange, an apple, or a peachlike fruit

Science Background

- Geologists use two main types of evidence to learn about Earth's interior: direct evidence from rock samples and indirect evidence from seismic waves.

- The three main layers of the Earth are the crust, the mantle, and the core.

- Both temperature and density increase with depth beneath Earth's surface.

Earth's Interior

Big Question How do scientists understand Earth's interior?

You will . . .
- Interpret scientific diagrams that show the inside of Earth.
- Describe the relative positions of Earth's layers: crust, mantle, and core.
- Explain how heat inside Earth causes changes in the layers.
- Differentiate among terms related to Earth's interior.

Talk About It

What do you think makes up the inside of Earth? Draw on the globe to show what you think occurs in Earth's inner layers.

Show your drawing to a partner. Talk about why and how scientists study the inside of Earth.

Predict
Look at the Big Question and the "You will . . ." statements at the top of the page. Tell what you think you are going to learn in this lesson.

I think I am going to learn about . . .

Frontload the Lesson

How do scientists understand Earth's interior?

Talk About It

Build Background Introduce students to the idea that they will be learning about the inside of Earth, or its interior. Encourage students to use their own ideas of the inside of Earth in their drawings. You might relate students' lack of certainty to the fact that scientists must use indirect evidence to infer the structure of the inside of Earth.

Content and Language

Predict

Model Read the objectives aloud. As students repeat after you, correct any mispronunciations that students are making. Show a picture of a pie. Explain that the pie crust is similar to Earth's crust.

Guide Discussion Ask students to choose one of the objectives. Have them predict where in the lesson they might learn about the topic.

Leveled Instruction

Early Beginner Ask students to identify and point to vocabulary terms they see throughout the lesson. Ask short questions that use each the term as the answer.

Beginner Ask students questions using short, complete sentences. Have students respond using single words or short phrases. Students might create a picture glossary for the terms, including distinct pictures with arrow indicators for the meanings of *conduction*, *convection*, and *radiation*.

Early Intermediate/Intermediate Encourage students to provide answers to questions in full sentences. They should also ask questions about concepts in the lesson. To encourage questions, ask students, *What puzzles you about Earth's interior? What do you want to know about Earth's core, or center?* Record their questions on chart paper for further reading practice.

Advanced/Transitioning Have students use complex sentences to answer questions and express complete ideas. Encourage students to write a few questions in English about what they would like to learn in their upcoming science lesson.

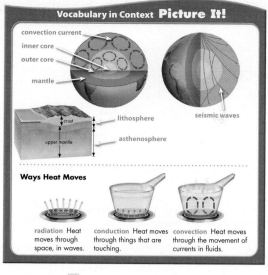

Vocabulary in Context **Picture It!**

convection current
inner core
outer core
mantle

seismic waves

crust
upper mantle

lithosphere
asthenosphere

Ways Heat Moves

radiation Heat moves through space, in waves.

conduction Heat moves through things that are touching.

convection Heat moves through the movement of currents in fluids.

Talk About It

Work with a partner. Use the pictures above to finish these sentences.

1. The deepest section of Earth is the . . . inner core.
2. The lithosphere has two parts—the upper mantle and the . . . crust.
3. Heat moves through the core and mantle by . . . convection currents.
4. The layer of Earth directly below the lithosphere is called the . . . asthenosphere.
5. Heat moves between two objects that are touching through . . . conduction.
6. Waves that move through Earth are called . . . seismic waves.

Your Turn

Talk with a partner about the terms in the Picture It box. Describe the different layers of Earth.

Earth's Interior **11**

Academic Vocabulary

- Explain that *evidence* is proof of something. Have students discuss how scientists find *evidence* about what Earth's layers are like. Write *direct* and *indirect* on the board. Discuss the difference between the two words. Explain that *direct evidence* is something we see with our eyes. Scientists use indirect evidence to figure out the nature of Earth's interior. For example, seismic waves travel at different speeds through liquids and solids. Scientists study how seismic waves travel to infer whether different layers are solid or liquid. This is *indirect evidence* of what the layers of Earth are made of.

- Cognates are words that are similar in two or more languages. For example, the Spanish word for *asthenosphere* is *astenósfera*. Encourage students to use cognates as a way of inferring the meanings of English words.

↻ Comprehensible Input

Vocabulary in Context: Picture It!

1. **Say the Term** Say each term slowly, artificially stressing each syllable. Have students repeat. Then say the term more naturally and have students repeat.

2. **Introduce Word Meaning** Connect each term to the visual that illustrates it.

3. **Demonstrate** Use gestures and visuals to demonstrate.

   - Choose a piece of fruit to demonstrate the terms *mantle*, *core*, and *crust*. As you say the word *mantle*, point to the mantle on the diagram. Gesture toward the thick middle part of the fruit to show how it is similar to the mantle on the diagram.

   - Then point to the inner and outer core in the diagram. Say, *This is Earth's core. It contains an inner core at the center and an outer core surrounding the inner core. The core of a fruit is deep inside the fruit. Similarly, the core of Earth is deep inside Earth.*

   - Move your fingers around the outside of the fruit. Say, *The crust of the Earth is the outermost layer, like the skin of a fruit.*

4. **Apply** After all of the terms have been discussed, have students demonstrate understanding with Talk About It.

Talk About It

Guide Discussion Ask students to look back at the pictures they completed at the start of the lesson. Ask them to use the Picture It terms to describe the pictures.

RTI Response to Intervention

If students have difficulty pronouncing the term *asthenosphere* . . .

Then pronounce each syllable separately and have the students repeat the syllables after you. Help them distinguish between the *s* and the *th* sounds.

Your Turn

Guide Discussion Encourage students to discuss each term one at a time and then relate the terms to one another.

Earth's Interior

 # Language Production

Do You Understand?

Comprehension Support If students have trouble matching up the answers on their own, allow them to work in groups to match terms and meanings. Encourage them to look back at the Picture It page to recall information about the location of each layer.

Model Demonstrate how students can ask themselves questions to help them complete the activity. Say, *Which layer is at the center of the Earth? Which layer forms the outer shell of Earth? What is this layer called?*

Talk About It

Guide Discussion Read the sentence starters aloud with students as they work together to complete the sentences.

Your Turn

Guide Discussion Listen to students discuss the structure of Earth. Make sure that they understand that the lithosphere includes the crust and the upper part of the mantle.

In Other Words

Model Point out that *interior* is a more formal way to say *insides* or *inner area*. Read the example sentence aloud for students. Then ask, *What is another way to say this? What is another word, or words, for* interior? Have students take turns reading the sentence aloud, choosing one of the yellow-highlighted words to fill in the space each time. Then have students suggest their own sentences that use the word *interior*.

Do You Understand?

Match each word with its meaning. Write the letter of the definition next to the word.

① crust ___c___	a. the crust and top section of the mantle together
② mantle ___e___	b. the center of Earth, made mostly of metals
③ core ___b___	c. solid rock layer that makes up the outside of Earth
④ lithosphere ___a___	d. the deeper section of the mantle
⑤ asthenosphere ___d___	e. layer of solid, hot rock above the core

Talk About It
Complete the sentences about Earth's structure and ways heat moves.
① Convection currents happen in the . . . mantle and outer core.
② The section of Earth that is liquid is the . . . core.
③ Heat moves from the sun to Earth by . . . radiation.
④ Dry land and the ocean floor are part of Earth's . . . crust, lithosphere.
⑤ The deeper section of the mantle is the . . . asthenosphere.
⑥ The crust and top of the mantle make up the . . . lithosphere.

Your Turn
Work with a partner. Compare your answers. Talk about the structure of Earth.

In Other Words

Earth's	interior	cannot be physically explored.
	inner region	
	inside	

12   Lesson 3

Leveled Language Proficiency

Students at each proficiency level should be able to perform the following tasks.

Listening/Speaking

Early Beginner/Beginner Gesture or point to respond to oral directions. Use single words in response to questions asking them to identify Earth's layers.

Early Intermediate Use hand gestures or short phrases to respond to questions. Tell where each layer of Earth is located.

Intermediate Follow oral directions with little to no help. Explain in complete sentences the three ways that heat is transferred.

Advanced/Transitioning Follow oral directions independently. Explain, using complete and complex sentences, the differences between Earth's layers, including the lithosphere and asthenosphere, and how heat is transferred inside Earth.

Think, Talk, and Write

Your Turn

Look at the arrows to see how heat moves. Then, match each picture to the word below that correctly labels it.

convection   conduction   radiation

Talk and Write About It

Complete the statements about how heat moves.

1. Look at the picture that shows conduction. Heat moves from _____ the cup to the hands .

2. Look at the picture that shows radiation. Heat moves from _____ the sun to the ice cream cone .

3. Look at the picture that shows convection. Heat moves _____ in currents that move through the air in the oven .

4. Heat is transferred from warmer objects to cooler objects .

Produce Language

Write about what you learned about Earth's layers. Use as many vocabulary terms as you can.

_____

_____

_____

_____

_____

Earth's Interior **13**

Leveled Language Proficiency

Students at each proficiency level should be able to perform the following tasks.

Reading/Writing

Early Beginner/Beginner Locate words that describe Earth's layers. Draw Earth's interior and surface layer and label the three main layers.

Early Intermediate Read to find references to ways heat is transferred. Write short phrases to describe three ways that heat is transferred.

Intermediate Comprehend phrases that describe the Earth's interior. Write complete sentences to tell how heat moves from Earth's core to its surface.

Advanced/Transitioning Read aloud sentences that describe the differences between Earth's layers. Write complete and original sentences that describe each layer and its characteristics.

⟳ Assess Understanding

Your Turn

Model If students need help identifying the word to describe each type of heat transfer, prompt them to look back at the Picture It section for a hint.

Talk and Write About It

On Their Own Encourage student groups to use the sentences to form questions about heat transfer. Have groups answer one another's questions and then write about heat transfer within Earth's layers.

Produce Language

On Their Own Have student pairs write and talk about Earth's layers. Use the words *inside* and *interior* and the words *outer layer* and *surface,* so that students become familiar with the distinctions between these terms.

Wrap Up

Table Talk Have students reflect on what they learned by referring to the Big Question. Encourage students to build fluency by reading their writing in groups or to the class.

✔ **Learned** and applied vocabulary related to Earth's interior

✔ **Spoken** statements about how heat moves in Earth's layers

✔ **Written** statements about the differences between Earth's layers

Lesson 4

Properties of Minerals

Vocabulary mineral, inorganic, crystal, streak, luster, Mohs hardness scale, cleavage, fracture, geode, crystallization, solution

Materials chalk and chalkboard, mineral samples (optional), clear plastic cups, water, salt, stirrers

 Science Background

- All minerals form by natural processes. A mineral is always a solid, with a definite chemical composition. The particles of a mineral line up in a repeating pattern, forming a crystal.

- All minerals are inorganic and form from elements or compounds that were not part of living things. Most minerals are formed either by the cooling of magma or lava or by the crystallization of materials in water.

- A mineral has a definite chemical composition. It always contains the same elements in definite proportions.

Frontload the Lesson

What is a mineral?

Talk About It

Build Background Read the directions aloud, asking students to find and read the word *mineral*. Then model thinking aloud by saying, *Did a person make this? Is it solid? Does it occur naturally? Did it come from a living thing?*

Content and Language

Predict

Model Read the Big Question and the objectives aloud and have students repeat. Clarify that a *property* is a characteristic or quality.

Guide Discussion Ask students to give other examples of characteristics or properties.

Big Question What is a mineral?

You will . . .
- Define *mineral* and describe how minerals are formed.
- Identify properties of minerals.
- Use terms related to minerals.

Talk About It

A mineral is not alive, and it does not come from a living thing. Minerals are solid. They can be found in nature and are not made by humans. Circle the pictures that you think show minerals.

Talk with a partner about the objects that you think are minerals.

Predict

Look at the Big Question and the "You will . . ." statements at the top of the page. Tell what you think you are going to learn about minerals.

I am going to learn about . . .

14   Lesson 4

Leveled Instruction

Early Beginner Encourage students to point to pictures to help them answer questions about minerals. When they do, say each word aloud for them to hear and repeat.

Beginner Provide sentence frames for students to help them start discussions, answer questions, and generate ideas for writing.

Early Intermediate/Intermediate. Ask questions using complex sentences. Expect answers about minerals in phrases or complete sentences.

Advanced/Transitioning Partner these students with beginning students. Have these advanced students model how to structure more detailed answers. Their answers should include the names of properties used to identify minerals, and processes such as crystallization as discussed in the lesson.

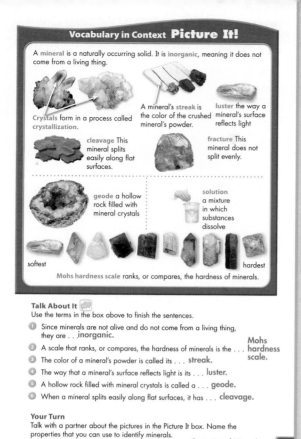

Vocabulary in Context Picture It!

A **mineral** is a naturally occurring solid. It is **inorganic**, meaning it does not come from a living thing.

Crystals form in a process called **crystallization.**

A mineral's **streak** is the color of the crushed mineral's powder.

luster the way a mineral's surface reflects light

cleavage This mineral splits easily along flat surfaces.

fracture This mineral does not split evenly.

geode a hollow rock filled with mineral crystals

solution a mixture in which substances dissolve

softest   hardest

Mohs hardness scale ranks, or compares, the hardness of minerals.

Talk About It
Use the terms in the box above to finish the sentences.

1. Since minerals are not alive and do not come from a living thing, they are . . . inorganic.
2. A scale that ranks, or compares, the hardness of minerals is the . . . Mohs hardness scale.
3. The color of a mineral's powder is called its . . . streak.
4. The way that a mineral's surface reflects light is its . . . luster.
5. A hollow rock filled with mineral crystals is called a . . . geode.
6. When a mineral splits easily along flat surfaces, it has . . . cleavage.

Your Turn
Talk with a partner about the pictures in the Picture It box. Name the properties that you can use to identify minerals.

Properties of Minerals **15**

Academic Vocabulary

- Explain to students that the word *solution* has multiple meanings. As used here, a *solution* is a mixture containing a solvent, such as water, and at least one solute. It has the same concentration and other properties throughout. But the word *solution* can also mean *explanation* or *answer,* as in: *The math problem has only one solution.*

- Point out to students that *property* can also mean "something owned by or belonging to a person or people," but that here it means "a characteristic or feature." Model using both meanings in a few examples, and encourage students to do the same.

- Students may notice that some of the terms are similar to words in their native language that have similar meanings. Point out that such words are called *cognates.* Help students see that cognates may be pronounced very differently even if their spellings are similar. For example, the Spanish word for *geode* is *geoda*.

↻ Comprehensible Input

Vocabulary in Context: Picture It!

1. **Say the Term** Say each term slowly, artificially stressing each syllable. Have students repeat. Then say the term more naturally and have students repeat.

2. **Introduce Word Meaning** Connect each term to the visual that illustrates it.

3. **Demonstrate** Use gestures and visuals to demonstrate.

   - As you say the word *crystal*, point to the quartz and halite.

   - Clarify the term *streak* by taking a piece of chalk and drawing a line on a chalkboard. Touch the chalk dust and point out that chalk is made of calcite, which is a mineral. The line on the board is a calcite streak.

   - Point to the images for *cleavage* and *fracture*. Emphasize how smooth and even the *cleavage* is, and contrast it with the unevenness of the *fracture*.

4. **Apply** After each term has been discussed, have students demonstrate understanding with Talk About It.

Talk About It

Guide Discussion Ask students to look back at the pictures in the opening Talk About It activity. Ask them to use the terms in the Picture It box to describe the minerals they see. Then have students review the Big Question. Elicit students' answers and use them to draw a cluster diagram or concept map on the board.

RTI Response to Intervention

If students have difficulty understanding the difference between *crystal* and *crystallization* . . .

Then remind them that words ending in *-ation* often describe a process. In this case, *crystallization* is the process by which *crystals* form.

Your Turn

Guide Discussion Encourage students to use words that describe properties of minerals, such as *streak* or *luster*. Before students begin, ask a volunteer to explain the meaning of *property*.

Properties of Minerals

↻ Language Production

Do You Understand?

Comprehension Support Before students start the activity, review the terms *mineral, crystal,* and *solution.* **CAUTION:** Remind students not to taste the salt or salt water.

Give each pair of students a plastic cup with a small amount of water, a few spoonfuls of salt, and a stirrer. (However, do not give students so much salt that some of it remains undissolved.) Tell students not to taste the salt or any other science materials. Have them dissolve the salt in water. Then have students wash their hands. Guide them in completing the activity in the book. Leave the cups out over several days to allow the water to evaporate (don't use too much water or it will take too long for it to completely evaporate). Once the water evaporates, it will leave behind a residue of salt. Have students compare the results with the pictures in their books.

Model Demonstrate how students can ask themselves questions to help them do the activity. Say, *What happens when you mix salt and water? What happens when the water evaporates?*

Talk About It

Guide Discussion Read the prompts aloud with students as they work together to complete the sentences.

Your Turn

Guide Discussion Listen to student discussions. Remind students of key properties of minerals. Say, *Minerals are solids. They have a definite chemical composition. They are not human-made. They are inorganic, meaning that they are not grown or shaped by living things.* Then ask, *How do they form?* Remind students of the process of crystallization. Clarify misunderstandings as needed.

Do You Understand?

1. Do the experiment with your teacher. (Do not taste or eat the salt or water.)
2. Circle the pictures that show crystals or crystallization.
3. Cross out the pictures that show a solution.

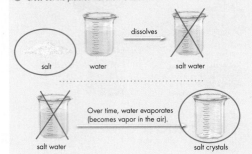

salt   water   dissolves   salt water

Over time, water evaporates (becomes vapor in the air).

salt water   salt crystals

Talk About It
Complete the sentences about each system.
1. Some minerals dissolve in water to form a . . . **solution.**
2. To make a saltwater solution, you mix water and salt particles called . . .**crystals.**
3. The particles in a mineral line up in a repeating pattern to form a crystal. This process is called . . . **crystallization.**
4. A naturally occurring, inorganic solid that has a crystal structure is called a . . . **mineral.**

Your Turn
How can the process of crystallization make minerals form? Work with a partner to write down your ideas.

16   Lesson 4

Leveled Language Proficiency

Students at each proficiency level should be able to perform the following tasks.

Listening/Speaking

Early Beginner/ Beginner Gesture or point in response to oral directions. Use a word or a short spoken phrase in response to questions about crystals and solutions.

Early Intermediate Respond to oral questions about minerals, asking for clarification or repetition as needed. Tell about crystallization using short spoken phrases or simple sentences.

Intermediate Follow oral directions with little or no help. Explain aloud, in complete sentences, how to dissolve crystals in water to form a solution.

Advanced/Transitioning Follow oral directions independently. Explain, using complete and complex spoken sentences, how salt mixed with water forms a solution, and how crystallization occurs when that solution evaporates.

Think, Talk, and Write

Your Turn

Look at the picture below. Draw a line to connect the process of forming minerals to the matching image.

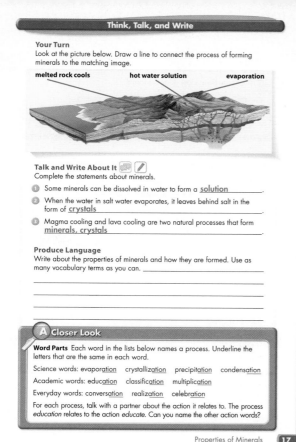

melted rock cools   hot water solution   evaporation

Talk and Write About It 💬 ✏️

Complete the statements about minerals.

1. Some minerals can be dissolved in water to form a **solution**.

2. When the water in salt water evaporates, it leaves behind salt in the form of **crystals**.

3. Magma cooling and lava cooling are two natural processes that form **minerals, crystals**.

Produce Language

Write about the properties of minerals and how they are formed. Use as many vocabulary terms as you can. _____

_____

_____

_____

_____

A Closer Look

Word Parts Each word in the lists below names a process. Underline the letters that are the same in each word.

Science words: evapor<u>ation</u>   crystall<u>ization</u>   precipit<u>ation</u>   condens<u>ation</u>

Academic words: educ<u>ation</u>   classific<u>ation</u>   multiplic<u>ation</u>

Everyday words: convers<u>ation</u>   realiz<u>ation</u>   celebr<u>ation</u>

For each process, talk with a partner about the action it relates to. The process *education* relates to the action *educate*. Can you name the other action words?

Properties of Minerals   **17**

Leveled Language Proficiency

Students at each proficiency level should be able to perform the following tasks.

Reading/Writing

Early Beginner/Beginner Locate words in text that describe the properties of minerals. Draw and label pictures to show the crystal structure of a mineral.

Early Intermediate Read to find a reference to crystallization. Write short phrases to describe the process of crystallization.

Intermediate Comprehend phrases in text that describe the steps involved in mineral formation. Write a description of how minerals can dissolve in water to form a solution, and how crystallization occurs when water in a solution evaporates.

Advanced/Transitioning Read grade-level textbooks that describe the crystallization of minerals from cooling magma and lava. Write complete sentences describing the process of crystallization from magma and lava.

 # Assess Understanding

Your Turn

Model Before students begin the activity, have them study the image. Model thinking aloud. Say, *I see land and water. Two of these processes involve water. Where might hot water, such as a mineral hot spring, be?* Encourage students to identify each word in the activity before matching it to the picture. If your students are familiar with the terms *lava* and *magma*, relate them to the term *melted rock* and to the red parts of the illustration.

Talk and Write About It

On Their Own Encourage student groups to talk about the lesson's Big Question. Have them brainstorm some ways minerals form *(evaporation, hot water solutions, cooling magma, and cooling lava)*.

A Closer Look

On Their Own Have students work in pairs to complete this word parts activity. Then have them brainstorm other examples for each category.

Produce Language

On Their Own After students have written their ideas, have them talk with a partner about their response. Encourage students to add details to their own writing based on any additional information their partner provided.

Wrap Up

Table Talk Have students reflect on what they learned. Encourage students to build fluency by reading their writing in groups or to the class.

✔ **Learned** and applied vocabulary related to minerals

✔ **Spoken** statements about the ways that minerals can form

✔ **Written** statements about the characteristics that can be used to identify minerals, including streak, luster, and relative hardness

Classifying Rocks

Vocabulary grain, texture, igneous rock, sedimentary rock, metamorphic rock, extrusive rock, intrusive rock, lava, magma, sediment, deposition, clastic rock, compaction, organic rock, cementation, chemical rock, foliated, rock cycle

Materials small rocks of different shapes, colors, textures; chalk or a cracker; fabric of varying textures; clay

Science Background

- Igneous rocks may form on or beneath the Earth's surface from magma or lava.

- Most sedimentary rocks form by deposition, compaction, and cementation.

- Any rock that forms from another rock as a result of changes in heat or pressure is a metamorphic rock.

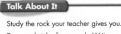
Classifying Rocks

Big Question How do rocks form?

You will . . .
- Describe and differentiate the three major ways rocks can form.
- Identify different types and features of rocks.
- Use terms related to rocks and the rock cycle.

Talk About It

Study the rock your teacher gives you.

Draw a sketch of your rock. Write words that describe it.

Talk with a partner.

How are your rocks the same? How are your rocks different?

My rock is . . .

My partner's rock is . . .

Predict

Look at the Big Question and the "You will . . ." statements at the top of the page. Describe what you think you are going to learn in this lesson.

I think I am going to learn about . . .

Frontload the Lesson

How do rocks form?

Talk About It

Build Background Distribute rock samples to student groups. Brainstorm some words with students that they might use to describe the rocks.

Content and Language

Predict

Model Read the Big Question and the objectives aloud. Use gestures to help explain the objectives.

Guide Discussion Ask students to repeat the objectives. Have them provide examples of things that can be organized into groups.

Leveled Instruction

Early Beginner/Beginner Provide students with additional visuals that clarify supporting vocabulary, such as *magma, lava,* and *grain.*

Early Intermediate/Intermediate Help students visualize how the rocks are classified by having them color-code the terms. For example, have students use a blue highlighter to mark words associated with igneous rocks, a yellow highlighter to mark words related to sedimentary rocks, and so on. Have them use these codes as they complete the activities.

Advanced/Transitioning Encourage students to keep a list of word parts that help them to understand the key vocabulary terms. Have them identify the origin of those parts as Greek or Latin and specify what the parts mean. Ask student volunteers to present their findings to the class.

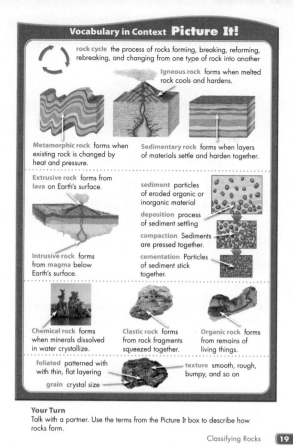

rock cycle the process of rocks forming, breaking, reforming, rebreaking, and changing from one type of rock into another

Igneous rock forms when melted rock cools and hardens.

Metamorphic rock forms when existing rock is changed by heat and pressure.

Sedimentary rock forms when layers of materials settle and harden together.

Extrusive rock forms from lava on Earth's surface.

sediment particles of eroded organic or inorganic material

deposition process of sediment settling

compaction Sediments are pressed together.

Intrusive rock forms from magma below Earth's surface.

cementation Particles of sediment stick together.

Chemical rock forms when minerals dissolved in water crystallize.

Clastic rock forms from rock fragments squeezed together.

Organic rock forms from remains of living things.

foliated patterned with with thin, flat layering

texture smooth, rough, bumpy, and so on

grain crystal size

Your Turn
Talk with a partner. Use the terms from the Picture It box to describe how rocks form.

Classifying Rocks **19**

Academic Vocabulary

- Point out that the word *igneous* comes from the Latin word *ignis*, which means "fire." Discuss how fire relates to the term *igneous*.

- Write the term *metamorphic* on the board. Underline *morph* and explain that the word part means "form." Use this information to help students better understand that the term *metamorphic* means *"having a changed form."*

- Write the terms *sedimentary* and *sediment* on the board. Explain that sedimentary rocks are made from sediment.

- Point out that the term *clastic* comes from the Greek word *klastos* meaning "broken into pieces." Use the Greek root to help students understand the meaning of *clastic*.

- Explain that deposition, compaction, and cementation are all processes. In each word a suffix, *-tion* or *-ation*, is added to a verb to form a noun. Write the words. Underline the verbs and discuss their meanings. For example, *compact* means "to press together." *Compaction* is "the process of pressing something together."

↻ Comprehensible Input

Vocabulary in Context: Picture It!

1. **Say the Term** Say each term slowly, artificially stressing each syllable. Have students repeat. Then say the term more naturally and have students repeat.

2. **Introduce Word Meaning** Connect each term to the visual that illustrates it.

3. **Demonstrate** Use gestures and visuals to demonstrate each term.

4. **Apply** After each term has been discussed, have students demonstrate understanding with Talk About It.

Talk About It

Guide Discussion Before students start their independent discussion, check for understanding with the following sentence starters:

1. *Three major groups of rocks are . . .* (metamorphic, igneous, and sedimentary.)

2. *The way a rock feels to the touch is its . . .* (texture.)

3. *The size of the crystals within a rock are the rock's . . .* (grain.)

4. *When layers of sediment settle and harden, they form . . .* (sedimentary rock.)

5. *Rock formed from the remains of living things is called . . .* (organic rock.)

RTI Response to Intervention

If students have difficulty remembering the /sh/ sound in *deposition, cementation,* or *compaction . . .*

Then write the terms on the board and underline the *-tion.* Point out that when a *t* is used in this way in a word, it makes a /sh/ sound. Give students more common examples, such as *action* or *nation.*

Your Turn

Guide Discussion Ask guiding questions, such as, *Do all rocks form in the same way?*

Classifying Rocks

↻ Language Production

Do You Understand?

Comprehension Support Before students begin the activity, discuss the diagram, particularly what the different arrows represent. Explain the meaning of the terms *weathering* and *erosion*. To be sure students understand the distinct nature of each major type of rock, use the board to draw or demonstrate a reminder. When discussing *sedimentary rocks,* take a piece of chalk or a cracker and crush it into pieces. Explain that sedimentary rock forms over time from pieces of other rocks and materials that stick together to form new rocks. Model compacting and cementing the cracker and chalk pieces together with water or clay.

If necessary, write the names of the three major groups of rocks on the board and have students copy them into the appropriate place on the chart.

Model Ask questions that help students determine which type of rock is formed. For example, say, *Which rocks form from melted materials? Which rocks form from rocks that have been weathered and eroded? Which rocks form after heat and pressure are applied?*

Talk About It

Guide Discussion Read the sentences aloud for students. Draw a three-column chart on the board with the heads *igneous rock, sedimentary rock,* and *metamorphic rock*. Write key words in each column that are associated with each rock type. Have students use the chart to help complete the sentences.

Your Turn

Guide Discussion Circulate around the room to listen to student discussions. Provide guidance as necessary. For a hands-on variation, have students use clay to make several small pebbles to represent sediment. They can then use the clay pebbles to model how the three steps form sedimentary rocks.

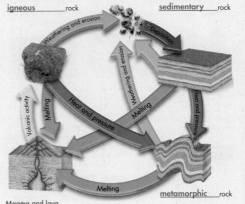

Do You Understand?

The diagram below shows the rock cycle. Label the three types of rocks that can form during the rock cycle.

<u>igneous</u> rock   <u>sedimentary</u> rock

Weathering and erosion

Deposition

Volcanic activity

Melting

Heat and pressure

Weathering and erosion

Melting

Heat and pressure

Melting

Magma and lava

<u>metamorphic</u> rock

Talk About It 🗨
Complete the sentences.

① Heat and pressure change other types of rocks into . . . metamorphic rocks.
② Rocks that form from cooled magma or lava are . . . igneous rocks.
③ Rocks that form when small pieces of rock stick together are . . . sedimentary rocks.
④ Three processes that form sedimentary rocks are . . . deposition, compaction, and cementation.
⑤ The series of processes that change rocks from one type into another is the . . . rock cycle.
⑥ Rocks with thin, flat layering are called . . . foliated.
⑦ The look and feel of a rock's surface is the rock's . . . texture.

Your Turn
Talk with a partner. Describe how deposition, compaction, and cementation turn sediment into sedimentary rock.

Leveled Language Proficiency

Students at each proficiency level should be able to perform the following tasks.

Listening/Speaking

Early Beginner/Beginner Gesture or point to images to identify rock types in response to verbal instruction. State key vocabulary terms aloud in response to questions about types of rocks.

Early Intermediate Respond to spoken questions about the rock cycle, using a visual aid to support the answers. Ask questions to clarify understanding of how rocks form.

Intermediate Respond orally to written questions about the rock cycle with little or no assistance. Summarize the rock cycle orally, with the support of a visual aid.

Advanced/Transitioning Answer oral comprehension questions about how different types of rock form. Summarize the rock cycle orally, without a visual aid.

Your Turn

Draw a line from each rock to the major group you think it belongs to. Discuss with a partner why you made the choices you did.

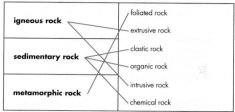

igneous rock	foliated rock
	extrusive rock
sedimentary rock	clastic rock
	organic rock
	intrusive rock
metamorphic rock	chemical rock

Talk and Write About It

Complete the statements about different types of rocks.

1. Organic, chemical, and clastic rocks are <u>types of sedimentary rocks</u>
2. Organic rocks are made from <u>things that were once living</u>.
3. Igneous rocks can be either <u>extrusive or intrusive</u>.
4. Metamorphic rocks are formed by a change in <u>heat or pressure</u>.
5. A metamorphic rock that is foliated has <u>thin, flat layers</u>.
6. During the rock cycle, <u>rocks change from one type to another</u>.

Produce Language

Read the Big Question. Write about how the three major groups of rocks form. Use as many vocabulary terms as you can.

_____
_____
_____
_____
_____
_____
_____
_____
_____

Classifying Rocks **21**

Leveled Language Proficiency

Students at each proficiency level should be able to perform the following tasks.

Reading/Writing

Early Beginner/Beginner Use knowledge of letters and sounds to decode words about rocks. Create a graphic that illustrates the rock cycle.

Early Intermediate Use text features, such as headings and captions, to understand a passage about rock types. Describe how each type of rock forms using simple sentences and illustrations.

Intermediate Distinguish cause from effect in a text about how rocks form. Write a paragraph about the rock cycle based on its visual representation.

Advanced/Transitioning Use Latin and Greek roots to better understand the meanings of key vocabulary terms. Write an organized, multiparagraph essay about the rock cycle that defines the term and relates it to each of the three major groups of rocks.

↻ Assess Understanding

Your Turn

Model With students' input, brainstorm details about the types of rocks in the second column. Include images, information about how they form, and unique characteristics.

Talk and Write About It

On Their Own Encourage students to use the matching activity to help them complete the sentences.

Produce Language

On Their Own Have students reread the Big Question. Help students to recall and classify key terms about the three types of rocks. Have volunteers read their work to the class, and ask classmates to offer additional details as necessary.

Wrap Up

Table Talk Have students reflect on what they learned. Encourage students to build fluency by reading their writing in groups or to the class.

✔ **Learned** and applied vocabulary related to rocks and the rock cycle

✔ **Spoken** statements about how rocks form

✔ **Written** sentences about different types of rocks

Lesson 6

Plate Tectonics

Vocabulary continental drift, Pangaea, mid-ocean ridge, sea-floor spreading, deep-ocean trench, subduction, plate, divergent boundary, convergent boundary, transform boundary, plate tectonics, fault

Materials Pangaea Map cutouts from Student Book Resources section, scissors, modeling compound, waxed paper

Science Background

- In 1910, Alfred Wegener proposed that all the continents were once joined in a single landmass, *Pangaea*.

- Sea-floor spreading adds crust to the ocean floor. The sea floor spreads away from the ridge and then sinks back into the mantle in a process called *subduction*.

- The theory of plate tectonics states that Earth's plates are in slow, constant motion, driven by convection currents in the mantle. The edges of plates meet at plate boundaries.

Frontload the Lesson

 How do moving plates change Earth's crust?

Talk About It

Build Background Give student pairs a Pangaea map and have them cut out the continents. Demonstrate how to move the pieces apart to the positions shown in maps *B* and *C*.

Content and Language

Predict

Model Read the objectives aloud. Write key words on the board for emphasis.

Guide Discussion Have students read the Big Question and the objectives with you and use the sentence starter to predict what they will learn.

 Big Question How do moving plates change Earth's crust?

You will . . .
- Identify the meaning of continental drift.
- Recognize that movements in the Earth's crust can form features such as mountains and valleys.
- Understand and use key terms related to plate tectonics.

Talk About It

A. 200 Million Years Ago   B. 115 Million Years Ago   C. Earth Today

1. Look at the map that your teacher gives you. Which of the above maps does it look *most* like?

2. Now cut out the map along the borders. Arrange the pieces that you cut out to look like the other two maps above. Are you moving the pieces together or apart?

3. Talk with a partner about what you think the maps represent.

Now, look at the blue terms in the Picture It box as your teacher reads them. Raise your hand if you hear any terms that describe the changes shown in the maps.

Predict

Look at the Big Question and the "You will . . ." statements at the top of the page. Describe what you think you are going to learn in this lesson.

I think I am going to learn about . . .

Leveled Instruction

Early Beginner/Beginner Ask students to point to vocabulary terms that contain the word *boundary*. Clarify the term by saying that the wall between your classroom and the one next door is the *boundary* where the two rooms meet. Point out that the way plates meet at boundaries can affect the makeup of the Earth's surface. Have students say the vocabulary terms aloud and point to the corresponding pictures.

Early Intermediate/Intermediate Have students create and label visuals in their notes, showing how the theory of plate tectonics affects the surface of the Earth and the ocean floor.

Advanced/Transitioning Encourage students to research Alfred Wegener to learn more about his ideas regarding continental drift. Invite small groups to summarize for the class, in poster form or on index cards, several findings that support Wegener's ideas.

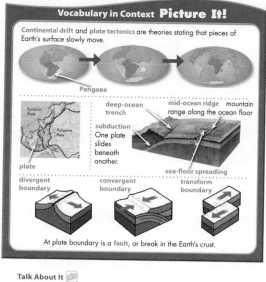

Vocabulary in Context **Picture It!**

Continental drift and plate tectonics are theories stating that pieces of Earth's surface slowly move.

Pangaea

deep-ocean trench

mid-ocean ridge — mountain range along the ocean floor

subduction
One plate slides beneath another.

plate

sea-floor spreading

divergent boundary

convergent boundary

transform boundary

At plate boundary is a **fault**, or break in the Earth's crust.

Talk About It

Work with a partner. Complete the sentences.

1. Wegener's idea that continents have moved over time is called . . . continental drift.
2. Earth's crust is broken into moving pieces called . . . plates.
3. The continents may have once formed one giant landmass called . . . Pangaea.
4. Mountain ranges that run along the middle of ocean floors are . . . mid-ocean ridges.
5. Part of the ocean floor sinks during the process called . . . subduction.
6. Mid-ocean ridges add new material to the ocean floor during . . . sea-floor spreading.

Your Turn

Talk with a partner about the three ways that Earth's plates move at boundaries. Use the words in the Picture It box.

Plate Tectonics **23**

Academic Vocabulary

- Help students to understand and pronounce the term *hypothesis* so that they may apply it in their science class. First, demonstrate pronunciation by saying the word slowly, emphasizing each syllable. Have students repeat after you. Then explain that, in science, a hypothesis is a possible explanation for a set of observations or a possible answer to a scientific question. Note that a hypothesis must be testable. Review scientific methodology, pointing out the step that involves hypothesis formation.

- Contrast the words *convergent* and *divergent*. Point out that the prefix *con-* can mean "together," and that plates come together at convergent boundaries. The prefix *dis-* can mean "away or apart," and plates move apart at divergent boundaries.

↻ Comprehensible Input

Vocabulary in Context: Picture It!

1. **Say the Term** Say each term slowly, artificially stressing each syllable. Have students repeat. Then say the term more naturally and have students repeat.

2. **Introduce Word Meaning** Connect each term to the visual that illustrates it.

3. **Demonstrate** Use gestures and visuals to demonstrate.

   - Emphasize the word *drift* as you say the term *continental drift*. Use the Pangaea puzzle pieces to break down the term to show drifting continents.

   - As you say the term *mid-ocean ridge*, push the edges of a piece of paper together to form a ridge. Point to a map and run your finger down the middle of the Atlantic Ocean to emphasize mid-ocean.

   - Use hand gestures to illustrate how the ocean floor moves in *sea-floor spreading* and *subduction*.

4. **Apply** After each term has been discussed, have students demonstrate understanding with Talk About It.

Talk About It

Guide Discussion Read the sentence starters aloud for students. Remind them to use the terms in the Picture It box to complete the sentences.

RTI Response to Intervention

If students have difficulty understanding the meaning of the word *subduction* . . .

Then point out that the prefix of the word is *sub-*, meaning "under." Give other examples of words with this prefix, such as *submarine, subsoil,* and *submerge*. Using your hands, show them how, in *subduction*, one plate moves under the other.

Your Turn

Guide Discussion Ask students to use hand motions to show what happens at each type of boundary, and to share their actions with the class.

Plate Tectonics

 # Language Production

Do You Understand?

Comprehension Support Before students start the activity, review the three types of plate boundaries. Distribute small blocks of modeling compound (or modeling clay) and waxed paper to the class. Remind students to avoid putting the compound in their mouths and to wash their hands when they finish the activity.

Model Show students how to move the blocks of modeling compound across a sheet of waxed paper. Then demonstrate how students can ask themselves questions to help them do the activity. Say, *How do plates move at a divergent boundary? What type of movement could break off a piece of crust to form a fault? What can happen when plates collide at a convergent boundary?*

Talk About It

Guide Discussion Read the sentences aloud with students. Have them work together to complete each one.

Your Turn

Guide Discussion Circulate around the room to listen to students describe how they modeled each type of plate boundary. Help them correct any mistakes or misunderstandings as needed.

A Closer Look

On Their Own Have students work in pairs to complete this word study activity. Then have them suggest new sentences using the words.

Do You Understand?

Use the materials your teacher gives you to model plate movements at boundaries.

Then label the boxes below with the type of boundary they model.

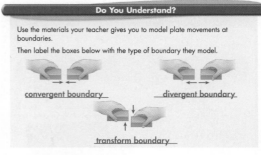

convergent boundary   divergent boundary

transform boundary

Talk About It
Complete the sentences.
1. Plates move past each other at a . . . transform boundary.
2. A break in the Earth's crust is a . . . fault.
3. Mountains may be formed when plates collide at a . . . convergent boundary.
4. A boundary where plates move away from each other is called a . . . divergent boundary.
5. Earth's plates are in slow, constant motion according to the theory of . . . plate tectonics.

Your Turn
Work with a partner. Take turns telling each other what you modeled. Be sure to use vocabulary terms to describe each model and its movements.

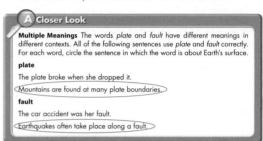

A Closer Look

Multiple Meanings The words *plate* and *fault* have different meanings in different contexts. All of the following sentences use *plate* and *fault* correctly. For each word, circle the sentence in which the word is about Earth's surface.

plate
The plate broke when she dropped it.
Mountains are found at many plate boundaries.

fault
The car accident was her fault.
Earthquakes often take place along a fault.

24 Lesson 6

Leveled Language Proficiency

Students at each proficiency level should be able to perform the following tasks.

Listening/Speaking

Early Beginner/Beginner Use gestures or point to illustrations or words to respond to oral directions. Use a word or a short phrase to describe plate tectonics and plate boundaries.

Early Intermediate Use short phrases to respond to oral directions. Use short phrases or simple sentences to describe plate tectonics and plate boundaries.

Intermediate Follow oral directions with little to no help. Use complete sentences to describe plate tectonics and to explain what happens at plate boundaries.

Advanced/Transitioning Follow oral directions independently. Use complete and complex sentences to describe how what happens at plate boundaries affects the Earth's surface.

Your Turn
Label the **mid-ocean ridge** and the **deep-ocean trench** on the diagram below. Then draw arrows showing the directions in which the sea floor is moving at these places.

mid-ocean ridge

deep-ocean trench

Talk and Write About It
Complete the statements.

1. Mountain ranges on the middle of some ocean floors are called
   mid-ocean ridges .

2. About 300 milion years ago, the continents may have been joined in one landmass called Pangaea .

3. The process in which oceanic crust sinks beneath a deep-ocean trench is called subduction .

4. Sea-floor spreading occurs at mid-ocean ridges .

5. Breaks in Earth's crust where rocks slip past each other are called faults .

Produce Language
Write about how the movement of Earth's plates causes changes in the Earth's surface. Use as many vocabulary terms as you can.

Plate Tectonics **25**

Leveled Language Proficiency

Students at each proficiency level should be able to perform the following tasks.

Reading/Writing

Early Beginner Work with a partner to identify words associated with pictures and processes. Copy words about sea-floor spreading, subduction, and plate tectonics.

Beginner Identify words associated with pictures and processes. Write short phrases about plate tectonics.

Early Intermediate Read about the movement of the Earth's plates and write short sentences summarizing the reading. Create short sentences about plate tectonics.

Intermediate Read labeled maps and diagrams that show continental drift and plate tectonics. Use complete sentences to write about plate tectonics.

Advanced/Transitioning Read aloud and comprehend sentences that describe continental drift and plate tectonics. Write detailed, complete sentences to apply these concepts when describing the Earth's surface.

↻ Assess Understanding

Your Turn

Model Read the instructions aloud with students. Briefly review the processes of sea-floor spreading and subduction with them, using hand gestures to show what happens during each process. Then have students label the diagram as indicated.

Talk and Write About It

On Their Own Have partners take turns reading and completing each statement orally. Then have each student write the responses on the lines provided.

Produce Language

On Their Own Have students write about what they learned and share their work with a partner. Invite those who wish to share their writing to do so on a class bulletin board or website.

Wrap Up

Table Talk Have students review the Big Question as a way to reflect on what they learned. Encourage students to build fluency by reading their writing in groups or to the class.

✔ **Learned** and applied vocabulary related to plate tectonics

✔ **Spoken** statements about how Earth's crust is divided into plates and how plates move at boundaries

✔ **Written** statements about plate boundaries, sea-floor spreading, and subduction

Lesson 7

Earthquakes

Vocabulary earthquake, stress, tension, compression, shearing, normal fault, reverse fault, strike-slip fault, focus, epicenter, seismograph, seismogram, P wave, S wave, surface wave

Materials stacks of books, toy blocks, clay

 Science Background

- Tension occurs where two plates pull apart. It can create a normal fault.

- Compression stress pushes plates together. It can create a reverse fault.

- Shearing stress moves rock in opposite directions. It occurs where two plates slip past each other. It can create a strike-slip fault.

- The focus is the point under Earth's surface where rock begins to move. The epicenter is the area on Earth's surface directly above the focus.

Frontload the Lesson

Why do earthquakes occur?

Talk About It

Build Background Have students review the pictures. Use books and blocks to demonstrate what happens in the images. Explain that these show how the plates of underground rock in Earth's surface can move at a fault, or break, in Earth's crust.

Content and Language

Predict

Model Read the Big Question and the objectives aloud and write key words on the board. Have students pronounce the key words with you.

Guide Discussion Have students use the sentence starter to say what they think they will learn.

Earthquakes

 Big Question Why do earthquakes occur?

You will . . .
- Describe how forces can cause changes in Earth's crust.
- Explain how earthquakes can happen and how they are measured.
- Compare and contrast three types of faults using new vocabulary.

Talk About It

Look at the picture below. Then answer the questions.

1. What happens when the books are pushed together?
2. What would happen if you slid the books in other directions?
3. What do you think causes an earthquake?

Predict

Look at the Big Question and the "You will . . ." statements at the top of the page. Tell what you think you are going to learn in this lesson.

> I think I am going to learn about . . .

26   Lesson 7

Leveled Instruction

Early Beginner/Beginner Use books or other objects to help students visualize the different faults and types of movements that cause earthquakes. Provide sentence frames for students to help them construct answers to questions about terms.

Early Intermediate/Intermediate Encourage students to create pictures to help them visualize different types of faults. Expect these students to work fairly independently.

Advanced/Transitioning Partner these students with beginning students. Have them model how they structure more detailed answers.

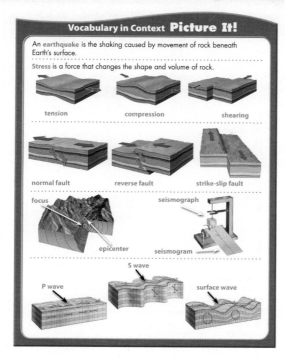

Vocabulary in Context **Picture It!**

An **earthquake** is the shaking caused by movement of rock beneath Earth's surface.

Stress is a force that changes the shape and volume of rock.

tension

compression

shearing

normal fault

reverse fault

strike-slip fault

focus

seismograph

epicenter

seismogram

S wave

P wave

surface wave

Your Turn
With a partner, talk about ways you could show what the terms mean. Work together to create a hand motion or action to show each type of stress and each type of fault.

Earthquakes   **27**

Comprehensible Input

Vocabulary in Context: Picture It!

1. **Say the Term** Say each term slowly, artificially stressing each syllable. Have students repeat. Then say the term more naturally and have students repeat.

2. **Introduce Word Meaning** Connect each term to the visual that illustrates it.

3. **Demonstrate** Use gestures and visuals to demonstrate the different types of stresses and faults.

4. **Apply** After each term has been discussed, have students demonstrate understanding with Talk About It.

Talk About It

Guide Discussion Before students start their independent discussion, check for understanding with the following sentence starters:

1. *The area on Earth's surface just above where an earthquake begins is called the* (epicenter).

2. *The first seismic waves in an earthquake are called* (P waves).

3. *Force that acts on rock to change its shape or volume is called* (stress).

4. *A fault that forms when stress pushes rocks toward each other is called a* (reverse fault).

5. *Seismic waves that can make the ground roll like ocean waves are called* (surface waves).

R T I Response to Intervention

If students have difficulty understanding the difference between the words *seismogram* and *seismograph* . . .

Then point out that words ending in *-gram* often mean a message or recording, while words ending in *-graph* often mean an instrument. Point out the similar relationship between a *telegram* and a *telegraph*.

Your Turn

Guide Discussion Have students demonstrate their hand motions for the class. Other students can identify the type of stress or fault being demonstrated.

Academic Vocabulary

- Some students may be struggling with the terms *shape* and *volume*. Remind them that volume is the amount of space that matter occupies. The shape of an object is based on its physical outline or form. When we say that *tension, compression,* and *shearing* can change the *shape* and *volume* of rock, we mean these forces can change the form and the amount of rock present in a given space.

- *Sheer* and *shear* are homophones—they sound alike but are spelled differently and have different meanings. *Sheer* can be an adjective that means thin and almost transparent. *Sheer* can also be an adverb meaning "completely." *Shear* is a verb that refers to the movement of two objects in opposite directions. For this reason, scissors, are also called *shears*.

- Point out that the words *stress* and *wave* can be both nouns and verbs. Provide a sample sentence for each. Then, have student pairs offer their own sample sentences.

- Students may be familiar with the everyday meanings of *stress* and *fault* as they relate to personality or human interaction. Encourage them to recall these meanings, but to practice and apply the precise Earth science meanings in this lesson.

Earthquakes

↻ Language Production

Do You Understand?

Comprehension Support Before students start the activity, take two books (to represent plates) and place on a table with bindings touching (to represent a fault line).

- Move books away from each other to model a *normal fault.*

- Then take books and move toward each other to model a *reverse fault.*

- Then take books and move them past each other to model a *strike-slip fault.*

Model If possible, before students do their drawing, have them model the movements with clay. Distribute clay to students to shape into two plates. Explain that students will use the clay to model the three types of stresses—tension, compression, and shearing. Point out the relationships between each type of stress and each type of fault. Demonstrate how students can ask themselves questions to help them do the activity. Say, *What type of motion happens with tension stress?* and *How do plates move to cause a strike-slip fault?* Have students wash their hands after using the clay.

Talk About It

Guide Discussion Read the statements aloud with students. Then have partners work together to complete the sentences.

Your Turn

Guide Discussion Circulate around the room to listen to student discussions. Ask comprehension questions or offer clarification as needed.

Do You Understand?

Draw blocks and arrows that represent each type of rock stress below. Be sure the arrows show the direction of the rock's movement.

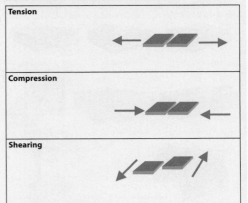

Talk About It
Complete the sentences about stress and faults.

1. Stress that pushes rocks together is called . . . compression.
2. Strike-slip faults are caused by the kind of stress called . . . shearing.
3. When rocks pull away from each other, they form a fault called a . . . normal fault.
4. Compression in Earth's crust causes faults called . . . reverse faults.
5. Normal faults are caused by the kind of stress called . . . tension.

Your Turn
Work with a partner. Take turns telling how each type of fault is formed by different types of stress.

Leveled Language Proficiency

Students at each proficiency level should be able to perform the following tasks.

Listening/Speaking

Early Beginner/Beginner Gesture or point to respond to oral directions. Use a word or a short phrase in response to questions about each kind of stress and the fault it can produce.

Early Intermediate Use hand gestures or short phrases to respond to questions and oral directions. Tell about each type of stress and its related fault using short phrases or simple sentences.

Intermediate Follow oral directions with little to no help. Explain aloud, in complete sentences, which type of stress causes which fault.

Advanced/Transitioning Follow oral directions independently. Explain, using complete and complex spoken sentences, the relationship between stress and faults.

Your Turn

Look at the chart below. Describe each kind of wave. Use words or pictures.

P waves	S waves	Surface waves
happen first, travel fast, compress and expand	happen second, move side to side	move slowly, create movements that cause ground to roll or buildings to shake

Talk and Write About It

Answer the questions about earthquakes.

1. What type of wave arrives after P waves during an earthquake?
   S waves

2. How do geologists record an earthquake's waves?
   using a seismograph that records a seismogram

3. What is the area beneath Earth's surface where an earthquake begins?
   focus

4. What is an earthquake's epicenter?
   the point on Earth's surface directly above the focus

Produce Language

Write about what you learned in this lesson. What are some types of movement that can cause an earthquake? As you write, use as many vocabulary terms as you can. _____

Leveled Language Proficiency

Students at each proficiency level should be able to perform the following tasks.

Reading/Writing

Early Beginner/Beginner Read key terms related to earthquakes that are associated with pictures or actions. Provide single-word responses to written questions about stress, faults, or seismic waves.

Early Intermediate Read key terms related to earthquakes without visual support. Write short phrases to describe stress, faults, and seismic waves.

Intermediate Comprehend written sentences related to earthquakes. Use complete sentences to describe how different stresses can create different faults.

Advanced/Transitioning Comprehend paragraphs that describe how stress and faults can cause earthquakes. Write a paragraph that summarizes the causes of earthquakes.

 # Assess Understanding

Your Turn

Model Review concepts about seismic waves before students start the activity. Model paraphrasing to help students complete the chart. For example, say, *I know that surface waves cause movements that make the ground shake* and write *create movements that make the ground shake* in the column under surface waves.

Talk and Write About It

On Their Own Have partners read and complete each question orally. Then have students write their responses individually

Produce Language

On Their Own Have students work in pairs to write about what they learned. When they complete the writing activity, have them share what they have written with another pair of students. Encourage pairs to ask at least one follow-up question about what they read.

Wrap Up

Table Talk Have students reflect on what they learned. Encourage students to build fluency by reading their writing in groups or to the class.

✔ **Learned** and applied vocabulary related to earthquakes

✔ **Spoken** statements about the stresses that cause faults and how these can cause earthquakes

✔ **Written** statements about the relationships among stresses, faults, and earthquakes

Volcanoes

Vocabulary volcano, magma, silica, magma chamber, lava, pipe, vent, crater, dormant, extinct, caldera, Ring of Fire, island arc, hot spot

Materials highlighters

 Science Background

- Volcanoes can form where plate boundaries diverge or converge. Island arcs are formed along deep-ocean trenches at converging boundaries.

- Volcanoes may form over hot spots, places where magma erupts through Earth's crust.

- All volcanoes have a magma chamber underneath them. Once magma leaves a vent, it is called lava.

- An active volcano is one that is erupting or may erupt soon. A dormant volcano may become active in the future. An extinct volcano is unlikely to erupt again.

↻ Frontload the Lesson

 How does a volcano erupt?

Talk About It

Build Background The Ring of Fire is a belt of volcanoes that circles the Pacific Ocean. The volcanoes form along the plate edges. Use the map on the next page to point out the boundaries of the Pacific plate.

↻ Content and Language

Predict

Model Read the Big Question and the objectives aloud and write key words on the board.

Guide Discussion Have students use the sentence starter to say what they think they will learn.

Volcanoes

 Big Question How does a volcano erupt?

You will . . .
- Learn how volcanoes form and where they are found.
- Identify the parts of a volcano.
- Describe what happens when a volcano erupts.

Talk About It

The Ring of Fire is a large group of volcanoes that circles the Pacific Ocean. With a pencil or pen, trace the volcanoes along the Ring of Fire.

Talk to a partner about the map.

1. This area is called the "Ring of Fire" because . . .
2. Scientists keep track of volcanic activity for many reasons, such as . . .

Predict
Look at the Big Question and the "You will . . ." statements at the top of the page. Describe what you think you are going to learn in this lesson.

   I think I am going to learn about . . .

Leveled Instruction

Early Beginner Ask students to point to vocabulary terms they see in the lesson and say the words aloud. Have students point to the diagrams to help them answer questions about volcanoes. Then say each word aloud for them to hear.

Beginner Ask students questions about volcanoes using simple sentences. Have them respond with single words or short phrases.

Early Intermediate/Intermediate Ask questions about volcanoes using complex sentences. Encourage students to answer in phrases or complete sentences.

Advanced/Transitioning These students should be able to give details about volcanoes. Ask questions using complex sentences and requiring answers that cannot be read directly from the book.

Vocabulary in Context **Picture It!**

volcano
crater
vent
lava
pipe
magma chamber

Ring of Fire

magma (contains silica)

A volcano that is not active is either **dormant** ("sleeping") or **extinct** ("dead").

island arc volcanoes that form at a plate boundary

caldera
a hole left when a volcano collapses

hot spot a weak place in Earth's crust

Talk About It

Work with a partner. Use the words in the box above to finish the sentences.

1. Molten rock that is underground is called . . . **magma.**
2. Once magma comes out of a volcano, it is called . . . **lava.**
3. One material contained in magma is . . . **silica.**
4. A weak place in Earth's crust where magma breaks through is a . . . **hot spot.**
5. A volcano that is "sleeping" is . . . **dormant.**
6. A volcano that will never erupt again is . . . **extinct.**
7. When a volcano collapses, it leaves a hole called a . . . **caldera.**

Your Turn

With a partner, talk about the pictures in the Picture It box. Discuss places on Earth where you might find volcanoes. Use the map to help you.

Volcanoes **31**

Academic Vocabulary

- *Erupt* and *molten* are two words that students will encounter frequently when they study volcanoes. Introduce those words when you introduce the science terms. You might use gestures to convey the meaning of *erupt*, and to introduce *molten*, use an illustration of molten chocolate or molten wax being poured into molds.

- The word *extinct* is used differently here than it is in life science. In life science, a species that is *extinct* has no more living members. In a sense, the species has disappeared from Earth. When a volcano becomes *extinct*, it is no longer active. That means it will never erupt again.

- Point out that several English and Spanish words related to volcanoes are cognates.

English	Spanish
volcano	volcán
magma	magma
lava	lava
extinct	extinto
crater	cráter
caldera	caldera

↻ Comprehensible Input

Vocabulary in Context: Picture It!

1. **Say the Term** Say each term slowly, artificially stressing each syllable. Have students repeat. Then say the term more naturally and have students repeat it again.

2. **Introduce Word Meaning** Connect each term to the visual that illustrates it.

3. **Demonstrate** Use gestures and visuals to demonstrate.

   - As you say the terms *magma* and *magma chamber*, point to the area of the diagram below the volcano. Then say the term *lava* and point to the surface of the volcano.

   - As you say *crater*, point to a crater. Make a bowl shape with your hands.

   - As you say *dormant*, mime sleeping. As you say *extinct*, draw an "X" over an erupting volcano. Then erase the eruption and say, *extinct; never; no more.*

4. **Apply** After all of the terms have been discussed, have students demonstrate understanding with Talk About It.

Talk About It

Guide Discussion Ask students to look at the Ring of Fire map. Encourage them to use the terms in the Picture It! box to describe volcanoes in the Ring of Fire.

RTI Response to Intervention

If students have difficulty understanding the way *ring* is used in *Ring of Fire* . . .

Then explain that the word *ring* is used here to describe something that circles an area. Ask six or seven volunteers to join hands in a circle, then point out that the circle they have formed can also be called a ring.

Your Turn

Guide Discussion Have students use the vocabulary terms in the Picture It box to describe their Ring of Fire map.

Volcanoes

↻ Language Production

Do You Understand?

Comprehension Support Before students start the activity, review the parts of a volcano. Then describe what happens when a volcano erupts. As you go through the sequence of events, point to the parts of the volcano that are involved.

Model Demonstrate how students can ask themselves questions to help them do the activity. Say, *What part of the volcano stores magma? How does magma travel from inside the volcano to the surface? Where is lava found? How is lava different from magma?*

Talk About It

Guide Discussion Read the sentence starters aloud with students as they work together to complete the sentences. Make sure that students understand *accumulates* in sentence 2. You may want to point out that it is a cognate of the Spanish *acumular*.

Your Turn

Guide Discussion Listen to student discussions as students talk about the structure of a volcano and the path that magma takes as the volcano erupts. Help them correct any mistakes or misunderstandings as needed.

A Closer Look

On Their Own Have students work in pairs to complete this activity. Ask them to scan their book to find one or two other science words with multiple meanings. *(Examples: vent, wave, stress, fault)* Then, ask students what other words they know that have more than one meaning.

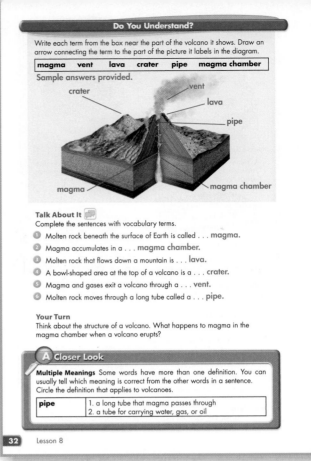

Do You Understand?

Write each term from the box near the part of the volcano it shows. Draw an arrow connecting the term to the part of the picture it labels in the diagram.

| magma | vent | lava | crater | pipe | magma chamber |

Sample answers provided.

Talk About It
Complete the sentences with vocabulary terms.
1. Molten rock beneath the surface of Earth is called . . . magma.
2. Magma accumulates in a . . . magma chamber.
3. Molten rock that flows down a mountain is . . . lava.
4. A bowl-shaped area at the top of a volcano is a . . . crater.
5. Magma and gases exit a volcano through a . . . vent.
6. Molten rock moves through a long tube called a . . . pipe.

Your Turn
Think about the structure of a volcano. What happens to magma in the magma chamber when a volcano erupts?

🔍 A Closer Look

Multiple Meanings Some words have more than one definition. You can usually tell which meaning is correct from the other words in a sentence. Circle the definition that applies to volcanoes.

| pipe | 1. a long tube that magma passes through
2. a tube for carrying water, gas, or oil |

Leveled Language Proficiency

Students at each proficiency level should be able to perform the following tasks.

Listening/Speaking

Early Beginner/Beginner Respond to oral directions that include visual clues by gesturing or pointing. Use a word or a short spoken phrase to respond to questions about parts of a volcano.

Early Intermediate Use short spoken phrases to respond briefly to questions about volcanoes. Identify important information about volcanoes using short spoken phrases or simple sentences.

Intermediate Demonstrate understanding of classroom discussions about volcanoes. Participate in discussions about volcanoes using appropriate and adequate words and phrases.

Advanced/Transitioning Follow complex oral directions independently. Use complete and complex spoken sentences to describe the parts of a volcano and the role each plays during an eruption.

Your Turn

Number the diagrams below to place them in the correct order to show how a caldera forms.

3   1   2

Talk and Write About It

Complete the statements to define some terms related to volcanoes.

1. A vent is <u>a crack that magma or gases come out of</u>
2. A caldera is formed <u>when a volcano collapses and leaves a hole</u>.
3. A magma chamber is <u>an underground space where magma accumulates</u>.
4. An extinct volcano is <u>a volcano that has stopped erupting</u>

Produce Language

Write about what you think is most interesting about volcanoes. Use as many vocabulary terms as you can.

_____

_____

_____

_____

_____

_____

_____

_____

_____

_____

_____

Volcanoes **33**

Leveled Language Proficiency

Students at each proficiency level should be able to perform the following tasks.

Reading/Writing

Early Beginner Identify words in text associated with volcano pictures or processes. Write words about volcanoes and calderas as labels for pictures and diagrams.

Beginner Read and point out correct labels on volcano diagrams. Write short phrases about volcanoes and calderas.

Early Intermediate Read short sentences describing volcano pictures and processes. Write short sentences about volcanoes and calderas.

Intermediate Use context clues to determine the meaning of unfamiliar words relating to volcanoes. Write complete sentences about volcanoes and calderas.

Advanced/Transitioning Comprehend written sentences about volcanic pictures and processes. Write complete sentences to describe the sequence of events involved in caldera formation. Revise the writing to improve the organization of ideas.

Assess Understanding

Your Turn

Model Read the instructions aloud to the students. Briefly review the vocabulary terms that apply to the diagrams. You also may wish to review what happens during a volcanic eruption. Then allow students to work with a partner to place the diagrams in the correct sequence.

Talk and Write About It

On Their Own Have partners take turns reading and completing each sentence starter orally. Then have each student write to complete the sentences.

Produce Language

On Their Own Have students review the Big Question and, as a class, collaborate on forming an answer. Then have students write about what they have learned. When they finish writing, invite students to read what they have written to a partner or to the class. Encourage students to ask each other questions about the material.

Wrap Up

Table Talk Have students reflect on what they have learned. Encourage students to build fluency by reading their writing in groups or to the class.

✔ **Learned** and applied vocabulary related to volcanoes and where and how they form

✔ **Spoken** statements about the parts of a volcano

✔ **Written** statements about what happens during an eruption and what may happen afterward

Lesson 9

Mapping Earth's Surface

Vocabulary map, equator, prime meridian, latitude, longitude, hemisphere, topographic map, contour line, index contour, contour interval, key, symbol, scale, globe, degree

Materials topographic maps, street maps, a globe, examples of scientific models

Science Background

- Maps and globes are drawn to scale and use symbols to represent features on Earth's surface.

- Distances on Earth are measured in degrees from the equator and prime meridian. Lines of latitude and longitude form a grid that can be used to find locations.

- Contour lines on topographic maps show elevation, relief, and slope.

Frontload the Lesson

 How does a map give people knowledge of an area on Earth?

Talk About It

Build Background Encourage students to visualize their walk or ride to and from school. Talk about different kinds of maps students have used or seen. Encourage them to think about how they can show real places and objects with symbols on their map.

Content and Language

Predict

Model Read the Big Question and the objectives aloud. Clarify any confusing words. For example, to explain *symbol*, draw a heart and point out that it is a *symbol* for love.

Guide Discussion Have students discuss with a partner some reasons people use maps.

 Big Question How does a map give people knowledge of an area on Earth?

You will . . .
- Describe the different details that different types of maps show.
- Identify how symbols on a map represent real objects.
- Use terms related to maps.

Talk About It

Maps are used to show where things are and what they are like. Draw a map showing how you get from school to your house. Add labels and include details.

Which features did you include on your map? How is your map different from your friends' maps?

Predict
Look at the Big Question and the "You will . . ." statements at the top of the page. Describe what you think you are going to learn in this lesson.

I think I am going to learn about . . .

Leveled Instruction

Early Beginner Ask students to point to images of their school and home on their maps when prompted.

Beginner Instruct students to add labels to their maps, such as *school, home*, street names, and so on.

Early Intermediate/Intermediate Provide students with maps. Ask students to use words and phrases to describe features of the map, such as the location shown, the type of map, and the meaning of symbols in the key.

Advanced/Transitioning After providing students with maps, have them write a paragraph explaining how a person would use the map—for example, to estimate driving distances or decide what places to visit on a vacation.

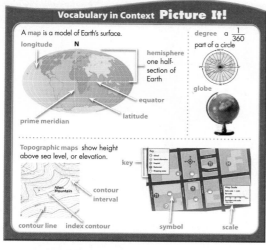

A map is a model of Earth's surface.

longitude   N

hemisphere one half-section of Earth

equator

prime meridian

latitude

degree a $\frac{1}{360}$ part of a circle

globe

Topographic maps show height above sea level, or elevation.

key

Allen Mountain

contour interval

contour line   index contour   symbol   scale

Talk About It
Work with a partner to finish the sentences.

1. One half-section of Earth is called a . . . **hemisphere.**

2. An imaginary line that separates the Northern and Southern hemispheres is the . . . **equator.**

3. An imaginary line that separates the Eastern and Western hemispheres is the . . . **prime meridian.**

4. If you travel all the way around the equator, you will travel 360 . . . **degrees.**

5. A picture or icon that stands for something on a map is called a . . . **symbol.**

6. The east-west lines on a map are lines of . . . **latitude.**

7. The north-south lines on a map are lines of . . . **longitude.**

Your Turn
Talk with a partner about the differences between the terms *equator* and *prime meridian* and between the terms *latitude* and *longitude.*

Mapping Earth's Surface   **35**

Academic Vocabulary

- Explain that the word *key* has multiple meanings. It can be used to describe an object used to open a door. However, in this lesson, it describes a guide that shows what symbols on a map represent.

- Point out that the word *scale* also has multiple meanings. It can be used to describe a tool used for weighing things. But in this lesson it describes the relationship between distance on a map and actual distance.

- Explain that the word *map* can be used as both a noun and a verb. A map is a diagram that gives you information about real places. You are *mapping* if you are making a map.

- Remind students of other *sphere* words, such as *atmosphere* and *geosphere*, which they learned and practiced in previous lessons.

Cultural Consideration

Studying maps provides an opportunity for students to talk about where they were born or where their families are from. Have students find points of latitude and longitude that correspond to places they or family members are from.

↻ Comprehensible Input

Vocabulary in Context: Picture It!

1. **Say the Term** Say each term slowly, artificially stressing each syllable. Have students repeat. Then say the term more naturally and have students repeat.

2. **Introduce Word Meaning** Connect each term to the visual that illustrates it.

3. **Demonstrate** Use gestures and visuals to demonstrate. For example:

   - For the terms *latitude* and *longitude*, trace the horizontal or vertical lines on a globe. Repeat using a map.

   - Trace the *equator* and *prime meridian* on a globe. Explain that the equator splits the globe into north and south halves, or *hemispheres*, and that the prime meridian splits it into east and west halves.

   - For the term *globe*, display a classroom globe. Show the part of the globe north of the equator and say, *This is the Northern Hemisphere.* Then point to the Southern Hemisphere and ask, *What do you think this hemisphere is called?*

   - For the term *map*, display several maps to show how maps can be used to show different features.

4. **Apply** After all of the terms have been discussed, have students demonstrate understanding with Talk About It.

Talk About It

Guide Discussion Call on volunteers to use the terms in the Picture It box. Use prompts, such as *Who can use the word* globe *in a sentence?*

RTI Response to Intervention

If students have difficulty saying or reading the word *hemisphere* . . .

Then point out that the word part *hemi-* means "half," and the word part *-sphere* refers to an object shaped like a ball or globe.

Your Turn

Guide Discussion Encourage students to use diagrams to clarify their explanations.

Mapping Earth's Surface

↻ Language Production

Do You Understand?

Comprehension Support Show students a few examples of topographic maps. Point out examples to students of the contour lines, index contours, and contour intervals. Call on volunteers to share their predictions of what these map symbols represent. Then explain that the contour interval is a set amount that the land feature rises between contour lines. The index contours are darker lines given at certain elevations, to make the map easier to read.

Model Read the directions in your own words. Model your thinking. Say, *I remember that maps like this show how the height, or elevation, of the land changes. What is the name of this type of map?*

Talk About It

Guide Discussion Review with students the differences between contour lines, index contours, and contour intervals. Call on volunteers to share their explanations.

Your Turn

Guide Discussion Check that students' descriptions of land features show that they understand how to read a topographic map.

A Closer Look

On Their Own Have students work in pairs to complete this word study activity. Invite a few volunteers to share their sentences.

Do You Understand?

Add labels to the map to answer these questions.

1. What type of map is this?
2. What do you call the lines on the map?
3. What do you call the spaces between the lines?

topographic map

contour line

▲Mount Wachusett

contour interval

Talk About It
Complete the sentences.

1. A map that shows elevation change is a . . . topographic map.
2. The lines on a topographic map are . . . contour lines.
3. The spaces between contour lines are . . . contour intervals.
4. Some maps have dark, heavy lines that are labeled with the elevation. This type of contour is called an . . . index contour.
5. A ball-shaped model of Earth is called a . . . globe.
6. "1 inch = 1 mile" is a map's . . . scale.

Your Turn
Work with a partner. Talk about the map shown here. Try to describe or draw what this part of Earth's surface might look like from the ground.

Ⓐ Closer Look

Multiple Meanings A degree is a unit of measure. There are different types of degrees, just as there are different types of units. A globe is divided into 360 degrees. If you travel halfway around the equator, you will have traveled 180 degrees. The word *degree* can also be used to tell how hot or cold something is. For example, "Water boils at a temperature of 100 degrees Celsius." Say two sentences using each meaning of *degree*.

36 Lesson 9   Sample answer: I traveled 4 degrees latitude on my vacation.; The directions say to preheat the oven to 350 degrees Fahrenheit.

Leveled Language Proficiency

Students at each proficiency level should be able to perform the following tasks.

Listening/Speaking

Early Beginner/Beginner Point to pictures in response to oral questions about features on maps. Orally identify the equator, prime meridian, a map, and a globe in a picture.

Early Intermediate Respond to simple questions about map features. Orally describe with simple sentences the difference between a map and a globe.

Intermediate Follow oral directions with little to no help. Explain with simple sentences and phrases the difference between words with multiple meanings, such as *scale, key,* and *degree.*

Advanced/Transitioning Follow multi-step oral directions independently. Orally explain some of the more abstract concepts related to maps, such as what a map scale shows and what degrees are.

Your Turn

Look at the map of Earth.

Draw and label the equator, the prime meridian, a line of latitude, and a line of longitude. Label a hemisphere. Add symbols, too. Include a map key to explain your symbols.

Student's drawings should show a world map that includes labels for equator, prime meridian, latitude, longitude, and hemisphere, as well as symbols and a key.

Talk and Write About It

Complete the statements about maps of Earth.

1. A map key tells __what the symbols represent__
2. The two imaginary lines that divide Earth into halves are called the __equator and the prime meridian__
3. The equator is located at 0° __latitude__
4. A topographic map shows __elevation and landforms__
5. Maps are drawn to scale because __Sample answer: it would be impossible to draw a map the same size as the part of Earth that it shows.__

Produce Language

Write about three things that you can find out from looking at a map or globe.

1. _____
2. _____
3. _____

Leveled Language Proficiency

Students at each proficiency level should be able to perform the following tasks.

Reading/Writing

Early Beginner/Beginner Point to the terms *map* and *globe* in text and use gestures or drawings to explain the difference between the two. Write labels for features on a map, such as the equator and prime meridian.

Early Intermediate Read and understand simple written directions. Write short phrases to describe the features of a topographic map.

Intermediate Answer comprehension questions after reading a short paragraph about maps. Write complete sentences that explain what maps can be used for.

Advanced/Transitioning Read paragraphs that explain topics related to maps. Write a short paragraph that interprets a topographic map.

 # Assess Understanding

Your Turn

Model Before beginning the activity, hold up a globe and have volunteers come to the front of the room to identify the features included in the activity. Provide prompts, such as *Where on the globe is the equator?* Clarify any misconceptions before students begin labeling.

Talk and Write About It

On Their Own Ask students if lines of latitude and longitude, the equator, and the prime meridian are real lines that you can see on the ground. Discuss how the lines are used to organize maps and provide specific locations for places on Earth.

Produce Language

On Their Own Encourage students to think about the types of maps they have learned about and the features that are often included on maps and globes. Ask students to explain when and how they might need to use a map.

Wrap Up

Table Talk Have students review the Big Question and reflect on what they learned. Encourage students to build fluency by reading their writing in groups or to the class.

✔ **Learned** and applied vocabulary related to lines on maps

✔ **Spoken** statements about features of maps and globes

✔ **Written** statements about what contour lines can tell about Earth's surface

Lesson 10

Soil on Earth's Surface

Vocabulary erosion, weathering, permeable, soil, bedrock, humus, fertility, loam, pH scale, soil horizon, topsoil, subsoil, decomposer, natural resource, soil conservation

Materials soil samples, paper or plastic cups, hand lenses (optional), white paper, plastic spoons

Science Background

- Soil is a mixture of rock particles, minerals, decayed plants and animals, water, and air.

- Soil forms when weathering breaks down rock and it mixes with other materials on the surface.

- Soil can lose its fertility due to soil erosion, but it can be conserved by contour plowing, conservation plowing, and crop rotation.

Frontload the Lesson

 How is soil formed?

Talk About It

Build Background Gather and distribute the cups, soil, paper, spoons, and optional hand lenses. Review safety procedures with students. Read through the activity aloud with students before they begin. Introduce the activity by having students discuss times they have seen rock, mud, sand, or soil outdoors. Have students dump the soil on white paper and use the spoon to spread it out. Discuss what they see. Remind students to wash their hands after the activity.

Content and Language

Predict

Model Read the Big Question and the objectives aloud. Ask a volunteer to tell one way that soil is different from rock.

Guide Discussion Ask students to choose one of the objectives and explain it in their own words.

 Big Question How is soil formed?

You will . . .
- Describe how soil forms.
- Explain how soil can be eroded and preserved.
- Use terms related to soil and weathering.

Talk About It

Step 1 Look at the cup of soil your teacher gives you. Dump it out on white paper. Use a spoon to spread the soil out. View the soil with a hand lens, if available. Talk about what you see. What are the different materials in the soil? Where do you think the different particles of soil came from?

Step 2 Follow your teacher's directions to clean up. Then wash your hands.

Step 3 Now look at the pictures below. What are some ways that mud, sand, or rocks might get worn down? Where might these materials end up?

Predict
Look at the Big Question and the "You will . . ." statements at the top of the page. Describe what you think you are going to learn in this lesson.

I think I am going to learn about . . .

Leveled Instruction

Early Beginner Ask students to choose a vocabulary term from the lesson. Encourage them to find pictures that illustrate the term.

Beginner Ask students questions about what is needed to have healthy soil. Invite them to name things that can help to make soil healthy for growing plants. If time allows, involve them in a classroom planting or transplanting (repotting) activity. Examine labels on soil packaging, and have students identify new and familiar soil-reated terms.

Early Intermediate/Intermediate Let students work independently. Ask them to explain the process of soil formation. They can draw and label diagrams that show the process of soil formation.

Advanced/Transitioning Encourage students to compare andcontrast different layers of the soil horizon. They may want to work on a classroom poster presenting the soil layers.

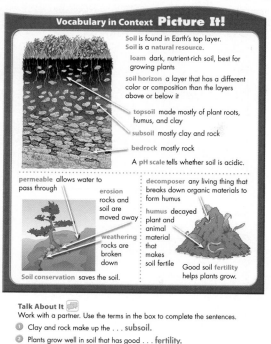

Vocabulary in Context Picture It!

Soil is found in Earth's top layer.
Soil is a natural resource.

loam dark, nutrient-rich soil, best for growing plants

soil horizon a layer that has a different color or composition than the layers above or below it

topsoil made mostly of plant roots, humus, and clay

subsoil mostly clay and rock

bedrock mostly rock

A **pH scale** tells whether soil is acidic.

permeable allows water to pass through

erosion rocks and soil are moved away

weathering rocks are broken down

Soil conservation saves the soil.

decomposer any living thing that breaks down organic materials to form humus

humus decayed plant and animal material that makes soil fertile

Good soil **fertility** helps plants grow.

Talk About It
Work with a partner. Use the terms in the box to complete the sentences.
1. Clay and rock make up the . . . subsoil.
2. Plants grow well in soil that has good . . . fertility.
3. A substance in soil made of organic material is . . . humus.
4. An earthworm is a . . . decomposer.
5. A solid layer of rock beneath soil is . . . bedrock.
6. Rocks or soil that let water pass through are . . . permeable.

Your Turn
Talk with a partner about soil and how soil forms.

Academic Vocabulary

- Explain that some of the words in the lesson are multiple-meaning words. In addition to its scientific meaning, the word *soil* also means "to stain," and the word *horizon* means "the line where the Earth and sky meet."

- Write the words *conservation* and *decomposer* on the board, and ask students to name the root words that form each longer word. Point out that the root words *conserve* and *decompose* are both verbs, and the suffixes *-er* and *-ation* turn them into nouns.

- The verb *to form* may be confusing, as *form* and *forms* have multiple meanings as either a noun or a verb. Practice with examples, such as: *Have you filled out the forms?* and *Do you know how soil forms?*

- Write the phrases *break down* and *break up* on the board. Point out that, while *up* and *down* are antonyms (opposite), the verbs *break down* and *break up* are synonyms, often interchangeable for one another. Have student pairs locate the words *break down* in the lesson and read the context. Then have them practice substituting *break up* in the same text.

↻ Comprehensible Input

Vocabulary in Context: Picture It!

1. **Say the Term** Say each term slowly, artificially stressing each syllable. Have students repeat. Then say the term more naturally and have students repeat.

2. **Introduce Word Meaning** Connect each term to the visual that illustrates it.

3. **Demonstrate** Use gestures and visuals to demonstrate. For example:

   - As you say the term *decomposer,* point to the picture of the earthworm. Say, Compose *means "to put together." The earthworm breaks up the soil. It is a* decomposer.

   - Say *weathering,* and point to the picture of the crack in the rock. Say, *Wind and water make up our* weather. *Wind and water break up rock. The process is called* weathering.

   - Repeat the word *topsoil.* Point to the picture of the soil horizons. Say, Topsoil *is the soil on the top layer.* Subsoil *is the soil underneath the top layer. Talk about what characterizes each soil layer.*

4. **Apply** After all of the terms have been discussed, have students demonstrate understanding with Talk About It.

Talk About It

Guide Discussion Ask students to use the terms from the Picture It box to describe what they see in the pictures.

RTI Response to Intervention

If students have difficulty understanding the meaning of the word *bedrock* . . .

Then review the concept by saying the word again with picture support or gestures. Explain that the layer is made of *rock.* It is referred to as *bed* because other things rest on top of it.

Your Turn

Guide Discussion Encourage students to discuss soil formation, using the illustrations as a guide. Encourage them to complete a sentence starter such as *Soil is made of . . .*

Soil on Earth's Surface

↻ Language Production

Do You Understand?

Comprehension Support Invite students to work in pairs or small groups to complete the activity. If students need help deciding whether each word is related to soil fertility, first, have them find any words that are in the column head "Words Related to Soil Fertility." *(soil, fertility).* Have them write these two words in the column. Then, allow them to look back at the Picture It box for further support.

Model Demonstrate how students can ask themselves questions to help them complete the activity. Say, *Is erosion needed for a patch of soil to produce healthy plants? What is erosion? Is humus needed for soil to produce healthy plants? What is humus? It is decayed organic material. I think it must add nutrients to the soil, and that would help make the soil fertile, or good for growing plants.*

Talk About It

Guide Discussion Read the sentences aloud with students as they work together to complete them.

Your Turn

Guide Discussion Listen to students talk about soil types they have seen. Remind them, if necessary, that they might see sand at a beach, loam in a garden, humus in an area with many plants and animals. If time allows, invite students to talk about how weathering changes and erosion moves soil.

In Other Words

Model Read the example sentence aloud for students and have them repeat it. Then ask, *What is another way to say this? What is another word, or words, for* consists of? Have students take turns reading the sentence aloud, choosing one of the yellow-highlighted words or phrases to fill in the space each time. Then have students suggest their own sentences that use the verb *to consist.*

Do You Understand?

Read the words in the box. Write each word in the correct column.

| erosion | weathering | soil | bedrock |
| humus | fertility | loam | decomposers |

Words Related to Soil Fertility	Words Unrelated to Soil Fertility
soil	erosion
humus	weathering
fertility	bedrock
loam	
decomposers	

Talk About It
Talk with a partner. Read and complete the sentences.
1. The kind of soil that plants grow best in is . . . loam.
2. Living things that break down soil are called . . . decomposers.
3. A rock layer deep underground is called . . . bedrock.
4. Soil gets washed away by . . . erosion.
5. Rocks and soil break down because of . . . weathering.

Your Turn
Work with a partner. Compare your answers. Talk about different soil types and where you might see them.

◀ In Other Words ▶

Soil	consists of	particles of rock and organic matter.
	contains	
	is made up of	

Leveled Language Proficiency

Students at each proficiency level should be able to perform the following tasks.

Listening/Speaking

Beginner/Beginner Gesture or point to respond to oral directions. Name the parts of the soil horizon while pointing to them in a picture.

Early Intermediate Use short phrases to respond to spoken questions. Explain the difference between *topsoil* and *subsoil* using spoken comparisons.

Intermediate Follow oral directions with little to no help. Explain in complete spoken sentences what materials are found in soil.

Advanced/Transitioning Follow oral directions independently. Explain, using complete and complex spoken sentences, the processes involved in breaking down materials that form soil.

Draw a line from each phrase on the left to the layer in the diagram that *best* fits the description. Then write the name of each layer.

Rocky layer under soil

Layer where loam is found

Layer with few decomposers

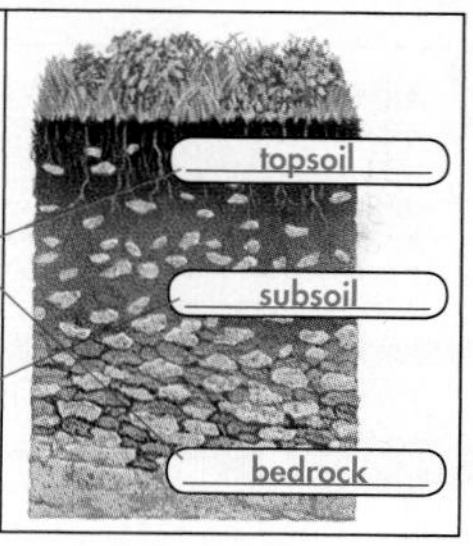

topsoil

subsoil

bedrock

Talk and Write About It 🖼️ ✏️

Complete the statements to show what you know about soil.

1. A soil horizon is <u>a division between layers of soil</u>.
2. Soil is carried away and worn away by <u>weathering and erosion</u>.
3. Decomposers are found <u>in the top layer of soil</u>.
4. New layers of soil are found on top of <u>bedrock</u>.
5. To tell if soil is acidic, you use <u>a pH scale</u>.
6. Humus is made up of <u>a mixture of decayed plants and animals</u>.
7. Erosion is a process in which <u>soil is washed away</u>.

Produce Language

Write what you learned about how soil is formed. Use as many vocabulary terms as you can.

_____
_____
_____
_____
_____
_____

Leveled Language Proficiency

Students at each proficiency level should be able to perform the following tasks.

Reading/Writing

Early Beginner/Beginner Locate words that describe soil. Write the names of soil layers.

Early Intermediate Read to find references to what soil is made of. Write short phrases to describe how soil forms.

Intermediate Comprehend phrases that describe weathering, erosion, and other soil processes. Write a complete sentence to tell how rock can break down to become soil over time.

Advanced/Transitioning Read aloud sentences that describe soil layers. Write complete and original sentences that explain the differences among the layers.

↻ Assess Understanding

Your Turn

Model As students complete the activity, have them add information to explain the layers of the soil horizon. Ask them to describe what can be found on each layer and how each layer is formed.

Talk and Write About It

On Their Own Encourage student groups to use the questions to form their own sentences that explain characteristics of soil.

Produce Language

On Their Own Invite student pairs to both write and talk about soil. Encourage them to talk about what makes up soil, how soil is formed, and how weathering and erosion affect soil.

Wrap Up

Table Talk Have students reread and discuss the Big Question as a way to reflect on what they learned. Encourage students to build fluency by reading their writing in groups or to the class.

✔ **Learned** and applied vocabulary related to weathering and soil formation

✔ **Spoken** statements about the layers of soil

✔ **Written** statements about how soil can be conserved

Lesson 11

Erosion

Vocabulary erosion, sediment, deposition, runoff, groundwater, stalactite, stalagmite, karst topography, glacier, ice age, valley glacier

Materials sand and soil for mounding, trays or bowls to hold sand, cups of water, paint trays, aprons, and gloves

 Science Background

- Weathering, erosion, and deposition act together in a cycle that wears down and builds up Earth's surface.

- Gravity, moving water, glaciers, waves, and wind are all agents of erosion.

- Wind erosion and deposition may form sand dunes and loess deposits.

Frontload the Lesson

 How does Earth's surface wear down and build up?

Talk About It

Build Background Review safety procedures and distribute aprons and gloves. Gather up materials ahead of time if possible. Give small groups of students a bowl or tray of sand and cup of water to complete the activity. Demonstrate effective ways to "blow gently" on the sand and to pour a "steady trickle" of water. Encourage groups to talk about what they see. Make sure students wash their hands.

Content and Language

Predict

Model Read the objectives aloud. As students repeat after you, point out that the lesson is about *erosion* and *deposition*, or the building up and wearing down of Earth's surface.

Guide Discussion Ask students to choose one of the objectives and give examples to describe it. Be sure that students understand that soil, rock, and sand are all materials that can be worn down or built up by water, wind, and gravity.

Erosion

 Big Question How does Earth's surface build up and wear down?

You will . . .
- Understand how Earth's surface is built up and worn down.
- Learn about different types of erosion.
- Use terms related to erosion.

Talk About It

Make a small hill with the sand your teacher gives you. Do the actions. Talk about what happens.

Step 1 Blow gently on the sand. What happens?
Step 2 Pour a steady trickle of water on the sand. What happens? Can you make a tiny river in the sand?
Step 3 Clean up the materials, following your teacher's directions, and then wash your hands.

Predict
Look at the Big Question and the "You will . . ." statements at the top of the page. Describe what you think you are going to learn in this lesson.

I think I am going to learn about . . .

Leveled Instruction

Early Beginner/Beginner Partner newcomers with more advanced students for the group activities. Assign group roles, such as observer, recorder, and reporter, that facilitate mixed grouping.

Early Intermediate/Intermediate Encourage students to work independently. Ask them to explain what they see. Provide sentence frames for their responses, such as: *When I . . . , I see that the soil . . .*

Advanced/Transitioning Encourage more advanced speakers to serve as reporters in their groups. Encourage these students to compare and contrast the different land features and processes they learn about in the lesson.

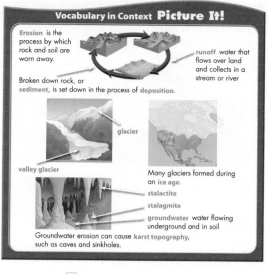

Erosion is the process by which rock and soil are worn away.

runoff water that flows over land and collects in a stream or river

Broken down rock, or **sediment**, is set down in the process of **deposition**.

glacier

valley glacier

Many glaciers formed during an **ice age**.

stalactite

stalagmite

groundwater water flowing underground and in soil

Groundwater erosion can cause **karst topography**, such as caves and sinkholes.

Talk About It

Work with a partner. Use the pictures above to complete the sentences.

1. The process of wearing away rocks and soil is called . . . erosion.
2. A large body of ice on land is called a . . . glacier.
3. Underground water that can shape the land is . . . groundwater.
4. A limestone deposit that hangs from the top of a cave is a . . . stalactite.
5. Water that flows from land into rivers . . . runoff.
6. Erosion and deposition move bits of broken rock called . . . sediment.

Your Turn

Talk with a partner about the pictures in the Picture It box. Tell how wind, water, and movement of rocks can change Earth's surface.

Erosion **43**

Academic Vocabulary

- Point out to students that the term *break down,* describing the process that rocks and earth materials go through during erosion, means "to break apart." You might also point out that the term is often used to discuss something that has broken, such as a car that *breaks down.* It may help students to know that *break down, break apart,* and *break up,* are all synonyms.

- When you discuss the term *sediment,* make sure that students understand the term *particles.* Demonstrate particles in the sand or soil samples.

- Point out a common misuse of the word *groundwater.* Students might think groundwater is water "on" the ground (which is really surface water). Groundwater is water that flows underground or through soil. Have students picture groundwater as "inside" the ground.

- Point out that the terms *stalagmite* and *stalactite* have a related meaning. Students can remember the terms if they think, *A stalactite must hold on <u>tight</u> to the ceiling. A stalagmite <u>might</u> reach the ceiling.* Students can also tell the words apart by remembering that *stalactite* has a *c* in it and comes down from the *ceiling,* while *stalagmite* has a *g* in it and comes up from the *ground.*

Comprehensible Input

Vocabulary in Context: Picture It!

1. **Say the Term** Say each term slowly, artificially stressing each syllable. Have students repeat. Then say the term more naturally and have students repeat.

2. **Introduce Word Meaning** Connect each term to the visual that illustrates it.

3. **Demonstrate** Use gestures and visuals to demonstrate each term. For example:

   - Explain that *sediment* can be made of particles of rock, soil, sand, or even the remains of dead plants and animals.

   - Then say *runoff,* and point to the picture of streams in the mountains. Say, *The word* runoff *is made of two words. What are they?*

   - Repeat with the words *ice age.* Point to the picture of the glacier. Say, *What would you guess the term* ice age *means? Look at the two words that make up the term.*

4. **Apply** After all of the terms have been discussed, have students demonstrate understanding with Talk About It.

Talk About It

Guide Discussion Ask students to look back at the pictures in the Picture It box. Ask them to use the Picture It terms to describe the images.

R T I Response to Intervention

If students have difficulty understanding the meaning of the word *deposition* . . .

Then Say, *Do you see the word* deposit *in the word* deposition? Deposit *means to put something down.* Deposition *is the act of putting something down.*

Your Turn

Guide Discussion Encourage students to discuss erosion, using the illustrations as a guide. Encourage them to complete a sentence such as *Earth materials move when* . . .

Erosion

Language Production

Do You Understand?

Comprehension Support Distribute the paint trays, sand or other soil, and containers for water. Review safety guidelines. Be sure students have smocks or aprons. If they are to handle the soil, have them wear gloves. Read through the activity steps with students before they begin. Check that they understand the question. Then, invite students to predict what will happen when they pour the water on the mound of soil. Then have them try it. Encourage discussion, by reminding students of their predictions, and by asking volunteers to describe what they observe, or see. Have students wash their hands after they have completed the activity.

Model Demonstrate how students can ask themselves questions to help them perform the activity. Say, *This water is similar to rain. Where will the water go when I pour it on top of the hill?*

Talk About It

Guide Discussion Read the sentences aloud with students as they work together to complete them. Remind students that they can use the Picture It box on the previous page for reference.

Your Turn

Guide Discussion Listen to students talk about ways that Earth is worn down and built up. Encourage students to search government sites online as well as classroom science books for pictures and descriptions of water, glacial, wave, and wind erosion. Have them discuss and describe any examples they find.

In Other Words

Model Point out that *process* is a more formal way to say *slow change*. Read the example sentence aloud for students. Then ask, *What is another way to say this? What is another word, or words, for* process? Have students take turns reading the sentence aloud, choosing one of the yellow-highlighted terms to fill in the space each time. Then have students suggest their own sentences that use the word *process*.

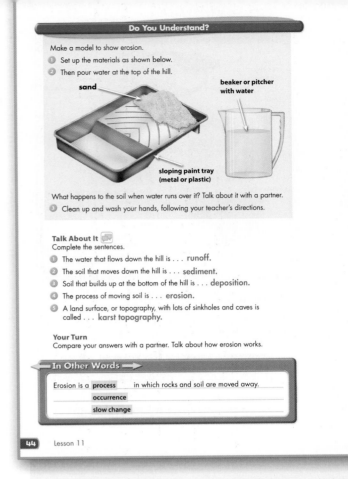

Do You Understand?

Make a model to show erosion.
1. Set up the materials as shown below.
2. Then pour water at the top of the hill.

sand

beaker or pitcher with water

sloping paint tray (metal or plastic)

What happens to the soil when water runs over it? Talk about it with a partner.
3. Clean up and wash your hands, following your teacher's directions.

Talk About It
Complete the sentences.
1. The water that flows down the hill is . . . runoff.
2. The soil that moves down the hill is . . . sediment.
3. Soil that builds up at the bottom of the hill is . . . deposition.
4. The process of moving soil is . . . erosion.
5. A land surface, or topography, with lots of sinkholes and caves is called . . . karst topography.

Your Turn
Compare your answers with a partner. Talk about how erosion works.

In Other Words

Erosion is a | process | in which rocks and soil are moved away.
| occurrence |
| slow change |

44   Lesson 11

Leveled Language Proficiency

Students at each proficiency level should be able to perform the following tasks.

Listening/Speaking

Early Beginner/Beginner Gesture or point to respond to oral directions. Say the word that matches a given definition or description.

Early Intermediate Use hand gestures or short phrases to respond to questions. Orally describe land features, such as glaciers and caves.

Intermediate Follow oral directions with little to no help. Explain in complete sentences what happens during the process of erosion.

Advanced/Transitioning Follow oral directions independently. Explain, using complete and complex sentences, how a cave can form and what features can be found in caves.

Match each word with its meaning. Write the letter of the definition next to the word.

1. _d_ erosion	a. water that moves over land carrying rock and soil with it
2. _c_ sediment	b. underground water that shapes the land
3. _e_ deposition	c. particles of rock, soil, and other material that is moved by erosion
4. _b_ groundwater	d. the process of moving weathered rock and soil from one place to another
5. _a_ runoff	e. materials that are carried from one place and built up in another place

Talk and Write About It
Complete the statements about erosion.

1. During deposition, sediment _builds up in one place_.
2. You might find groundwater in _an underground cave_.
3. Runoff moves _downhill into streams_.
4. Erosion occurs when _wind or water moves soil_.
5. A stalagmite is a limestone column that _builds up from the bottom of a cave_.
6. A stalactite is a limestone column that _builds down from the top of a cave_.
7. An ice age is a time _when many glaciers form_.

Produce Language
Write what you learned in this lesson about how Earth's surface is built up and worn down. Use as many vocabulary terms as you can.

_____
_____
_____
_____
_____
_____
_____

Erosion **45**

Leveled Language Proficiency

Students at each proficiency level should be able to perform the following tasks.

Reading/Writing

Early Beginner/Beginner Locate words that label land features and geologic processes. Write words that help to describe and define key vocabulary.

Early Intermediate Read to find definitions of key terms. Write short phrases that explain a process.

Intermediate Comprehend phrases that describe erosion and deposition. Write complete sentences that describe cause and effect.

Advanced/Transitioning Read aloud definitions of erosion and deposition. Write complete and original sentences that explain how different factors can cause erosion or deposition.

Assess Understanding

Your Turn

Model As students complete the activity, have them navigate through the lesson to find pictures that illustrate each word. Point out that they may be able to use the same picture to illustrate several words in the exercise.

Talk and Write About It

On Their Own Encourage student groups to use the questions to form their own sentences that explain the process of erosion.

Produce Language

On Their Own Have student pairs both write and talk about how erosion shapes the land. Ask them to talk about the different types of erosion and give examples of each.

Wrap Up

Table Talk Have students reread and discuss the lesson's Big Question as a way to reflect on what they learned. Encourage students to build fluency by reading their writing in groups or to the class.

✔ **Learned** and applied vocabulary related to erosion

✔ **Spoken** statements about how Earth's surface is worn down and built up

✔ **Written** statements about forces that shape Earth's surface

Lesson 12

Fossils and Earth's History

Vocabulary fossil, carbon film, trace fossil, relative age, absolute age, law of superposition, extrusion, intrusion, index fossil, unconformity, radioactive decay, half-life, Geologic Time Scale

Science Background

- Fossils provide evidence about the history of life and past environments on Earth.

- In horizontal sedimentary rock layers, the oldest layer is generally at the bottom.

- When using radioactive dating, scientists compare the amount of a radioactive element left in a rock. Over time, the radioactive element decays into a nonradioactive, stable element.

- To make Earth's history easier to understand, geologists use the Geologic Time Scale.

 Frontload the Lesson

 How do scientists learn about Earth's history?

Talk About It

Build Background Read the definition of *fossils*. Encourage students to tell about any fossils they may have seen. Tell them that fossils are traces, of living things from long ago.

Content and Language

Predict

Model Read the objectives aloud. As students repeat after you, correct any mispronunciations they make. Define and explain unfamiliar words, such as *evidence*.

Guide Discussion Encourage students to use the sentence starter to discuss the relationship between the Big Question and the objectives.

Fossils and Earth's History

Big Question How do scientists learn about Earth's history?

You will . . .
- Understand what fossils show about the history of life on Earth.
- Learn how scientists tell the age of fossils.
- Use terms related to fossils and Earth's history.

Talk About It

Fossils are the preserved remains or traces of living things. Look at the pictures. Talk about which animal formed each fossil.

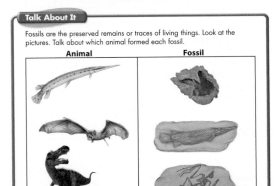

Animal	Fossil

Predict

Look at the Big Question and the "You will . . ." statements at the top of the page. Describe what you think you are going to learn in this lesson.

I think I am going to learn about . . .

46 Lesson 12

Leveled Instruction

Early Beginner Point to the pictures to identify each, saying *fossil, bat,* and so on. Ask students to repeat each word and point to the correct picture.

Beginner Provide sentence starters to help students construct answers to the questions. Example: *I predict that _____.*

Early Intermediate/Intermediate These students should work fairly independently. Ask students to read directions and completion items aloud, providing help as needed.

Advanced/Transitioning Ask these students to explain their answers as they complete the activities. Invite them to explain their thoughts and observations.

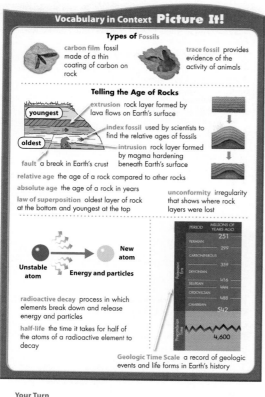

Vocabulary in Context Picture It!

Types of Fossils

carbon film fossil made of a thin coating of carbon on rock

trace fossil provides evidence of the activity of animals

Telling the Age of Rocks

youngest

oldest

extrusion rock layer formed by lava flows on Earth's surface

index fossil used by scientists to find the relative ages of fossils

intrusion rock layer formed by magma hardening beneath Earth's surface

fault a break in Earth's crust

relative age the age of a rock compared to other rocks

absolute age the age of a rock in years

law of superposition oldest layer of rock at the bottom and youngest at the top

unconformity irregularity that shows where rock layers were lost

Unstable atom → New atom, Energy and particles

radioactive decay process in which elements break down and release energy and particles

half-life the time it takes for half of the atoms of a radioactive element to decay

PERIOD	MILLIONS OF YEARS AGO
PERMIAN	251
CARBONIFEROUS	299
DEVONIAN	359
SILURIAN	416
ORDOVICIAN	444
CAMBRIAN	488
	542
	4,600

Geologic Time Scale a record of geologic events and life forms in Earth's history

Your Turn
Talk with a partner about types of fossils, what you can learn from rocks, and how you can tell the age of rocks.

Academic Vocabulary

- Explain that the word *geologic* comes from the root word, *geo-*, meaning "Earth." *Geology* and *geologist* come from the same root.

- Guide students through decoding the word *paleontologist*. The prefix *paleo-* means "old" or "ancient." The suffix *–ologist* refers to someone who studies. So *paleontologist* means "someone who studies ancient prehistory," as represented by fossils.

- Introduce any unfamiliar words by pronouncing them a few times with students. Explain that the word *preserve* means "to keep in existence" or "to make last."

- Emphasize to students that the word *evidence* refers to any material, observable event, or fact that proves or disproves something.

↻ Comprehensible Input

Vocabulary in Context Picture It!

1. **Say the Term** Say each term slowly, artificially stressing each syllable. Have students repeat. Then say the term more naturally and have students repeat.

2. **Introduce Word Meaning** Connect each term to the visual that illustrates it.

3. **Demonstrate** Use gestures and visuals to demonstrate each term.

4. **Apply** After each term has been discussed, have students demonstrate understanding with Talk About It.

Talk About It

Guide Discussion Before students start their independent discussion, check for understanding with the following sentence starters:

1. *A fossil made of a thin layer of carbon is a . . .* (carbon film).

2. *An animal's tracks can form a . . .* (trace fossil).

3. *The bottom layer of sedimentary rock is the oldest. This law is the called the . . .* (law of superposition).

4. *A rock's age in years is its . . .* (absolute age).

5. *A place where rock layers are lost is an . . .* (unconformity).

6. *The time it takes for half of a radioactive element to decay is its . . .* (half-life).

R T I Response to Intervention

If students have difficulty understanding the meaning of the terms *absolute and relative age . . .*

Then review the concept by comparing students' absolute ages with their relative ages, as compared with the ages of their siblings or classmates.

Your Turn

Guide Discussion Encourage students to look at prefixes such as *in-* (meaning "inside" or "inward"), *ex-* (meaning "outside" or "outward"), *super-* (meaning "over" or "above"), and *un-* (meaning "not").

Language Production

Do You Understand?

Comprehension Support Before students start the activity, review the rock diagram in the Picture It box. Explain that sedimentary rock layers form when sediment is deposited on the ground and hardens into rock. The oldest layer is usually at the bottom. Read the vocabulary terms out loud as you point out and explain each term in the diagram. Advise students to use *both* a pencil *and* an eraser to complete the activity.

Model Read all instructions. Model using a pencil and an eraser to complete the work through the steps. Demonstrate how students should look for action words, such as *draw* or *add*, in each statement.

Talk About It

Guide Discussion Read the directions chorally with students and have them work with their partners to complete the sentences. For each sentence, have students point to the place in their diagram that shows what is being described.

Your Turn

Guide Discussion Listen to students as they explain their diagrams. Help them correct any mistakes or misunderstandings.

Do You Understand?

Follow the instructions to draw a diagram. Add labels to your drawing. Look back at the Picture It box for help.

1. Draw one layer of rock at the bottom of the box.
2. Add a layer on top of it.
3. Add another rock layer. Draw a fossil in it.
4. Magma has pushed into the two bottom rock layers and hardened. Draw this intrusion.
5. A volcano has added a layer of lava, which has cooled into rock. Draw this extrusion.
6. Add a layer of rock on top.

Talk About It

Use the terms from the Picture It box to complete the sentences.

1. The rock layer that forms first is the . . . oldest rock.
2. The rock layer that forms last is the . . . youngest rock.
3. The age of a rock compared to other rocks is its . . . relative age.
4. Fossils that show the relative age of rock are . . . index fossils.
5. Magma that hardens inside or underneath other rock layers is an . . . intrusion.
6. Lava that hardens on top of other rock layers is an . . . extrusion.

Your Turn

Explain to a partner how you made your diagram. Tell what you did first, second, next, and so on. Use the vocabulary terms.

48   Lesson 12

Leveled Language Proficiency

Students at each proficiency level should be able to perform the following tasks.

Listening/Speaking

Early Beginner/Beginner Repeat vocabulary terms correctly, and identify each one on the rock diagram using gestures, single words, or short phrases.

Early Intermediate Listen carefully to connect new information to prior knowledge. Use short phrases and expressions in discussions with peers about fossils.

Intermediate Follow oral directions with little to no help. Explain in complete sentences the vocabulary terms and use sequence words correctly to describe the order in which sediment or rock layers are deposited.

Advanced/Transitioning Follow oral directions independently. Present spoken explanations of fossil formation.

Look at the rock layer diagram. Write the name of each major span of geologic time on the lines to the right.

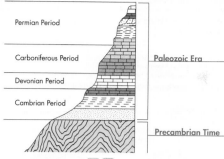

Permian Period

Carboniferous Period

Devonian Period   Paleozoic Era

Cambrian Period

Precambrian Time

Talk and Write About It
Complete the statements about the rock layers of the Grand Canyon, as pictured above.

1. The Geologic Time Scale is a record of ___geological events___.

2. It is known that the rock layer that formed in Precambrian time is the oldest because _it is the bottom layer_

3. The youngest layer in the Grand Canyon formed _during the Permian period_

4. The law of superposition states that the youngest rock _is the top layer_

5. The absolute age of the youngest Grand Canyon rock layer is _____ _251 to 299 million years old_

Produce Language
Write what you learned about how scientists find the age of rocks and fossils. Use as many vocabulary terms as you can.

_____

_____

_____

Fossils and Earth's History   **49**

Leveled Language Proficiency

Students at each proficiency level should be able to perform the following tasks.

Reading/Writing

Early Beginner/Beginner Locate words that describe diagrams of Earth's layers, and draw pictures to represent key vocabulary terms about fossils.

Early Intermediate Read simple phrases and recognize words relating to fossils. Write short phrases to describe the ages of rock layers.

Intermediate Read and comprehend phrases related to Earth's history. Write a description of what scientists can learn from fossils and rocks.

Advanced/Transitioning Read aloud sentences related to radioactive decay and half-lives. Write complete sentences describing the methods scientists use to date rocks and fossils.

↻ Assess Understanding

Your Turn

Model Point out the eras and periods on the Geologic Time Scale. Tell students that scientists developed this time scale based on what index fossils told them about the relative age of rock layers, and what radioactive decay showed about the absolute age of rock layers.

Point out the layers on the rock diagram of the Grand Canyon. Explain that each layer formed during a different period on the Geologic Time Scale.

Talk and Write About It

On Their Own Invite student groups to explain how fossils might have helped paleontologists develop the Geologic Time Scale.

Produce Language

On Their Own Have student pairs write and talk about ways that scientists learn about Earth's history by studying rocks and fossils. Encourage them to use as many vocabulary terms as they can. Let them refer back to pictures and diagrams in the lesson as needed.

Wrap Up

Table Talk Have students reflect on what they learned. Encourage students to build fluency by reading their writing in groups or to the class.

✔ **Learned** and applied vocabulary related to fossils and Earth's history

✔ **Spoken** statements about absolute and relative ages of Earth's layers

✔ **Written** statements about how scientists can tell the age of rocks and fossils

Lesson 13

Earth's Water

Vocabulary water cycle, evaporation, condensation, precipitation, transpiration, eutrophication, permeable, unsaturated zone, impermeable, saturated zone, water table, tributary, watershed, reservoir

Science Background

- The water cycle moves water between land, water sources, and the atmosphere.

- Water seeps between soil particles and through cracks and spaces in rock layers and gradually moves into underground areas.

- A river system consists of a river and all of the streams and smaller rivers that flow into it.

Earth's Water

 Big Question How does water move through and around Earth?

You will . . .
- Learn how water moves in the water cycle.
- Identify parts of river systems.
- Use new vocabulary terms related to the water cycle.

Talk About It

Where is water found on Earth? Talk with a partner about each picture below. Then brainstorm a list of places water is found.

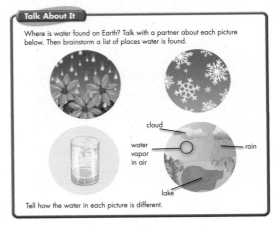

cloud
water vapor in air
rain
lake

Tell how the water in each picture is different.

Predict
Look at the Big Question and the "You will . . ." statements at the top of the page. Describe what you think you are going to learn in this lesson.

I think I am going to learn about . . .

50 Lesson 13

Frontload the Lesson

 How does water move through and around Earth?

Talk About It

Build Background Review the three forms of water with students. Write *solid, liquid,* and *gas* and sketch an example of each. Use examples from nature, such as a glacier, rain, and water vapor. Use these as a starting point for students' list of where they find water on Earth.

Content and Language

Predict

Model Read the Big Question and the objectives aloud. Correct any mispronunciations that students make as they read. Demonstrate position words, such as *through* and *around*. Use a classroom globe to emphasize word meaning as you say these words.

Guide Discussion Ask students to restate one of the objectives in their own words and predict what they might learn.

Leveled Instruction

Early Beginner Ask students to say each part of the water cycle, and point to each one in a diagram as they say it aloud.

Beginner Ask students to form their own question about one of the vocabulary words from the lesson. Their question may try to clarify meaning or better understand a concept related to the word. Answer each question students have.

Early Intermediate/Intermediate Ask students to compare different places where water falls on Earth. For example, ask them to compare a reservoir and a tributary. Ask, *Which is moving water and which is still water?* Ask, *Which is used by humans?*

Advanced/Transitioning Challenge these students to find vocabulary words and concepts from the lesson that have to do with groundwater and how it gets underground. Ask them to read short passages about groundwater in classroom books or magazines and then to explain how water moves underground.

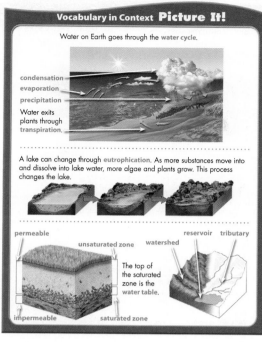

Water on Earth goes through the water cycle.

condensation
evaporation
precipitation
Water exits
plants through
transpiration.

A lake can change through eutrophication. As more substances move into and dissolve into lake water, more algae and plants grow. This process changes the lake.

permeable

unsaturated zone   watershed   reservoir   tributary

The top of
the saturated
zone is the
water table.

impermeable   saturated zone

Your Turn
With a partner, talk about the pictures in the Picture It box. Discuss how water moves through the air and soil.

Earth's Water   **51**

Academic Vocabulary

- Point out to students that some terms from the lesson are compound words, such as *groundwater, watershed,* and *wetland.* These are words that are one word made from two different words combined. Also point out the open compound words from the lesson—words that are two words treated a compound because the two parts mean one thing together: *water cycle, water table, unsaturated zone, saturated zone.*

- Write the suffix *-ion* on the board and have students name the vocabulary terms that use this suffix. Repeat with the prefixes *un-* and *im-* and have students name the terms that use these prefixes. Then discuss what these word parts mean based on what the students know about the meanings of the vocabulary terms.

- The word *impermeable* means "raincoat" in Spanish. Discuss or demonstrate materials that are permeable and impermeable. Say, *If I pour water on soil it will permeate or seep into the soil. If I pour water on a rock, it will roll off or sit on top of the rock. The soil is permeable, and the rock is impermeable. Most clothes are permeable to rain. A raincoat is impermeable to rain.*

↻ Comprehensible Input

Vocabulary in Context: Picture It!

1. **Say the Term** Say each term slowly, artificially stressing each syllable. Have students repeat. Then say the term more naturally and have students repeat.

2. **Introduce Word Meaning** Connect each term to the visual that illustrates it.

3. **Demonstrate** Use gestures and visuals to demonstrate each term.

4. **Apply** After each term has been discussed, have students demonstrate understanding with Talk About It.

Talk About It

Guide Discussion Before students start their independent discussion, check for understanding with the following sentences:

1. *When water changes from liquid to gas, it* (evaporates).

2. *When water vapor rises and cools, it may* (condense).

3. *Rain and snow are examples of* (precipitation).

4. *Water moves out of plants through the process called* (transpiration).

5. *Water can pass through* (permeable) *materials and the* (unsaturated) *zone.*

6. *Water cannot pass through* (impermeable) *materials or the* (saturated) *zone.*

7. *Water for human use is stored in* (reservoirs).

RTI Response to Intervention

If students have difficulty pronouncing the word *eutrophication* . . .

Then Repeat the word slowly several times, stressing each syllable.

Your Turn

Guide Discussion Call on volunteers to explain parts of the water cycle.

Language Production

Do You Understand?

Comprehension Support Before students start the activity, point to each picture and have students talk about what they see. In addition to words such as *evaporation*, *condensation*, or *precipitation*, encourage students to use other water-related words, such as *puddle*, *cloud*, *raindrops*, *glass of water*, or *snowflakes*.

Model Demonstrate how students can ask themselves questions to help them do the activity. Say, *In which part of the water cycle does water move up into the air? In which part of the cycle does water fall from the sky?*

Talk About It

Guide Discussion Encourage students to refer to the pictures and labels in the Picture It! box for help with this exercise.

Your Turn

Guide Discussion Listen to pairs of students as they compare their answers. Help them correct any mistakes or misunderstandings about how water moves through Earth's land and atmosphere.

A Closer Look

Model If students have difficulty thinking of other words with the suffix *-able*, write the words *renewable*, *agreeable*, and *doable* on the board. Call on volunteers to explain what each word means. Then ask students for other examples.

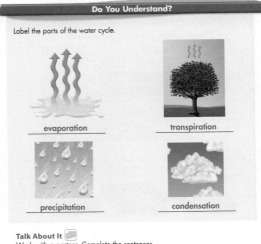

Do You Understand?

Label the parts of the water cycle.

evaporation

transpiration

precipitation

condensation

Talk About It
Work with a partner. Complete the sentences.
1. Water moves around Earth in the . . . water cycle.
2. Water is given off by the leaves of trees during . . . transpiration.
3. During precipitation, water can fall into a . . . , . . . , or . . . reservoir, watershed, tributary.
4. Water droplets gather into clouds during a process called . . . condensation.

Your Turn
Work with a partner. Compare your answers. Talk about other ways water moves during the different stages of the water cycle.

A Closer Look

Word Parts The suffix *-able* means "capable of being." Which two terms in this lesson contain the suffix *-able*? What do these terms mean?

Leveled Language Proficiency

Students at each proficiency level should be able to perform the following tasks.

Listening/Speaking

Early Beginner/Beginner Gesture or point to respond to oral directions. Use a word or a short phrase in response to questions about the water cycle.

Early Intermediate Respond to a description of a *water table* by finding a picture of it in the lesson. Describe another meaning of the word *table* by using a complete sentence.

Intermediate Listen to a description of *permeable* and *impermeable* materials. Paraphrase what is being said, using complete sentences.

Advanced/Transitioning Listen and contribute to a discussion about the water cycle. Use complete and complex sentences to explain how water moves between different locations on Earth and in the atmosphere.

Your Turn
Draw the arrows to show the stages of the water cycle. Complete the diagram to show each stage.

Drawings should include clouds in sky, precipitation, and arrows coming up from lake and from plant life, going to clouds, and down from clouds to Earth/mountain.

Talk and Write About It
Complete the statements about how water moves on Earth.

① The steps of the water cycle are <u>evaporation, transpiration, condensation, precipitation</u>

② When people collect water in one area, it is called a <u>reservoir</u>.

③ Water in a tributary flows into <u>larger rivers</u>.

④ A watershed is <u>a land area that supplies water to a river system</u>.

Produce Language
Write about how water cycles on Earth. Use as many vocabulary terms as you can.

_____
_____
_____
_____
_____

Earth's Water **53**

Leveled Language Proficiency

Students at each proficiency level should be able to perform the following tasks.

Reading/Writing

Early Beginner/Beginner Locate words that describe the movement of water. Draw and label pictures to show at least two different stages of the water cycle.

Early Intermediate Read to find a reference to permeable materials. Write short phrases to describe permeability.

Intermediate Comprehend written phrases that describe the movement of water through the water cycle. Write a description of how plants contribute water to the water cycle.

Advanced/Transitioning Read aloud sentences that describe where water moves on land. Write complete sentences describing the changes that occur as water moves through a river system.

↻ Assess Understanding

Your Turn

Model Before students complete the activity, have them review the Big Question. Students should then compare the diagram to water cycle diagrams they have seen in the lesson. Remind them that they will need to add some drawing and some arrows to the diagram in order to turn it into a labeled picture of the water cycle. Remind them that the arrows on the diagram should show which direction water flows through the cycle.

Talk and Write About It

On Their Own Encourage students to work together to complete the sentences if they have difficulty doing it on their own. Encourage them to look back at the lesson to get ideas if necessary.

Produce Language

On Their Own Have student pairs both talk and then write about ways that water moves throughout Earth in a cycle. Have them name the distinct stages of the water cycle and name places on Earth where water is found.

Wrap Up

Table Talk Have students reflect on what they learned. Encourage students to build fluency by reading their writing in groups or to the class.

✔ **Learned** and applied vocabulary related to the movement of water on Earth

✔ **Spoken** statements about how water moves during the water cycle

✔ **Written** statements about places where water is stored and found on Earth

Lesson 14

The Oceans

Vocabulary salinity, wave, current, climate, El Niño, intertidal zone, neritic zone, open-ocean zone, plankton, seamount, trench, continental slope, continental shelf, abyssal plain, mid-ocean ridge, tsunami

Materials a globe, a map showing ocean currents

Science Background

- Ocean water varies in salinity, temperature, and depth.

- Most waves form when winds transmit their energy to water.

- Deep currents are caused by differences in density of ocean water. Surface currents are driven mainly by winds.

- Ocean zones include the intertidal zone, the neritic zone, and the open-ocean zone.

Frontload the Lesson

What are some qualities of Earth's oceans?

Talk About It

Build Background Read the instructions with students. Ask students who have been to the ocean to tell what they saw while there. Then read the vocabulary terms aloud as students copy them on cards. Leave time for sorting the cards. Encourage student pairs to describe words they know to one another.

Content and Language

Predict

Model Read the Big Question and the objectives aloud. As students repeat after you, correct any mispronunciations.

Guide Discussion Ask students to read the objectives aloud with you. Then, have them use the sentence starter to make a prediction.

The Oceans

Big Question What are some qualities of Earth's oceans?

You will . . .
- Describe how ocean water varies in salinity, temperature, and depth.
- Differentiate waves and currents.
- Identify ocean zones and features of the ocean floor.
- Understand and use vocabulary terms related to the ocean.

Talk About It

Step 1 Copy the science terms in the Picture It box on index cards as your teacher reads them aloud.

Step 2 Then place the cards into three piles.

wave	depth	current

Pile 1 I have never heard of this word before.

Pile 2 I have heard this term before, but I don't know how it is used in science.

Pile 3 I understand the meaning of this term in science.

Step 3 Talk with a partner about your Pile 3 words. Share what you know with one another. Then, find a new partner and discuss Pile 3 words again. Now see if you want to move any cards from Pile 1 into other piles.

Predict

Look at the Big Question and the "You will . . ." statements at the top of the page. Describe what you think you are going to learn in this lesson.

I think I am going to learn about . . .

Leveled Instruction

Early Beginner Point to pictures and objects, such as salt, and say each word aloud for students. Have them repeat. Turn on a fan or have students make a folded-paper fan to have students feel air moving, and say *wind*.

Beginner Point to pictures and diagrams to provide explanation. Have students repeat the vocabulary words you use. Model each activity.

Early Intermediate/Intermediate Encourage students to work fairly independently. Use visual and physical demonstrations to help students connect new vocabulary terms with familiar words in both English and in their native languages. Ask questions and tell students to respond in complete sentences.

Advanced/Transitioning Explain and discuss concepts with students, using complex sentences. Ask questions and tell students to respond using complete sentences.

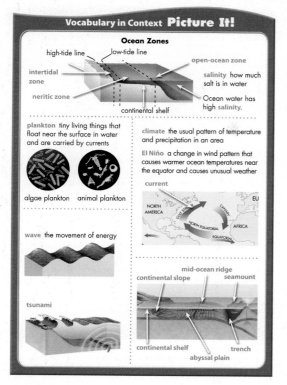

Academic Vocabulary

- Begin by writing the term *salinity* on the board. Underline the letters *sal*, and explain that *sal* is the Latin word for "salt."

- Explain that the term *intertidal* has a prefix and a base word. The prefix *inter-* means "between." The base word *tide* refers to the rise and fall of ocean water produced by the pull of the sun and moon. *Intertidal* means "between the tides."

- The suffix *-al*, which means "of," is also part of the word *continental*. The base word *continent* combined with the suffix means "of a continent." The term *abyssal* comes from the root word *abyss*, which means "something that is so deep it cannot be measured." Tell students that, although the abyssal plain is very large and deep, scientists have measured its depth.

- Explain that the term *wave* can mean either "a swell in water" or "a fluttering of the hand or flag."

- Encourage students to practice using words for comparing and contrasting terms. Beginning students use the words *more* and *less* to modify adjectives such as *deep* and *salty*. Intermediate students can use comparative and superlative forms of adjectives such as *deeper, deepest; saltier, saltiest.*

↻ Comprehensible Input

Vocabulary in Context: Picture It!

1. **Say the Term** Say each term slowly, artificially stressing each syllable. Have students repeat. Then say the term more naturally and have students repeat.

2. **Introduce Word Meaning** Connect each term to the visual that illustrates it.

3. **Demonstrate** Use gestures and visuals to demonstrate.

4. **Apply** After each term has been discussed, have students demonstrate understanding with Talk About It.

Talk About It

Guide Discussion Before students start their independent discussion, check for understanding with the following sentence starters:

1. *The zone between lines for high tide and low tide is the . . .* (intertidal zone).

2. *A giant wave formed on the ocean floor is a . . .* (tsunami).

3. *A volcanic mountain on the ocean floor is a . . .* (seamount).

4. *Temperature and rainfall are part of an area's . . .* (climate).

5. *The ocean zone starting at the low-tide line is the . . .* (neritic zone).

6. *The deepest ocean zone is the . . .* (open-ocean zone).

R T I Response to Intervention

If students have difficulty pronouncing the word *tsunami* . . .

Then explain that the word comes from Japanese, so some letters are pronounced differently from the way they are pronounced in many English words. Review the pronunciation of the *ts* and the vowels.

Your Turn

Guide Discussion Encourage students to draw a picture or diagram of several vocabulary terms, and then explain the terms to a partner.

The Oceans

 ## Language Production

Do You Understand?

Comprehension Support Before students start the activity, review the terms in the illustration, and ask them if they have any questions.

Model Demonstrate how students can ask themselves questions to do the activity. Say, *What is the first zone called? It is between the tide lines. If I don't remember, I can look back at the Picture It box.*

Talk About It

Guide Discussion Read the sentences aloud with students as they work together to complete the items.

Your Turn

Guide Discussion Listen to student discussions. Help them correct any mistakes or misunderstandings as needed.

A Closer Look

On Their Own Have students work in pairs to complete this word study activity. Then have them suggest other sentences or familiar phrases using the term *current* as an adjective and as a noun. Challenge groups of students to use the noun form of the word in each of the science contexts mentioned.

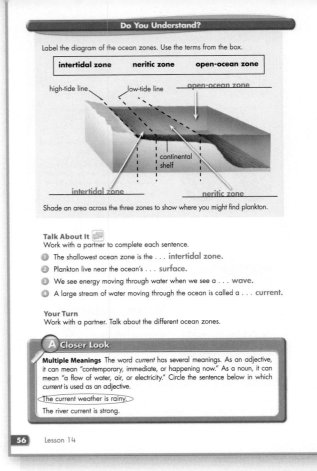

Do You Understand?

Label the diagram of the ocean zones. Use the terms from the box.

| intertidal zone | neritic zone | open-ocean zone |

high-tide line   low-tide line   open-ocean zone

continental shelf

intertidal zone   neritic zone

Shade an area across the three zones to show where you might find plankton.

Talk About It
Work with a partner to complete each sentence.

1. The shallowest ocean zone is the . . . intertidal zone.
2. Plankton live near the ocean's . . . surface.
3. We see energy moving through water when we see a . . . wave.
4. A large stream of water moving through the ocean is called a . . . current.

Your Turn
Work with a partner. Talk about the different ocean zones.

A Closer Look

Multiple Meanings The word *current* has several meanings. As an adjective, it can mean "contemporary, immediate, or happening now." As a noun, it can mean "a flow of water, air, or electricity." Circle the sentence below in which *current* is used as an adjective.

The current weather is rainy.

The river current is strong.

Leveled Language Proficiency

Students at each proficiency level should be able to perform the following tasks.

Listening/Speaking

Early Beginner Point to appropriate pictures in response to oral directions. Use a word or gesture in response to questions about ocean vocabulary.

Beginner Point to appropriate pictures in response to oral directions. Respond appropriately using ocean vocabulary.

Early Intermediate Use short phrases to respond to questions about ocean temperature, salinity, or depth. Respond to multi-sentence directions during activities.

Intermediate Follow oral directions with little or no help. Identify, using complete sentences, ocean zones and features of the ocean floor.

Advanced/Transitioning Follow oral directions independently. Speak complete, complex sentences to describe features of the ocean floor.

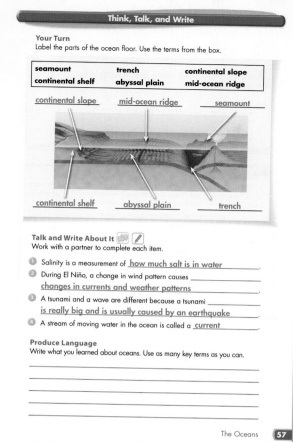

Your Turn

Label the parts of the ocean floor. Use the terms from the box.

| seamount | trench | continental slope |
| continental shelf | abyssal plain | mid-ocean ridge |

continental slope   mid-ocean ridge   seamount

continental shelf   abyssal plain   trench

Talk and Write About It 💬 ✏️
Work with a partner to complete each item.

1. Salinity is a measurement of <u>how much salt is in water</u>.
2. During El Niño, a change in wind pattern causes <u>changes in currents and weather patterns</u>.
3. A tsunami and a wave are different because a tsunami <u>is really big and is usually caused by an earthquake</u>.
4. A stream of moving water in the ocean is called a <u>current</u>.

Produce Language
Write what you learned about oceans. Use as many key terms as you can.

_____
_____
_____
_____
_____

The Oceans **57**

Leveled Language Proficiency

Students at each proficiency level should be able to perform the following tasks.

Reading/Writing

Early Beginner/Beginner Match an ocean floor diagram with printed words. Write terms to label the diagram.

Early Intermediate Read sentences about characteristics of the ocean. Write short phrases to describe at least two characteristics.

Intermediate Read and discuss sentences relating to the ocean. Write a description of the different ocean zones.

Advanced/Transitioning With some support, read about the oceans in a grade-level science textbook. Peer-edit another student's sentences about ocean features.

↻ Assess Understanding

Your Turn

Model Work with students to label one of the features in the diagram. For example, say, *I know that trenches are the deepest parts of the ocean, so I find the deepest part in the picture.*

Talk and Write About It

On Their Own Read the instructions aloud with students. Encourage student pairs to begin by discussing the sentences and then to collaborate in writing answers. Tell students that they can look back at the Picture It box for help.

Produce Language

On Their Own To answer the Big Question, have student pairs both write and talk about the characteristics of the ocean. Encourage them to use as many vocabulary terms as they can.

Wrap Up

Table Talk Invite students to reflect on what they learned. Encourage students to build fluency by reading their writing in groups or to the class.

✔ **Learned** and applied vocabulary related to ocean waters

✔ **Spoken** statements about characteristics of waves and currents

✔ **Written** statements about ocean zones and the ocean floor

Lesson 15

The Atmosphere

Vocabulary weather, atmosphere, water vapor, density, air pressure, barometer, altitude, troposphere, stratosphere, mesosphere, thermosphere

Materials a beach ball or other round object

 Science Background

- The atmosphere of Earth is made up of nitrogen, oxygen, carbon dioxide, water vapor, and other gases, as well as particles of solids and droplets of liquids.

- Air pressure changes in different parts of the atmosphere. As altitude decreases, air pressure increases. As altitude increases, air pressure decreases.

- The layers of Earth's atmosphere are the troposphere, stratosphere, mesosphere, and thermosphere. The ozone layer is found in the stratosphere. Earth's weather takes place in the troposphere.

Frontload the Lesson

THE BIG ? **What are the characteristics of the atmosphere?**

Talk About It

Build Background Show students a ball and explain that every ball has the shape of a *sphere*. Then explain that the atmosphere makes an invisible sphere around Earth.

Content and Language

Predict

Model Have students read the objectives aloud. Model how to read through difficult words, such as *altitude*. Say, *I may learn the meaning of this word as I keep reading.*

Guide Discussion Ask students to choose one of the objectives and predict what they might learn about that topic.

The Atmosphere

 Big Question What are the characteristics of the atmosphere?

You will . . .
- Learn what makes up Earth's atmosphere.
- Understand how changes in altitude affect air pressure.
- Identify the four main layers of Earth's atmosphere.
- Use and understand key terms related to Earth's atmosphere.

Talk About It

Earth is surrounded by the atmosphere. Look at the picture of things you might see in the sky. How high above Earth do you think each one is? Circle the object that is so far from Earth's surface that it is not in Earth's atmosphere.

Predict

Look at the Big Question and the "You will . . ." statements at the top of the page. Describe what you think you are going to learn in this lesson.

I think I am going to learn about . . .

58   Lesson 15

Leveled Instruction

Early Beginner Ask students to say the name of each layer of the atmosphere, and point to each one in a diagram as they say it aloud.

Beginner Have students choose a picture from the lesson and form a phrase or complete sentence about it if possible.

Early Intermediate/Intermediate Ask students to choose two layers of the atmosphere and compare them. For example, they might compare the highest and lowest levels. Have them make a comparison statement with little or no help.

Advanced/Transitioning Ask these students to find vocabulary terms from the lesson that have to do with weather, including how it is measured. Then have them explain the terms to their classmates, using visuals.

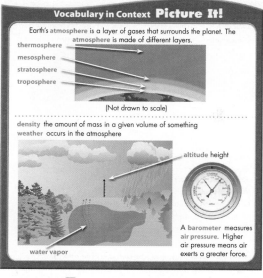

Vocabulary in Context **Picture It!**

Earth's **atmosphere** is a layer of gases that surrounds the planet. The **atmosphere** is made of different layers.

thermosphere
mesosphere
stratosphere
troposphere

(Not drawn to scale)

density the amount of mass in a given volume of something
weather occurs in the atmosphere

altitude height

water vapor

A **barometer** measures **air pressure**. Higher air pressure means air exerts a greater force.

Talk About It
Work with a partner. Use the terms in the box above to finish these sentences.

1. The lowest layer of the atmosphere is the . . . troposphere.
2. A barometer is a tool that measures . . . air pressure.
3. A measurement of something's distance above the ground is called . . . altitude.
4. Water in the form of a gas is called . . . water vapor.
5. *Sunny* and *rainy* are words that describe . . . weather.

Your Turn
Talk with a partner about the pictures in the Picture It box. What is falling from the cloud? What is rising from the lake?

The Atmosphere   **59**

Academic Vocabulary

- Point out the suffix *-meter* in the word *barometer*. Remind students that the word *meter* refers to measurement. Then explain that a *barometer* is a tool for measuring pressure in the atmosphere. Ask students to name other words that use the word part *-meter* as a suffix, such as *thermometer*.

- Explain the idiom *made up of*. Tell students that the words themselves do not help them to figure out the meaning of the phrase. When we say the atmosphere is "made up of" different layers, we mean that there are different layers that are part of the atmosphere. To illustrate the point, have them tell you different parts that a sandwich is "made up of."

- Cognates are words that have the same or similar roots and meanings in two languages. Have students share any vocabulary terms they recognize as cognates of words in their first language. For example, the Spanish word for *atmosphere* is *atmósphera*.

↻ Comprehensible Input

Vocabulary in Context: Picture It!

1. **Say the Term** Say each term slowly, artificially stressing each syllable. Have students repeat. Then say the term more naturally, and have students repeat.

2. **Introduce Word Meaning** Connect each term to the visual that illustrates it.

3. **Demonstrate** Use gestures and visuals to demonstrate.

   - Demonstrate altitude, air pressure, and density by showing different heights with your hands and body. Crouch down and say, *This represents a low altitude. The air pressure is greater closest to Earth's surface. The air is thicker, denser.* Stand on tiptoe and say, *This represents a high altitude. The air pressure is less at a high altitude. The air is thinner, less dense.*

   - Sketch a model of Earth and its layers of atmosphere on the board. To illustrate changes in altitude and air pressure, use the same sentences you said above.

4. **Apply** After all of the terms have been discussed, have students demonstrate understanding with Talk About It.

Talk About It

Guide Discussion Ask students to choose a word related to each picture in the Picture It! box and use it in a sentence.

RTI Response to Intervention

If students have difficulty pronouncing the layers of the atmosphere . . .

Then divide each word into two parts. Repeat the parts slowly and have students repeat (*atmo sphere*). Then put the parts together to form each word (*atmo sphere, atmosphere*).

Your Turn

Guide Discussion Encourage students to talk about different kinds of weather they are familiar with. Explain that all weather activity happens in the troposphere.

The Atmosphere

Language Production

Do You Understand?

Comprehension Support Before students start the activity, read each term aloud along with the students. Remind them that they can look back at the similar diagram in the Picture It! box.

Model Read the first term with students. Say, *I know that the mesosphere is not the lowest layer of the atmosphere. Which layer is it? Let's try to remember. We can always check the diagram in the Picture It! box if we can't remember.* Guide students in labeling the layers.

Talk About It

Guide Discussion Have students work in groups if they have trouble completing the sentences.

Your Turn

Guide Discussion Listen to student discussions. Help correct any mistakes or misunderstandings about each layer of the atmosphere. If students are having trouble deciding what to talk about, list ideas on the board together, such as *weather, altitude, air pressure,* and *density.*

A Closer Look

On Their Own Ask students to underline the word part independently. Then have them use their own words to explain the word *sphere* and how it relates to the layers of the atmosphere.

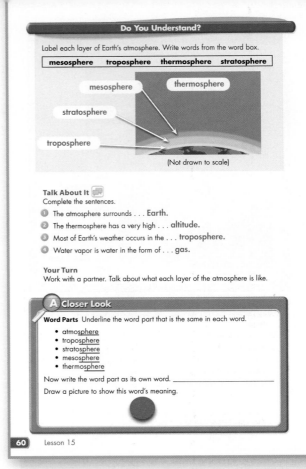

Do You Understand?

Label each layer of Earth's atmosphere. Write words from the word box.

| mesosphere | troposphere | thermosphere | stratosphere |

mesosphere   thermosphere

stratosphere

troposphere

(Not drawn to scale)

Talk About It
Complete the sentences.
1. The atmosphere surrounds . . . Earth.
2. The thermosphere has a very high . . . altitude.
3. Most of Earth's weather occurs in the . . . troposphere.
4. Water vapor is water in the form of . . . gas.

Your Turn
Work with a partner. Talk about what each layer of the atmosphere is like.

A Closer Look

Word Parts Underline the word part that is the same in each word.
- atmo<u>sphere</u>
- tropo<u>sphere</u>
- strato<u>sphere</u>
- meso<u>sphere</u>
- thermo<u>sphere</u>

Now write the word part as its own word. _____
Draw a picture to show this word's meaning.

60   Lesson 15

Leveled Language Proficiency

Students at each proficiency level should be able to perform the following tasks.

Listening/Speaking

Early Beginner/Beginner Gesture or point to identify the layers of the atmosphere, as they are spoken out loud. Use a word or a short spoken phrase in response to questions about Earth's atmosphere.

Early Intermediate Respond to a spoken description of *water vapor* by finding a picture in the lesson that could illustrate the term. Use a short phrase or sentence to orally describe what water vapor is.

Intermediate Listen to a description of *air pressure.* Paraphrase what is being said, using complete sentences.

Advanced/Transitioning Listen and respond to a discussion about the layers of the atmosphere. Use complete and complex sentences to orally explain the difference between the troposphere and the stratosphere.

Your Turn

Draw a picture to show each term. Then write a sentence about each picture.

Weather	Water Vapor	Barometer
Drawings should illustrate the word in each box. Sentences will vary, but should mention the term and be relevant to the concept and picture drawn.		
_____ _____ _____ _____	_____ _____ _____ _____	_____ _____ _____ _____

Talk and Write About It

Complete the statements about the atmosphere.

1. Earth's weather happens in the lowest layer of the <u>atmosphere</u>.
2. Wood floats in water, but a brick sinks, because wood and a brick have different <u>densities</u>.
3. The tool that measures air pressure is called a <u>barometer</u>.
4. The layers of the atmosphere are the <u>troposphere, stratosphere, mesosphere, and thermosphere</u>.

Produce Language

Write about what you learned about the Earth's atmosphere. Use as many vocabulary terms as you can. _____
_____
_____
_____
_____
_____

The Atmosphere **61**

Leveled Language Proficiency

Students at each proficiency level should be able to perform the following tasks.

Reading/Writing

Early Beginner/Beginner Locate words that describe the characteristics of the atmosphere. Draw and label pictures to show what happens at the lowest layer of the atmosphere.

Early Intermediate Read to find a reference to air pressure. Write short phrases to describe air pressure.

Intermediate Comprehend phrases that describe the characteristics of the atmosphere. Write a description of how two of the layers differ from each other.

Advanced/Transitioning Read aloud sentences that describe how weather changes in the atmosphere. Write complete sentences describing the changes that can occur with air pressure.

↻ Assess Understanding

Your Turn

Model Before students complete the activity, have them first identify places where the terms *weather, water vapor,* and *barometer* appear in the lesson. Then ask them to practice by explaining the pictures in the lesson. Finally, have students work on their own example by completing the activity.

Talk and Write About It

On Their Own Encourage student groups to work together to complete the sentences if they have difficulty completing them on their own. Allow them to look back at the lesson for ideas if necessary.

Produce Language

On Their Own Revisit the Big Question with students. Then have student pairs both write and talk about what happens in each layer of Earth's atmosphere. Ask them to name the distinct layers in order of increasing altitude.

Wrap Up

Table Talk Have students use their writing as a springboard to discuss the Big Question. Encourage students to build fluency by reading their writing in groups or to the class.

✔ **Learned** and applied vocabulary related to Earth's atmosphere

✔ **Heard** statements about each layer of the atmosphere

✔ **Read** statements about the differences and similarities between the layers of Earth's atmosphere

Energy in the Atmosphere

Vocabulary electromagnetic waves, radiation, scattering, greenhouse effect, temperature, thermal energy, thermometer, heat, convection, conduction, convection currents, Coriolis effect, latitude

Materials a globe

 Science Background

- Earth's atmosphere is heated by radiation from the sun.

- Heat is transferred in three ways: convection, conduction, and radiation. In the troposphere, heat is transferred mostly by convection.

- Winds are caused by differences in air pressure. These differences are caused by unequal heating of Earth's surface.

Frontload the Lesson

 How does the sun's energy affect Earth's atmosphere?

Talk About It

Build Background Ask students how heat travels from the sun to Earth. At this point in the lesson, accept their ideas uncritically. When they have finished the lesson, review the meaning of the term *radiation* and ask students to recall their earlier discussion.

Content and Language

Predict

Model Read the Big Question and the objectives aloud. As students repeat after you, correct any mispronunciations that students are making. Repeat the term *temperature* and clap as you say each syllable.

Guide Discussion Ask students to use their own words to describe one of the objectives.

Energy in the Atmosphere

 Big Question How does the sun's energy affect Earth's atmosphere?

You will . . .
- Describe the sun's role in warming Earth.
- Identify three ways heat is transferred.
- Use terms related to energy in the atmosphere.

Talk About It

Copy each term from Picture It on a piece of paper. As your teacher reads each term, __underline__ it with colored pencils or crayons.

- Want to Know
- Have Heard
- Know

Step 1 Underline the terms you know in __green__.

Step 2 Underline the terms you have heard but are not sure of in __yellow__.

Step 3 Underline the terms that you want to know in __red__.

What do you know about each term? Explain, using the sentence starters.

- I want to know what . . . means.
- I think . . . means . . .
- I know . . . means . . .

Predict
Look at the Big Question and the "You will . . ." statements at the top of the page. Tell what you think you are going to learn in this lesson.

I think I am going to learn about . . .

Leveled Instruction

Early Beginner/Beginner Pair beginners with more advanced students. Have the members of the pair collaborate to interpret the visuals in Picture It. Encourage beginners to try to pronounce the English terms they are learning.

Early Intermediate Throughout the lesson, encourage students to use simple sentences to relate the terms to the visuals and to define terms in their own words, using their native language to supplement English.

Intermediate Have students describe the Coriolis effect, either orally or in writing.

Advanced/Transitioning Many people have the misconception that the greenhouse effect is a bad thing. Have advanced and transitioning students do research and prepare a report explaining why life could not exist on Earth without the greenhouse effect.

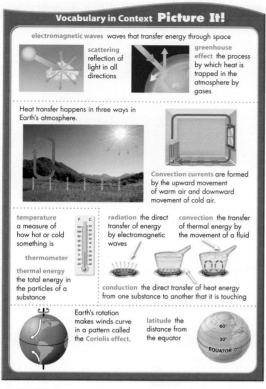

electromagnetic waves waves that transfer energy through space

scattering
reflection of
light in all
directions

greenhouse
effect the process
by which heat is
trapped in the
atmosphere by
gases

Heat transfer happens in three ways in
Earth's atmosphere.

Convection currents are formed
by the upward movement
of warm air and downward
movement of cold air.

temperature
a measure of
how hot or cold
something is

thermometer

thermal energy
the total energy in
the particles of a
substance

radiation the direct
transfer of energy
by electromagnetic
waves

convection the transfer
of thermal energy by
the movement of a fluid

conduction the direct transfer of heat energy
from one substance to another that it is touching

Earth's rotation
makes winds curve
in a pattern called
the Coriolis effect.

latitude the
distance from
the equator

Your Turn
Talk with a partner about the images in Picture It. Talk about sources of heat
that you are familiar with. Draw pictures to show sources of heat.

Energy in the Atmosphere 63

Academic Vocabulary

- Write the terms *thermal energy* and *thermometer* on the board and underline *therm-*. Have students explain how the two words are related and then have them list other words that use the word part, such as *thermos, thermostat,* and *thermal blanket.*

- Write the terms *greenhouse effect* and *Coriolis effect* on the board. Then write the Big Question, *How does the sun's energy affect Earth's atmosphere?* Underline the word *effect* in the two terms and the word *affect* in the Big Question. Explain that *effect* is a noun, or a thing, as in *cause and effect.* The word *affect* is usually used as a verb as in the sentence *The cold weather affected the crops.*

- Cognates are words that have the same or similar roots and meanings in two languages. Have students share any vocabulary terms they recognize as cognates to words in their first languages.

↻ Comprehensible Input

Vocabulary in Context: Picture It!

1. **Say the Term** Say each term slowly, artificially stressing each syllable. Have students repeat. Then say the term more naturally and have students repeat.

2. **Introduce Word Meaning** Connect each term to the visual that illustrates it.

3. **Demonstrate** Use gestures and visuals to demonstrate each term.

4. **Apply** After each term has been discussed, have students demonstrate understanding with Talk About It.

Talk About It

Guide Discussion Encourage students to first complete the sentences without looking. Then, as needed, have them consult the images in the Picture It box.

1. *Visible light is one type of . . .* (electromagnetic wave.)

2. *Light is dispersed or spread out in a process called . . .* (scattering.)

3. *Earth is kept at a comfortable temperature by the . . .* (greenhouse effect.)

4. *The effect of Earth's rotation on the direction of winds is called the . . .* (Coriolis effect.)

5. *A place's distance from the equator is its . . .* (latitude.)

R T I Response to Intervention

If students have difficulty pronouncing the term *electromagnetic waves . . .*

Then point out the two parts of the word *electromagnetic: electro-* and *-magnetic.* Remind students of the familiar words *electricity* and *magnet.* Have students practice saying each word part and then the two parts together.

Your Turn

Guide Discussion Ask students to list objects that emit heat. Have students think of things that warm them up when they are cold, such as fires, radiators, the sun, or a hot shower.

Language Production

Do You Understand?

Comprehension Support Before students start the activity, discuss the three ways that heat can be transferred. Have students share their ideas and list some examples of each type of heat transfer.

Model Demonstrate how students can ask themselves questions to help them complete the activity. Say, *Which type of heat transfer involves two objects touching each other? Which type of heat transfer involves the movement of liquids?*

Talk About It

Guide Discussion Read the sentence starters aloud with students as they work together to complete the sentences. If students have trouble distinguishing *convection, conduction,* and *radiation,* refer them to the diagram in Picture It. Discuss the three-part diagram of the electric burners. Point out that the diagram showing radiation does not have an object on it, so radiation does not involve transmission through objects that touch one another. Help students distinguish the difference between conduction and convection by pointing out the convection currents in the water in the pan on the third burner.

Your Turn

Guide Discussion Listen in and watch as students act out the three types of heat transfer. Correct any misconceptions. Invite volunteers to act out one of their ideas for the class.

In Other Words

Model Read the example sentence aloud for students and have them repeat it. Then ask, *What is another way to say this? What is another word, or words, for the verb* measure? Have students take turns reading the sentence aloud, choosing one of the yellow-highlighted words to fill in the space each time. Then have students suggest their own sentences that use forms of the verbs *measure, determine,* and *quantify.* Have students share their experiences of measuring. What have they measured? What tools or methods did they use to measure? How did they record or use their measurement? Why was it important?

Do You Understand?

Heat is transferred in three ways: *convection, conduction,* and *radiation.* Add labels to the image to show the three ways.

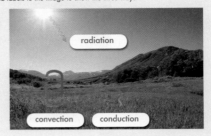

Talk About It
Complete the sentences.

1. Energy comes from the sun in the form of . . . radiation.
2. The transfer of heat by movement within a gas or liquid is called . . . convection.
3. The transfer of heat between two objects that are touching is called . . . conduction.
4. When hot air rises and cool air sinks, the result is the formation of . . . convection currents.
5. Thermal energy is the total energy of motion in . . . the particles of a substance.
6. The words *hot* and *cold* describe an object's . . . temperature.

Your Turn
Work with a partner. Take turns acting out three ways that heat can be transferred. Guess which types of heat transfer your partner is acting out.

In Other Words

Use a thermometer to **measure** the temperature.
　　　　　　　　　　　 quantify
　　　　　　　　　　　 determine

Leveled Language Proficiency

Students at each proficiency level should be able to perform the following tasks.

Listening/Speaking

Early Beginner/Beginner Use pictures, actions, or objects to respond to oral questions. Ask and respond to questions about familiar content, such as *Which object is hot?*

Early Intermediate In response to an oral prompt, speak simple sentences to explain the Coriolis effect. Orally narrate stories with a beginning, middle, and end about a familiar experience involving heat transfer.

Intermediate In response to hearing the terms *conduction* and *convection,* give verbal explanations of how the concepts are similar and different. Participate in discussions using appropriate words related to three types of heat transfer.

Advanced/Transitioning Follow multiple-step oral directions independently. Elaborate on personal stories about experiences with hot and cold weather.

Your Turn

The greenhouse effect and the Coriolis effect describe two ways that energy behaves in the atmosphere. Add arrows to the pictures to show how each works.

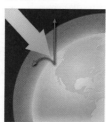

greenhouse effect

Coriolis effect

Talk and Write About It

Complete the statements about how energy behaves in Earth's atmosphere.

1. The greenhouse effect keeps Earth warm by <u>trapping some heat</u>

2. The Coriolis effect is a result of <u>Earth's rotation or spinning</u>.

3. Degrees of latitude tell you <u>how far away from the equator you</u> are

4. When you measure how hot or how cold an object is, you are measuring the object's <u>temperature</u>.

Produce Language

Write about how the greenhouse effect helps determine the temperature of the atmosphere. What would Earth be like without the greenhouse effect?

_____

_____

_____

_____

_____

Energy in the Atmosphere   **65**

Leveled Language Proficiency

Students at each proficiency level should be able to perform the following tasks.

Reading/Writing

Early Beginner/Beginner Read and understand previously learned vocabulary. Write labels on pictures of new concepts such as *greenhouse effect* and *heat transfer*.

Early Intermediate Use context to understand meaning of new vocabulary. Write a description of a familiar experience with heat.

Intermediate Apply knowledge of word analysis to better understand new vocabulary. Write a personal account of an experience with heat that has a focus and includes details.

Advanced/Transitioning Read passages about global winds and summarize the important ideas from the reading. Revise writing about the greenhouse or Coriolis effect to include more precise language and details.

↻ Assess Understanding

Your Turn

Model Discuss the greenhouse effect and the Coriolis effect with students before beginning the activity. On the board write the following sentences to serve as support for students: *The greenhouse effect traps some heat in the atmosphere. The Coriolis effect causes winds in the northern hemisphere to curve to the right and winds in the southern hemisphere to curve to the left.*

Talk and Write About It

On Their Own Encourage students to look back at the Picture It terms to help clarify meanings. In particular, refer them to the diagram of the greenhouse effect. Make sure they understand that the curving arrow on the left demonstrates the retention of energy by greenhouse gases. In contrast, the straight arrow on the right does not show the greenhouse effect; rather, it shows the reflection of some of the sun's energy back into space.

Produce Language

On Their Own Before writing, have students talk with a partner about why the greenhouse effect is important for life on Earth.

Wrap Up

Table Talk Have students review the Big Question and reflect on what they learned. Encourage students to build fluency by reading their writing in groups or to the class.

✔ **Learned** and applied vocabulary related to how the sun's energy affects Earth's atmosphere

✔ **Heard** statements about three types of heat transfer

✔ **Written** statements about the greenhouse effect

Lesson 17

Clouds and Precipitation

Vocabulary water cycle, evaporation, condensation, humidity, dew point, cirrus, cumulus, stratus, precipitation, rain gauge, flood, drought

Materials hand mirrors (optional)

 Science Background

- Rain, sleet, freezing rain, snow, and hail are all types of precipitation. They form based on atmospheric temperatures and dew points.

- Droughts are usually caused when dry weather systems remain in one place for weeks or months at a time. Floods can affect areas in a short amount of time.

 Frontload the Lesson

 What causes clouds and precipitation?

Talk About It

Build Background Most students will know that precipitation falls from clouds. Encourage discussion by asking what happens to soil and plants when no clouds form for a long period of time in an area. Also discuss what happens when there are clouds but no rain, and when there is a long period of heavy rain.

Content and Language

Predict

Model Read the Big Question and the objectives aloud. Repeat difficult words such as *precipitation*. Use gestures to show precipitation falling.

Guide Discussion Ask students to choose one of the objectives and tell what they think they will learn about that topic.

Clouds and Precipitation

 Big Question What causes clouds and precipitation?

You will . . .
- Identify the three main types of clouds.
- Learn about the different forms of precipitation.
- Understand what causes flooding and droughts.
- Understand and use key terms related to clouds and precipitation.

Talk About It

Talk about what clouds look like.

What connection do you think there is between clouds and the weather?

Predict
Look at the Big Question and the "You will . . ." statements at the top of the page. Describe what you think you are going to learn in this lesson.

I think I am going to learn about . . .

Leveled Instruction

Early Beginner Ask students to repeat the name of each cloud type after you read it aloud and to name each cloud type as you point to it.

Beginner Ask students to choose a picture from the lesson and ask a question about it using a complete sentence.

Early Intermediate/Intermediate Ask students to choose two forms of precipitation and compare them. For example, they might compare rain and snow. Have them explain each one and tell how they are alike and different.

Advanced/Transitioning Partner these students with beginning students. Have them point out pictures in the lesson that illustrate vocabulary words. Have them explain each of the concepts to the beginning level students.

Vocabulary in Context **Picture It!**

Clouds form as part of Earth's water cycle.
Humidity is the amount of water vapor in the air.

- cirrus
- cumulus
- evaporation
- precipitation
- stratus

The temperature at which condensation begins is the dew point.

drought   flood   rain gauge

Talk About It
Work with a partner. Use the words in the box above to complete the sentences.

1. Rainfall can be measured with a . . . **rain gauge.**
2. Clouds form in the process called . . . **condensation.**
3. When there is not enough rainfall, the result may be a . . . **drought.**
4. Too much rain or snow in an area can cause a . . . **flood.**
5. Rain is one form of . . . **precipitation.**

Your Turn
Talk with a partner about the terms in the Picture It box. Use some of the terms to talk about how you think clouds form.

Clouds and Precipitation   **67**

Academic Vocabulary

- Say the word *flood* for students and tell them that the word can be used in different ways. It can be a noun, as in *There is a flood in the valley.* It can also be used as a verb, as in *The river flooded yesterday.* Use the word in various sentences and ask students to identify whether it is used as a noun or a verb.

- Students may benefit from reviewing the terms *condensation, precipitation,* and *evaporation,* by looking back at the lesson on "Earth's Water."

- Explain that the term *relative* (as in *relative humidity*) is a multiple-meaning word. As a noun, it means "a member of a family." As an adjective, it means "compared to something else." Use the term in sample sentences and have students identify whether it is a noun or an adjective.

- Have students share any vocabulary terms they recognize as cognates of words in their first languages.

↻ Comprehensible Input

Vocabulary in Context: Picture It!

1. **Say the Term** Say each term slowly, artificially stressing each syllable. Have students repeat. Then say the term more naturally and have students repeat.

2. **Introduce Word Meaning** Connect each term to the visual that illustrates it.

3. **Demonstrate** Use gestures and visuals to demonstrate.

   - As you say the word *cirrus* aloud, write the word on the board. Stress that the *c* in *cirrus* makes the soft *c* sound, or the *s* sound.

   - Repeat the process as you write the word *cumulus* on the board. Say the word aloud and stress that the *c* in the word makes the hard *c* sound.

   - Ask students to breathe on hand mirrors. Have students observe the moisture deposited on the mirror, and explain that they have observed the process of condensation. Relate this to cloud formation.

4. **Apply** After each term has been discussed, have students demonstrate understanding with Talk About It.

Talk About It

Guide Discussion Ask students to choose a term from Picture It and use it in a sentence.

RTI Response to Intervention

If students have difficulty pronouncing the word *humidity* . . .

Then point out that the word includes the base word *humid.* Say *humid* aloud and have students repeat after you. Repeat the entire word again slowly pointing out that the emphasis or accent changes from the first syllable to the second.

Your Turn

Guide Discussion Encourage students to talk about different kinds of clouds. As they review the lesson concepts and vocabulary, encourage them to describe the connection between clouds and weather.

Clouds and Precipitation

↻ Language Production

Do You Understand?

Comprehension Support Stress that the quality of the drawings is not the most important part of the activity. What is important to show is how the cloud types differ.

Model Demonstrate how students can ask themselves questions to help them do the activity. Have them ask, *What kind of cloud is very high in the sky?*

Talk About It

Guide Discussion Have students work in pairs or small groups if they have trouble completing the sentences. Encourage them to use their drawings and the pictures on the previous page for guidance.

Your Turn

Guide Discussion Listen to student discussions as they compare their answers. Help students use the Picture It box to correct any mistakes or misunderstandings they have about the three cloud types.

In Other Words

On Their Own Have students underline the *-ation* suffix in each word. To encourage recollection of the three processes, review the pictures in the "Earth's Water" lesson. Then have students identify other words with the *-ation* suffix. If they have difficulty, you might list words such as *estimation, calculation,* and *radiation*.

Do You Understand?

Read each description of clouds. Write the name of each cloud. Then draw a picture.

• high in the sky • wispy, like feathers	• flat, spread out • low in the sky	• puffy like cotton
cirrus	stratus	cumulus

Talk About It
Complete the sentences.
1. Three types of clouds are . . . Sample: cirrus, stratus, cumulus.
2. High, wispy clouds are . . . cirrus.
3. Clouds that form in flat layers are . . . stratus.
4. Thick, puffy clouds are . . . cumulus.
5. When clouds change, you may see changes in the . . . weather.

Your Turn
Work with a partner. Compare your answers. Talk about how each type of cloud is different from the others.

A Closer Look

Word Parts The suffix *-ation* can mean "the process of." Underline the ending in each word. Then, tell a partner what happens during each process.
- evaporation Liquid water changes to water vapor.
- condensation Water vapor changes to liquid water.
- precipitation A form of water falls from the sky.

Leveled Language Proficiency

Students at each proficiency level should be able to perform the following tasks.

Listening/Speaking

Early Beginner/Beginner Gesture or point in response to oral directions. Use a word or a short spoken phrase in response to questions about the three cloud types.

Early Intermediate Respond to a spoken description of the *water cycle* by finding pictures in the lesson that illustrate different parts of the water cycle. Use a short spoken phrase to tell about the different parts of the water cycle.

Intermediate Listen to a description of *dew point.* Paraphrase what is being said during a discussion of clouds and weather.

Advanced/Transitioning Follow oral directions independently. Explain, using complete and complex spoken sentences, what type of weather is associated with each cloud type.

Your Turn

Use colored pencils to change each scene. Color a scene with a flood in the first box. Color a scene with a drought in the second box. Then write a sentence to tell about each picture.

1. Illustration should be changed to show the whole area flooded with water.

2. Illustration should be changed to show the whole area lacking water.

1. A flood is an area with too much water.

2. A drought is an area with not enough water for living things.

Talk and Write About It

Complete the statements about how water affects Earth.

1. The dew point is the temperature at which condensation forms.

2. Types of precipitation are rain, snow, hail, sleet.

3. Types of clouds are cirrus, cumulus, stratus.

4. Evaporation occurs when water becomes water vapor.

5. Condensation occurs when water vapor forms water droplets.

Produce Language

Write what you have learned about clouds and precipitation.

_____
_____
_____
_____
_____

Clouds and Precipitation **69**

Leveled Language Proficiency

Students at each proficiency level should be able to perform the following tasks.

Reading/Writing

Early Beginner/Beginner Locate words that describe different parts of the water cycle. Draw and label pictures to show what happens at each part of the cycle.

Early Intermediate Read to find a reference to dew point and humidity. Write short phrases to describe each of these terms.

Intermediate Comprehend phrases that describe the characteristics of each cloud type. Write a description of how the cloud types differ from each other.

Advanced/Transitioning Read aloud sentences that describe how clouds can be used to predict the type of weather that may occur soon. Write sentences about how clouds form.

↻ Assess Understanding

Your Turn

Model Before students complete the activity, have them talk about the differences between a drought and a flood. Encourage them to use their own phrases or sentences to describe each. Then have them draw over the existing pictures to show how too much water or insufficient water would affect the areas during a flood or drought.

Talk and Write About It

On Their Own Encourage student groups to work together to complete the sentences if they have difficulty doing it on their own. Allow them to look back at the lesson to get ideas if necessary.

Produce Language

On Their Own Have student pairs talk and write about how clouds and precipitation are related. Encourage students to loook back at the Big Question. Have them discuss the question, using lesson vocabulary to express their ideas.

Wrap Up

Table Talk Have students reflect on what they learned. Encourage students to build fluency by reading their writing in groups or to the class.

✔ **Learned** and applied vocabulary related to clouds and precipitation

✔ **Spoken** statements about each of the cloud types

✔ **Written** statements about different types of precipitation, and about how the water cycle makes clouds

Predicting the Weather

Vocabulary tropical, polar, jet stream, front, cyclone, thunderstorm, hurricane, storm surge, tornado, meteorologist, isobar, isotherm, air mass, maritime, continental

Science Background

- Maritime air masses form over oceans and continental air masses form over continents. Tropical, warm air masses form in the tropics, and polar, cold air masses form near the arctic circles.

- A front is the boundary where two air masses meet and is often where storms and changeable weather patterns begin. There are four types of fronts: cold, warm, stationary, and occluded.

- Jet streams are bands of high-speed winds about 10 kilometers above Earth's surface, which generally blow from west to east, moving air masses.

⟳ Frontload the Lesson

How do scientists describe and predict the weather?

Talk About It

Build Background Ask students to think of what they have seen on television or in movies to help them answer the questions if they do not have experience with all of the storms.

⟳ Content and Language

Predict

Model Read the objectives aloud. Clarify the meaning of the word *predict* by giving a relevant example of a weather prediction.

Guide Discussion Ask students to identify the important words—or key words—in the objectives. Explain any unfamiliar terms. Then suggest that students use the words they identified as important to say what they think they will learn.

Predicting the Weather

 Big Question How do scientists describe and predict the weather?

You will . . .
- Compare and contrast different types of storms.
- Identify the symbols that appear on a weather map.
- Understand and use key terms to label a weather map.

Talk About It

Look at the pictures of storms.

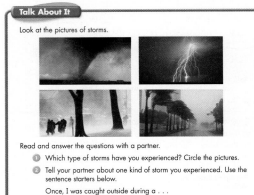

Read and answer the questions with a partner.

1 Which type of storms have you experienced? Circle the pictures.

2 Tell your partner about one kind of storm you experienced. Use the sentence starters below.

Once, I was caught outside during a . . .

I saw major damage, including . . .

Predict
Look at the Big Question and the "You will . . ." statements at the top of the page. Describe what you think you are going to learn in this lesson.

I think I am going to learn about . . .

70 Lesson 18

Leveled Instruction

Early Beginner/Beginner Help students categorize the vocabulary when appropriate. For example, say, *Tropical, polar, maritime, and continental are all types of air masses.* Have them organize the vocabulary into categories in their notes.

Early Intermediate/Intermediate Where appropriate, help students learn the vocabulary by looking at word parts. For example, point out how the root of the word *continental* is *continent*, meaning a large land mass.

Advanced/Transitioning Have students connect the material to their everyday lives by narrating about weather patterns in their local area from recent weeks. Ask them to apply the vocabulary terms to their narrations.

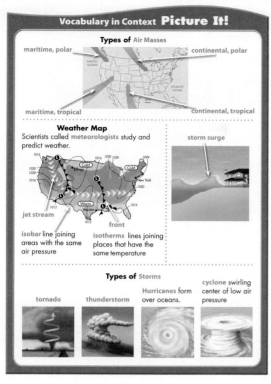

Vocabulary in Context Picture It!

Types of Air Masses

maritime, polar   continental, polar

maritime, tropical   continental, tropical

Weather Map
Scientists called **meteorologists** study and predict weather.

storm surge

jet stream

isobar line joining areas with the same air pressure

isotherms lines joining places that have the same temperature

Types of Storms

tornado   thunderstorm   Hurricanes form over oceans.   **cyclone** swirling center of low air pressure

Your Turn
Work with a partner to study the types of storms shown in the Picture It box. Then talk about how they are alike and how they are different.

Academic Vocabulary

- Point out the multiple-meaning word *mass* in the term *air mass*. Explain to students that this word can mean a large amount of a substance (such as air), or the amount of matter in an object.

- Point out the multiple-meaning word *front*. It can mean the area where two air masses meet, the part of something that faces forward, or a location where the fighting happens in a war. Give examples for each use of the word.

- Point out that the suffix *-ologist* is often used in science. It means "one who studies." Explain that a meteorologist doesn't study "meteors," as one might expect, but rather studies the events in Earth's atmosphere, also known as weather. Ask students to give other examples using this suffix (*biologist, geologist,* and so on).

- Write the word *thunderstorm*. Explain that this is a closed compound word, or two words put together to form one. Write the term *storm surge*. Explain that this is an open compound word. The two words are used together but are written separately.

- Students may notice similarities between a hurricane and a cyclone. A hurricane is a cyclone that develops over tropical ocean areas.

↻ Comprehensible Input

Vocabulary in Context: Picture It!

1. **Say the Term** Say each term slowly, artificially stressing each syllable. Have students repeat. Then say the term more naturally and have students repeat.

2. **Introduce Word Meaning** Connect each term to the visual that illustrates it.

3. **Demonstrate** Use gestures and visuals to demonstrate.

4. **Apply** After each term has been discussed, have students demonstrate understanding with Talk About It.

Talk About It

Guide Discussion Before students start their independent discussion, check for understanding with the following statements.

1. *A person who predicts weather is a . . .* (metereologist).

2. *The place where two air masses meet is called a . . .* (front).

3. *Air masses that from over the ocean are called . . .* (maritime air masses).

4. *Air masses that form over land are called . . .* (continental air masses).

RTI Response to Intervention

If students have difficulty distinguishing the meanings of the words *isobar* and *isotherm* . . .

Then write both terms, as well as the words *barometer* and *thermometer*, on the board. Underline the identical word parts. Point out that a barometer measures air pressure, and that a thermometer measures temperature. Explain that an *isobar* marks an area with the same air pressure and an *isotherm* marks an area with the same temperature.

Your Turn

Guide Discussion Circulate around the room to listen to students' discussions. Select two or three students to share their stories with the class.

Predicting the Weather

↻ Language Production

Do You Understand?

Comprehension Support Have students look at the words in the word bank before starting the activity. Discuss the meanings of each term as a class. Then, have students label the map.

Model Think aloud as you label one term for students. Say to students, *I know that the jet stream moves from west to east. So I look on the map to find something that moves in that direction. I see the series of white arrows, and I label it.* Have students complete the activity.

Talk About It

Guide Discussion Read the statements aloud with students. Have them work together to complete the sentences. You may need to review the meaning of *air pressure*. Help students use the index to find the pages where this term is introduced and practiced.

Your Turn

Guide Discussion Before students begin, explain that there are no isotherms on this map. Instead, colors are used to indicate areas with similar temperatures. Shades of blue indicate cooler areas, green indicates middle-range temperatures, and yellow and red indicate warmer temperatures. Model how to describe weather patterns by saying, *A meteorologist might say, "There is a cold front moving across the Midwestern states. Expect temperatures to cool in Wisconsin."* You may want to write terms such as *cold front, warm front, temperature,* and *air pressure* on the board.

In Other Words

Model Point out that a familiar meaning of *key* may be as a common noun that names a "thing." Ask students for examples, definitions, or translations of this meaning. Then explain that *key* is also an adjective meaning "important" or "critical." Read the example sentence aloud for students and have them repeat it. Then ask, *What is another way to say this? What is another word, or words, for* key? Have students take turns reading the sentence aloud, choosing one of the yellow-highlighted words to fill in the space each time. Then have students suggest their own sentences that use the word *key* as an adjective.

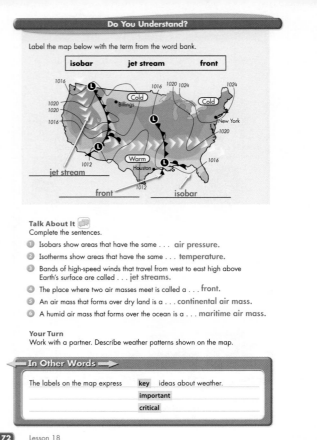

Do You Understand?

Label the map below with the term from the word bank.

| isobar | jet stream | front |

Talk About It
Complete the sentences.

1. Isobars show areas that have the same . . . air pressure.
2. Isotherms show areas that have the same . . . temperature.
3. Bands of high-speed winds that travel from west to east high above Earth's surface are called . . . jet streams.
4. The place where two air masses meet is called a . . . front.
5. An air mass that forms over dry land is a . . . continental air mass.
6. A humid air mass that forms over the ocean is a . . . maritime air mass.

Your Turn
Work with a partner. Describe weather patterns shown on the map.

In Other Words

The labels on the map express	key	ideas about weather.
	important	
	critical	

Leveled Language Proficiency

Students at each proficiency level should be able to perform the following tasks.

Listening/Speaking

Early Beginner/Beginner Point to appropriate areas of the map as a response to oral directions. Name different types of storms and air masses.

Early Intermediate Point to appropriate areas of the map in response to questions. Use short phrases and simple sentences to talk about the weather map.

Intermediate Follow oral directions with little to no help. Describe weather orally, using complete sentences.

Advanced/Transitioning Follow oral directions independently. Explain to others, in spoken conversation, the symbols and concepts of the weather map.

Think, Talk, and Write

Your Turn

Look at the pictures. What type of storm does each picture show? Label each picture.

thunderstorm   _hurricane_   _tornado_

Talk and Write About It

Complete these statements about the weather.

1. A meteorologist is a scientist who _studies and tries to predict weather_.
2. Thunderstorms usually bring _lightning and rain_
3. Hurricanes form over _oceans_
4. Because the center of a hurricane has swirling winds, a hurricane is a kind of _cyclone_
5. When a hurricane hits the coast, it can cause a dome of water called a _storm surge_
6. A tornado is a storm with a _whirling storm cloud, shaped like a cone or funnel that touches Earth's surface_
7. In weather science, a front is the place where _two air masses meet_

Produce Language

Write about what meteorologists do and how their work helps people.

_____
_____
_____
_____
_____
_____

Predicting the Weather   **73**

Leveled Language Proficiency

Students at each proficiency level should be able to perform the following tasks.

Reading/Writing

Early Beginner/Beginner Locate words that describe the types of fronts, air masses, and storms. Label pictures or diagrams illustrating each concept.

Early Intermediate Read descriptions of weather patterns with some assistance. Write short phrases to describe weather.

Intermediate Read and comprehend vocabulary terms in context. Write a description of different types of storms using complete sentences.

Advanced/Transitioning Read independently about meteorology. Write detailed paragraphs using complete sentences to describe weather and the way meteorologists predict it.

↻ Assess Understanding

Your Turn

Model Read instructions aloud to students. Refer students back to the Picture It box and review the terms with them. Encourage language production by having students describe what they see in each picture. Extend discussion, if desired, by displaying other storm pictures in the classroom or by having students search for such pictures in magazines or online.

Talk and Write About It

On Their Own Pair more advanced students with beginners to complete the sentences.

Produce Language

On Their Own Have students recall and describe the weather reporting they have seen, heard, or read in various news sources. If necessary, provide sentence frames, such as *Metereologists provide . . . , which can help people prepare for . . . by . . . .* to help students write their descriptions.

Wrap Up

Table Talk Refer students back to the Big Question and call on volunteers to contribute partial answers. Have students reflect on what they learned. Encourage students to build fluency by reading their writing in groups or to the class.

✔ **Learned** and applied vocabulary related to describing and predicting the weather

✔ **Spoken** statements describing the different types of weather and how they are predicted

✔ **Written** statements showing the way that weather is described and predicted, using key vocabulary in the correct manner

Lesson 19

Climate

Vocabulary temperate zone, monsoon, tundra, permafrost, ice age, climate, greenhouse gases, fossil fuel, global warming

Materials globe, flashlight, colored pencils or crayons

Science Background

- Scientists classify climates according to temperature and precipitation.

- The last ice age ended about 10,000 years ago.

- The burning of fossil fuels, such as oil and natural gas, releases greenhouse gases, such as carbon dioxide, into the air. This increase in greenhouse gas production has caused the temperature of the atmosphere to rise.

Climate

Big Question What factors determine and affect climate?

You will . . .
- Understand the factors that determine and affect climate.
- Learn the six main climate regions.
- Understand and use key words to discuss climate.

Talk About It

Copy each term from Picture It onto an index card. As your teacher reads the terms, create three piles of cards.

Step 1 Place the terms that you know in **Pile 1.**

Step 2 Place the terms that you have heard but that you don't know in **Pile 2.**

Step 3 Place the terms you have never heard in **Pile 3.**

What do you know about each term? Explain, using the sentence frames for support.

Pile 1—I know . . . means . . .

Pile 2—I think . . . means . . .

Pile 3—I do not know what . . . means.

global warming

ice age

tundra

Predict

Look at the Big Question and the "You will . . ." statements at the top of the page. Describe what you think you are going to learn in this lesson.

I think I am going to learn about . . .

Frontload the Lesson

What factors determine and affect climate?

Talk About It

Build Background Have students create index cards as described. Read each term aloud as students sort the cards. Ask volunteers to explain the difference between weather and climate.

Content and Language

Predict

Model Read the Big Question and the objectives aloud. Model skipping over certain words as you infer the general meaning of the objectives. Then write the academic words *factors, determine,* and *affect* on the board. Substitute near synonyms, *things* for "factors" and *influence* for "determine and affect." Explain that these stand-in words are less precise.

Guide Discussion Ask students to use their own words to describe one of the objectives. Then have them make their predictions.

Leveled Instruction

Early Beginner Ask students to point to each zone on the map and repeat the name of the zone after a higher-proficiency partner says it.

Beginner Ask students questions about climate and climate change using simple sentences. Have them respond with single words or short phrases.

Early Intermediate/Intermediate Have students work independently or in pairs. Students should use full sentences with some details to describe climate and climate change.

Advanced/Transitioning Partner these students with students of lower language proficiency. Have them model how to correctly pronounce the names of climate zones. Also encourage students, particularly those who are transitioning, to use their grade-level science textbook to learn about climate and climate change.

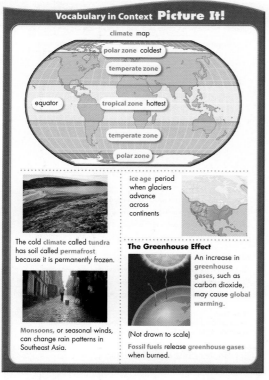

Vocabulary in Context Picture It!

climate map

polar zone coldest

temperate zone

equator   tropical zone hottest

temperate zone

polar zone

The cold **climate** called **tundra** has soil called **permafrost** because it is permanently frozen.

ice age period when glaciers advance across continents

Monsoons, or seasonal winds, can change rain patterns in Southeast Asia.

The Greenhouse Effect

An increase in **greenhouse gases**, such as carbon dioxide, may cause **global warming**.

(Not drawn to scale)

Fossil fuels release **greenhouse gases** when burned.

Your Turn
Work with a partner. Look at the picture called "The Greenhouse Effect." Talk about what the arrows might mean.

Climate   75

Academic Vocabulary

- Point out the word *zone* in the terms *temperate zone, polar zone,* and *tropical zone.* Note how the words *temperate, polar,* and *tropical* describe the climate in each zone. Students may have heard *school zone* or *traffic zone.* Explain that *zones* are special areas set off because of a specific purpose or characteristic.

- Discuss how the academic word *variation* is often used in referring to weather or climate. The word *variation* means "a slight change." Rainfall, temperature, and wind often vary. They are rarely the same year after year. Make sure students understand that the academic word *vary* means "to change slightly" and has the same root as *variation.*

- Point out the word parts *perma-* and *-frost* in the word *permafrost. Perma-* comes from the same root as *permanent,* which means "lasting forever." The word part *-frost* comes from the same root as the word forms *freeze* or *frozen. Permafrost* is ground that remains permanently frozen.

↻ Comprehensible Input

Vocabulary in Context: Picture It!

1. **Say the Term** Say each term slowly, artificially stressing each syllable. Have students repeat. Then say the term more naturally and have students repeat.

2. **Introduce Word Meaning** Connect each term to the visual that illustrates it.

3. **Demonstrate** Use gestures and visuals to demonstrate.

4. **Apply** After all of the terms have been discussed, have students demonstrate understanding with Talk About It.

Talk About It

Guide Discussion Before students start their independent discussion, check for understanding with the following sentences:

1. *Between the tropical and polar zones are the . . .* (temperate zones).

2. *In a tundra, frozen layers of soil are called . . .* (permafrost).

3. *Warm winds that can cause months of rain in Southeast Asia are called . . .* (monsoons).

4. *A natural change in Earth's orbit caused ice to cover much of the Earth during an . . .* (ice age).

5. *Gases that trap heat in Earth's atmosphere are called . . .* (greenhouse gases).

6. *Greenhouse gases are released from burning . . .* (fossil fuels).

RTI Response to Intervention

If students have difficulty pronouncing the word *temperate* in the term *temperate zone . . .*

Then write the words *temperature* and *temperate* on the board. Read each word aloud slowly and then naturally, with students repeating. Point out that the *-ate* ending of *climate* and *temperate* are pronounced the same way.

Your Turn

Guide Discussion Prompt students to explain the diagrams using vocabulary terms. (The arrows in the diagram indicate the movement of heat.)

Climate

↻ Language Production

Do You Understand?

Comprehension Support Before students begin the activity, point to the horizontal lines on the map. Be sure that students understand that the directions call for labeling all five zones, even though the word box contains only three labels.

Model Demonstrate how students can ask themselves questions to help them do the activity. Say, *Where is the polar zone? Let me think of the word* polar. *It means "cold." The polar zones must be zones where there is cold weather.*

Talk About It

Guide Discussion Read the statements aloud with students as they use vocabulary terms to complete the sentences. Encourage students to point to places on the map that correspond to each sentence as they complete it.

Your Turn

Guide Discussion Listen to student discussions as they talk about what they wrote. Help them by giving them weather-related terms like *hot, cold, warm,* and *moderate.*

In Other Words

Model Read the sentence aloud for students. Then ask, *What is another way to say this? What is another word, or words, for* affect? Encourage students to read the sentence aloud in turn, each time choosing a new highlighted word for the term *affect.* You may want to expand the discussion by discussing the difference between the academic words *affect* and *effect.* Additionally, advanced students can compare the precise meanings of *affect* and *determine.* Point out that there is smaller influence conveyed by *affect,* and much greater influence conveyed by *determine.* Explain that *factors* are any things that cause or contribute to an effect or result.

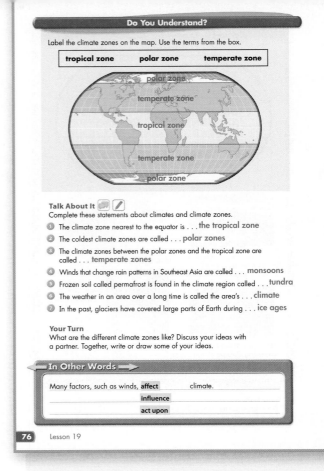

Do You Understand?

Label the climate zones on the map. Use the terms from the box.

tropical zone	polar zone	temperate zone

polar zone
temperate zone
tropical zone
temperate zone
polar zone

Talk About It
Complete these statements about climates and climate zones.
1. The climate zone nearest to the equator is . . . the tropical zone
2. The coldest climate zones are called . . . polar zones
3. The climate zones between the polar zones and the tropical zone are called . . . temperate zones
4. Winds that change rain patterns in Southeast Asia are called . . . monsoons
5. Frozen soil called permafrost is found in the climate region called . . . tundra
6. The weather in an area over a long time is called the area's . . . climate
7. In the past, glaciers have covered large parts of Earth during . . . ice ages

Your Turn
What are the different climate zones like? Discuss your ideas with a partner. Together, write or draw some of your ideas.

⟵ In Other Words ⟶

Many factors, such as winds,	**affect**	climate.
	influence	
	act upon	

Leveled Language Proficiency

Students at each proficiency level should be able to perform the following tasks.

Listening/Speaking

Early Beginner/Beginner Point to appropriate areas of diagrams and maps as a response to oral directions. Use words and short phrases in response to questions about climate and climate change.

Early Intermediate/Intermediate Understand simple oral sentences that describe the different climate zones. Use simple sentences to talk about climate and climate change.

Advanced/Transitioning Understand discussions about global warming. Use multiple complex sentences to talk about climate and climate change.

Your Turn

Greenhouse gases keep Earth warm. Draw arrows to show how greenhouse gases do this.

(Not drawn to scale)

Talk and Write About It

Complete the following sentences about greenhouse gases and the greenhouse effect.

1. Greenhouse gases trap energy that comes from the _sun._
2. Greenhouse gases are released when _people burn fossil fuels._
3. An increase in greenhouse gases may change Earth's climates because greenhouse gases _absorb heat and increase the temperature of the atmosphere._

Produce Language

How might global warming affect climate zones and living things on Earth? Use as many vocabulary terms as you can in your answer.

_____
_____
_____
_____
_____
_____

Climate **77**

Leveled Language Proficiency

Students at each proficiency level should be able to perform the following tasks.

Reading/Writing

Early Beginner Locate terms that describe the climate regions and types. Write labels on a climate map.

Beginner Identify vocabulary terms associated with the maps and diagrams in the lesson. Write short phrases about climate and climate change.

Early Intermediate/Intermediate Read and comprehend a description of global warming with some assistance. Write phrases or short sentences to describe the factors that affect climate change.

Advanced/Transitioning Read sentences that include key content vocabulary terms. Write a paragraph about global warming using complete sentences that correctly include vocabulary terms.

↻ Assess Understanding

Your Turn

Model Demonstrate with your finger the path of sunlight and show how some of the sun's energy stays in Earth's atmosphere. Enhance the content with questions such as, *Has anyone ever been inside a greenhouse? What does it feel like?*

Talk and Write About It

On Their Own As students work, encourage them to think about the greenhouse effect by asking, *What do we do that uses fossil fuels? What do you know about what happens when fossil fuels burn?*

Produce Language

On Their Own Have students write about the effects of global warming on the Earth. Encourage students to use the information they already know, and explain that they will learn more about this topic when they study the content lesson. Have student pairs exchange and discuss their writing, and circle any key terms.

Wrap Up

Table Talk Have students review and discuss the Big Question. Then have students reflect on what they learned. Encourage students to build fluency by reading their writing in groups or to the class.

✔ **Learned** and applied vocabulary related to climate and climate change

✔ **Spoken** statements describing the climate regions and types and the factors that determine and affect climate

✔ **Written** statements describing the factors that determine and affect climate

Earth in Space

Vocabulary satellite, planet, meteor, comet, star, constellation, axis, rotation, revolution, orbit, calendar, solstice, equinox

Materials index cards, ball; optional: star chart, foam ball skewered through center with dowel, calendar, solar-system diagram, globe, lamp

Science Background

- Earth moves in two major ways: rotation and revolution.

- Earth has seasons because its axis is tilted. The northern part of Earth is tilted toward the sun for part of the year, and the southern part is tilted toward the sun for the rest of the year.

- Many objects including stars, meteors, comets, constellations, and the moon are visible in the night sky.

 Frontload the Lesson

 How do Earth and the sun interact?

Talk About It

Build Background Give each student pair a ball, and/or demonstrate each action. Explain that when something spins, it rotates. Spinning in one complete circle is called one *rotation*. One complete circle around a center object (or person) is called one *revolution*.

Content and Language

Predict

Model Read the Big Question and the objectives aloud. Use pictures to further explain objectives.

Guide Discussion Ask students to discuss or demonstrate the meaning of the term *interact* in the Big Question.

 Big Question How do Earth and the sun interact?

You will . . .
- Explain how Earth's movement causes days, nights, and seasons.
- Identify objects seen in the night sky.
- Understand and use terms related to Earth's movement in space.

Talk About It

Write the terms from the Picture It box on cards as your teacher reads them. Then, take turns doing the following actions.

1. Spin a ball. Notice the center of the ball as it spins.
2. Have one person stand in place to represent the sun. The other carries the ball around "the sun" in a circle.

Look at your cards. Find the words *rotation* and *revolution*. Which word fits each action? Use the two words to describe Earth's motion.

rotation	revolution

1. Earth spinning around its center line is a . . .
2. Earth traveling around the sun is a . . .

Predict
Look at the Big Question and the "You will . . ." statements at the top of the page. Describe what you think you are going to learn in this lesson.

I think I will learn about . . .

Leveled Instruction

Early Beginner/Beginner The beginner can point out or draw objects in the night sky that he or she is familiar with. Beginners can consult with more advanced students to label the drawings with vocabulary terms and other everyday words in both English and in the students' native languages.

Early Intermediate Students should be building toward independent use of language. Have students use the images in the Picture It box to help contrast the meanings of *planet* and *satellite*.

Intermediate These students should work with little assistance. Have students list several objects that can be seen in the day and the night sky. They should be able to choose a few objects and write a sentence about each one.

Advanced/Transitioning Students should list many objects that can be found in the day and the night sky and describe the difference between *rotation* and *revolution*.

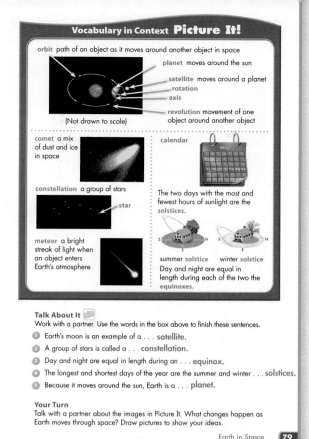

orbit path of an object as it moves around another object in space

planet moves around the sun

satellite moves around a planet
rotation
axis

revolution movement of one object around another object

(Not drawn to scale)

comet a mix of dust and ice in space

calendar

constellation a group of stars
star

The two days with the most and fewest hours of sunlight are the solstices.

meteor a bright streak of light when an object enters Earth's atmosphere

summer **solstice**   winter **solstice**

Day and night are equal in length during each of the two the equinoxes.

Talk About It
Work with a partner. Use the words in the box above to finish these sentences.

1. Earth's moon is an example of a . . . satellite.
2. A group of stars is called a . . . constellation.
3. Day and night are equal in length during an . . . equinox.
4. The longest and shortest days of the year are the summer and winter . . . solstices.
5. Because it moves around the sun, Earth is a . . . planet.

Your Turn
Talk with a partner about the images in Picture It. What changes happen as Earth moves through space? Draw pictures to show your ideas.

Earth in Space **79**

Academic Vocabulary

- If students have trouble with the word *axis,* point out that it is similar to the familiar word *axle,* such as you would find connected to the wheels of a car. Have volunteers describe the similarity.

- Cognates are words in different languages that have similar spellings and meanings. For example, the Spanish word for *meteor* is *meteoro.* Encourage students to use cognates to infer and learn the meanings of English words.

Cultural Consideration

- If students are from Southern Hemisphere, discuss the fact that December starts the summer and June the winter in these areas. Additionally, if students are from equatorial or tropical climates, they will realize that the seasons vary only mildly in these regions. Encourage open discussion of these different experiences. Have students formulate questions and hypotheses about what causes the differences. As they read or do research on the topic, they can use their questions as a purpose for reading.

Comprehensible Input

Vocabulary in Context: Picture It!

1. **Say the Term** Say each term slowly, artificially stressing each syllable. Have students repeat. Then say the term more naturally and have students repeat.

2. **Introduce Word Meaning** Connect each term to the visual that illustrates it.

3. **Demonstrate** Use gestures and visuals to demonstrate. For example:

   - For the terms *rotation, revolution, orbit,* and *axis,* use a foam ball with a dowel through its center. Move the ball accordingly to show how Earth rotates and travels in its *orbit,* with its *axis* tilted in relation to the sun.

   - Point to a real calendar to demonstrate the meaning of *calendar.*

   - Point out that Earth is just one example of a *planet* in our solar system. Show students images of other *planets* in the solar system.

   - Correct a common misunderstanding of the term *satellite* as referring only to human-made devices. Reinforce the scientific definition of *satellite* as *any* object that orbits a planet.

   - Display a star chart, and have volunteers each point out one *constellation.*

4. **Apply** After each term has been discussed, have students demonstrate understanding with Talk About It.

Talk About It

Guide Discussion Assign partners and have pairs discuss and draw images of the changes they can see in the sky from the position of Earth.

RTI Response to Intervention

If students have difficulty pronouncing the long and short vowels in *solstice* . . .

Then isolate the word part *sol,* the Spanish word (and Latin root) for "sun." Have students pronounce *sol* and *solstice* a few times together.

Your Turn

Guide Discussion Ask students guiding questions, such as, *Why do we have day and night? What is a year?*

Earth in Space

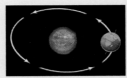 **Language Production**

Do You Understand?

Comprehension Support Before students start the activity, point out that Earth rotates and revolves. As you say each word, model these two movements. For rotation, spin a ball, or spin yourself around. For revolution, move the ball around one hand or circle one hand around the other.

Model Demonstrate how students can ask themselves questions to help them do the activity. Say, *How does Earth move to make a rotation? How does it move to make a revolution?*

Talk About It

Guide Discussion Read the sentence starters aloud with students as they work together to complete the sentences.

Your Turn

Guide Discussion Listen to and encourage student discussions. Clarify discussion points as they arise. Use a globe or foam ball (skewered with a dowel), and a lamp or flashlight and drawings to show how Earth's rotation causes the day and night cycle, and how Earth's tilted axis and revolution causes the year cycle. If feasible, have student volunteers do demonstrations.

Do You Understand?

Earth is always moving. Earth rotates and revolves. Label each image below with the term **rotation** or **revolution.**

(Not drawn to scale)

revolution   rotation

Talk About It
Work with a partner. Complete the sentences.

① When Earth spins one time around its axis, it has completed one . . . **rotation.**
② When Earth completes one circle around the sun, it has completed one . . . **revolution.**
③ Earth spins, or rotates, around a tilted . . . **axis.**
④ The path of Earth around the sun is called Earth's . . . **orbit.**
⑤ The sun is an example of a . . . **star.**
⑥ A group of stars, such as the Big Dipper, that astronomers connect to form a picture is called a . . . **constellation.**

Your Turn
Work with a partner. Find Earth's orbit and Earth's axis in the pictures above. Add arrows to the pictures to show each of these terms.

Leveled Language Proficiency

Students at each proficiency level should be able to perform the following tasks.

Listening/Speaking

Early Beginner/Beginner Use pictures, actions, or objects to respond to oral questions. Respond to questions using pictures, gestures, or objects.

Early Intermediate Understand single-sentence questions about Earth in space. Ask simple questions with the aid of pictures and gestures.

Intermediate Exhibit good comprehension of oral descriptions related to Earth's rotations and revolutions. Verbally contrast rotation and revolution using complex sentences.

Advanced/Transitioning Discuss and describe examples of rotation and revolution in everyday life. Answer complex, inferential questions about the movement of Earth relative to the sun.

Your Turn

Each year, there are two **equinoxes** and two **solstices**.

Label each picture as either an **equinox** or a **solstice**.

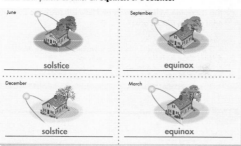

June — solstice

September — equinox

December — solstice

March — equinox

Talk and Write About It

Complete the statements about Earth's movement and objects in the sky.

1. In the sky, meteors appear as <u>streaks of light</u>.
2. Comets are made up of <u>a mix of dust and ice</u>.
3. A calendar shows <u>days, weeks, months, and year</u>.
4. One year is the time it takes Earth to <u>orbit around the sun one time</u>.

Produce Language

Write about two ways that Earth moves. Explain how this movement affects our lives on Earth. Sample answers given.

1. <u>Earth rotates on its axis. One rotation takes 24 hours, or one day and night. As one side of Earth faces the Sun, we see daylight. Then, as we face away from the sun, we experience the darkness of night.</u>

2. <u>Earth revolves around the sun. One revolution takes one year. During the year, on parts of Earth, we experience seasons—summer when the tilt of Earth allows direct sunlight, and winter when it causes us to receive less direct sun.</u>

Earth in Space **81**

Leveled Language Proficiency

Students at each proficiency level should be able to perform the following tasks.

Reading/Writing

Early Beginner/Beginner Match pictures related to the solstice and equinox with words. Complete sentence starters with vocabulary related to these topics.

Early Intermediate Comprehend printed text consisting of simple sentences. Write questions about the solstice and equinox.

Intermediate Interpret written information about the solstice and equinox. Use complex sentences to provide written descriptions of the solstice and equinox.

Advanced/Transitioning Read short newspaper articles about Earth in space. Write a paragraph that compares the winter and summer solstices.

↻ Assess Understanding

Your Turn

Model Use a globe tilted on its axis and a lamp to show how Earth's tilt causes the seasons as it travels around the sun. At four positions related to the two solstices and two equinoxes, point out how the sun's light hits Earth—either directly or at an angle. Point out that—because of the tilt—the northern and southern hemispheres experience winter and summer at different times of the year.

Talk and Write About It

On Their Own Encourage students to look back at the Picture It terms to help clarify meanings.

Produce Language

On Their Own Before writing, have students reread the Big Question and their predictions about what they would learn in the lesson. Ask them to write about how their predictions compare to what they learned about how Earth's relationship to the sun causes the days, night, and seasons. Finally, ask them to discuss how the days, nights, and seasons affect their daily lives.

Wrap Up

Table Talk Have students reflect on what they learned. Encourage students to build fluency by reading their writing in groups or to the class.

✔ **Learned** and applied vocabulary related to Earth's movement in space

✔ **Spoken** statements about objects in space and how Earth moves

✔ **Written** statements about how Earth's movement affects our lives

Lesson 21

Gravity, Earth, and the Moon

Vocabulary force, gravity, mass, weight, moon phase, eclipse, solar eclipse, umbra, penumbra, lunar eclipse, tide, spring tide, neap tide, maria, crater, meteoroid

Materials pictures of high and low tides

 Science Background

- The strength of the force of gravity between two objects depends on the masses of the objects and the distance between them.

- Inertia and gravity combine to keep Earth in orbit around the sun and the moon in orbit around Earth.

- The changing relative positions of the moon, Earth, and the sun cause phases of the moon and eclipses.

- Tides are caused by differences in how much gravity from the moon and the sun pulls on different parts of Earth.

Frontload the Lesson

 What is gravity and how is it related to Earth's orbit and the moon's orbit?

Talk About It

Build Background Show students additional images of beaches at high and low tides.

Content and Language

Predict

Model Read the Big Question and the objectives aloud. Use pictures and gestures to support your explanations.

Guide Discussion Repeat the objectives, having students chorally read with you. Have volunteers explain the objectives in their own words.

 Big Question What is gravity and how is it related to Earth's orbit and the moon's orbit?

You will . . .
- Understand how gravity affects the movement of objects in space.
- Learn about the moon's phases and eclipses.
- Identify the cause of tides on Earth.
- Understand and use terms related to gravity and the moon.

Talk About It

Look at the two pictures of the sand castle. What is happening to it?

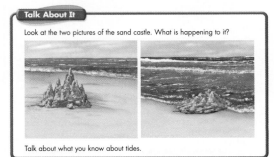

Talk about what you know about tides.

Predict
Look at the Big Question and the "You will . . ." statements at the top of the page. Describe what you think you are going to learn in this lesson.

I think I am going to learn about . . .

Leveled Instruction

Early Beginner/Beginner Beginners can work with more advanced students. The advanced students can write words and phrases for the beginners to copy onto their pictures.

Early Intermediate Students can use pictures on the Picture It! page to help organize ideas about gravity and the moon. List key terms and phrases for students to use to build sentences.

Intermediate Since these students need little assistance, have them observe the moon in the evening and then report their observations to the class. Encourage students to supplement their reports with visuals.

Advanced/Transitioning Ask these students to work with students of lower level language proficiency. Expect advanced and transitioning students to provide detailed descriptions and examples related to gravity and the moon.

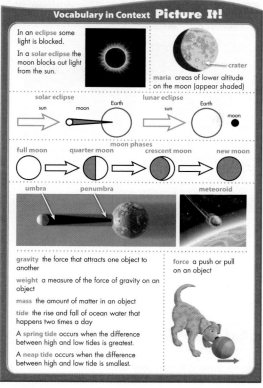

In an **eclipse** some light is blocked.

In a **solar eclipse** the moon blocks out light from the sun.

crater

maria areas of lower altitude on the moon (appear shaded)

solar eclipse

sun   moon   Earth

lunar eclipse

sun   Earth   moon

moon phases

full moon   quarter moon   crescent moon   new moon

umbra   penumbra   meteoroid

gravity the force that attracts one object to another

weight a measure of the force of gravity on an object

mass the amount of matter in an object

tide the rise and fall of ocean water that happens two times a day

A **spring tide** occurs when the difference between high and low tides is greatest.

A **neap tide** occurs when the difference between high and low tide is smallest.

force a push or pull on an object

Your Turn
Talk about experiences you have had with forces, tides, eclipses, and gravity.

Gravity, Earth, and the Moon **83**

Academic Vocabulary

- Point out the Spanish words *sol* and *luna*, which translate to *sun* and *moon*. Ask students how they can use these words to help them remember what solar and lunar eclipses are.

- Point out that the term *umbra* comes from a Latin word meaning "shade or shadow." Add that the prefix *pen-* means "almost." Have students explain how they can use this information to remember the meanings of the terms *umbra* and *penumbra*.

- Write the term *maria* on the board. Explain that *maria* is the plural form of the word *mare* (mahr-ey). Emphasize the difference between the term and the name *Maria*.

↻ Comprehensible Input

Vocabulary in Context: Picture It!

1. **Say the Term** Say each term slowly, artificially stressing each syllable. Have students repeat. Then say the term more naturally and have students repeat.

2. **Introduce Word Meaning** Connect each term to the visual that illustrates it.

3. **Demonstrate** Use gestures and visuals to demonstrate each term.

4. **Apply** After all of the terms have been discussed, have students demonstrate understanding with Talk About It.

Talk About It

Guide Discussion Before students start their independent discussion, check for understanding with the following sentence starters:

1. *A push or pull on an object is a . . .* (force).

2. *The force that pulls things to Earth is called . . .* (gravity).

3. *Changes in how the moon looks are called . . .* (moon phases).

4. *The parts of the shadow during an eclipse are called the . . .* (umbra) *and the . . .* (penumbra).

5. *Holes we see on the moon are actually . . .* (craters).

6. *Craters on the moon are made by . . .* (meteoroids).

RTI Response to Intervention

If students have difficulty pronouncing the word *inertia* . . .

Then write it on the board and say it slowly, emphasizing the /sh/ sound. Ask students to suggest other words in which *ti* sounds like /sh/ . . .

Your Turn

Guide Discussion Encourage students to use classroom objects, such as books, pencils, or markers to talk about the terms *force, inertia, gravity, mass,* and *weight*.

Gravity, Earth, and the Moon

↻ Language Production

Do You Understand?

Comprehension Support Before students start the activity, have them review the depictions of the terms *maria, crater,* and *meteoroid* in Picture It!, page 83.

Model Demonstrate how students can ask themselves questions to help them do the activity. Say, *What effect have meteoroids had on the surface of the moon?*

Talk About It

Guide Discussion Read the sentence starters aloud with students as they work together to complete the sentences. Use pictures or gestures to help show the meanings of the sentences.

Your Turn

Guide Discussion If time permits, encourage students to create a Venn diagram to compare maria and craters. (Similarity: they are both features on the surface of the moon. Differences: craters are holes, while maria are dark and flat; craters were formed by the impact of meteoroids, while maria are hardened lava flows.)

A Closer Look

On Their Own Have students work in pairs to complete this word study activity. Then have them suggest other words with multiple meanings.

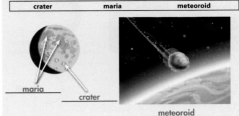

Do You Understand?

Write a label for each picture. Use the terms in the box.

| crater | maria | meteoroid |

maria

crater

meteoroid

Talk About It 🖵
1. Pits on the surface of the moon are called . . . craters.
2. Chunks of rock from space that hit the moon are called . . . meteoroids.
3. A push or a pull on an object is called a . . . force.
4. The force that pulls objects to each other is called . . . gravity.
5. The amount of matter in an object is the object's . . . mass.
6. When you measure the force of gravity on an object you measure the object's . . . weight.
7. During one day, tides . . . rise and fall twice.

Your Turn
Work with a partner. Talk about the surface of the moon. Also talk about tides.

> **A Closer Look**
>
> **Multiple Meanings** Look at the word *force.* The scientific meaning of the word *force* is "a push or a pull." Another meaning of the word *force* is "to make someone do something." Draw a picture for each meaning.

84 Lesson 21

Leveled Language Proficiency

Students at each proficiency level should be able to perform the following tasks.

Listening/Speaking

Early Beginner/Beginner Use pictures, gestures, or objects to respond to oral questions about tides. Use a key word or a short phrase to respond orally to a question about gravity and the moon.

Early Intermediate Use hand gestures or short phrases to respond to oral questions about tides. Respond orally with short phrases or simple sentences to questions about gravity, tides, and the movement of the moon.

Intermediate Demonstrate comprehension of the main points of a discussion about tides. Orally compare and contrast solar and lunar eclipses.

Advanced/Transitioning Understand discussions and explanations about the moon's movements. Orally explain with complex sentences the meanings of key ideas and terms about tides and gravity.

Your Turn

The drawings show the positions of Earth, the sun, and the moon during an eclipse. Is it a solar eclipse or a lunar eclipse? Label the drawing *solar eclipse* or *lunar eclipse*. Then label the umbra and the penumbra.

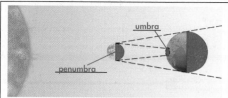

umbra

penumbra

Talk and Write About It

Complete the statements about gravity, Earth, and the moon.

1. The changing shapes of the moon we see from Earth are called <u>moon phases</u>

2. Two types of eclipses are <u>solar eclipses and lunar eclipses</u>.

3. Two parts of the shadow that are cast during an eclipse are called <u>the umbra and penumbra</u>

4. Large dark spots on the moon are called <u>maria</u>

5. The round pits on the moon are called <u>craters</u>

6. Craters on the moon were caused by <u>meteoroids</u>

Produce Language

Write about ways that the moon affects our lives on Earth. Use as many vocabulary terms as you can.

_____

_____

_____

_____

_____

_____

Gravity, Earth, and the Moon   **85**

Leveled Language Proficiency

Students at each proficiency level should be able to perform the following tasks.

Reading/Writing

Early Beginner/Beginner Match key terms to pictures or objects. Write a list of words and phrases related to the moon.

Early Intermediate Use context as a clue to word meaning while reading about gravity and the moon. Write short descriptions of what happens during an eclipse.

Intermediate Summarize sections of text about gravity and the movement of the moon. Use key words and phrases to write about how the movement of the moon affects the Earth environment.

Advanced/Transitioning Read and understand paragraphs about eclipses and the moon. Write short paragraphs describing what happens during an eclipse.

↻ Assess Understanding

Your Turn

Model Before students begin the activity, discuss how a solar and a lunar eclipse are different. Ask, *What do we see during a solar eclipse? Why? What do we see during a lunar eclipse? Why? Why are the words* solar *and* lunar *used to describe these events?*

Talk and Write About It

On Their Own Have students work together in pairs. Circulate among the pairs, helping students who are having difficulty. Listen to students' pronunciations, and correct any errors.

Produce Language

On Their Own Before students start writing, have a few volunteers share their ideas orally with the class. Write key terms and phrases that come up in the discussion on the board for students to use in their writing.

Wrap Up

Table Talk Have students reread the Big Question and reflect on what they learned. Encourage students to build fluency by reading their writing in groups or to the class.

✔ **Learned** and applied vocabulary related to gravity, tides, and the movement of the moon

✔ **Spoken** statements comparing different types of tides and different types of eclipses

✔ **Written** statements about how the movement of the moon affects our lives on Earth

Exploring Space

Vocabulary rocket, thrust, velocity, satellite, space shuttle, space station, space probe, rover, vacuum, microgravity, space spinoff, remote sensing, geostationary orbit

Materials balloon, globe

Science Background

- NASA has used space shuttles to take satellites into orbit, repair damaged satellites, and carry astronauts to and from space stations. A space station provides a place for experiments in space. Space probes collect data about the solar system.

- Conditions in space that differ from those on Earth include being a near vacuum, having extreme temperatures, and having microgravity.

♻ Frontload the Lesson

 How does exploring space benefit people?

Talk About It

Build Background Inflate a balloon and hold the opening closed with your fingers. Point the balloon in a direction away from people. Let go of the balloon and have students observe what happens. Relate the demonstration to how real rockets and jets use a backward thrust of air or other gases which push against the matter in the surrounding air. A rocket moves forward when gases shooting out of the back of the engine push it in the opposite direction.

♻ Content and Language

Predict

Model Read the Big Question and the objectives aloud. Explain any unfamiliar words using accessible language, such as *tools* in place of *technology*.

Guide Discussion As students discuss what they think they are going to learn, ask them what they most want to learn.

Exploring Space

 Big Question How does exploring space benefit people?

You will . . .
- Identify technology that makes exploring space possible.
- Recognize ways that people benefit from space exploration.
- Understand and use terms related to space exploration.

Talk About It

Rockets are an important technology that scientists use to explore space.

Watch as your teacher makes a balloon travel around the room. Talk about what makes it move. Describe what you saw.

1. When my teacher lets go of the balloon it . . .
2. I think this happens because . . .
3. Listen as your teacher reads the words in the Picture It box. Raise your hand if you hear any words that remind you of the balloon's movement.

Predict
Look at the Big Question and the "You will . . ." statements at the top of the page. Describe what you think you are going to learn in this lesson.

I think I am going to learn about . . .

Leveled Instruction

Early Beginner/Beginner Partner beginners with students of higher level language proficiency. The advanced student can show images of machines and then ask *yes or no* questions, such as *Is this a satellite?*

Early Intermediate Students should be building toward independence. Provide sentence frames and images of space exploration technology to help students produce full sentences.

Intermediate These students should be able to work with little assistance. They should produce sentences about space exploration that include some details.

Advanced/Transitioning Partner these students with students of lower level language proficiency. Have them model detailed examples related to space exploration.

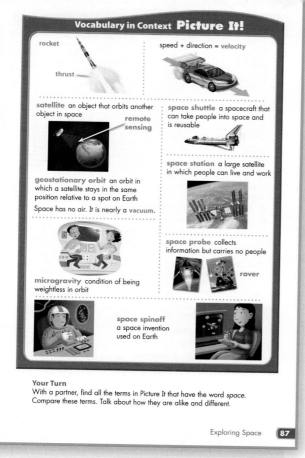

rocket

thrust

speed + direction = **velocity**

satellite an object that orbits another object in space

remote sensing

space shuttle a spacecraft that can take people into space and is reusable

space station a large satellite in which people can live and work

geostationary orbit an orbit in which a satellite stays in the same position relative to a spot on Earth

Space has no air. It is nearly a **vacuum.**

space probe collects information but carries no people

rover

microgravity condition of being weightless in orbit

space spinoff a space invention used on Earth

Your Turn
With a partner, find all the terms in Picture It that have the word *space*. Compare these terms. Talk about how they are alike and different.

Academic Vocabulary

- Explain that *spinoff* means "an unintended benefit that comes from some other effort." Divide the word into its two component parts and explain each part. Discuss or draw what happens when you "spin" the beaters on a mixer and the dough or batter flies off.

- Students are probably familiar with a vacuum cleaner. Explain that, in a vacuum, all air and other matter needs to be absent.

- Write the term *geostationary orbit* on the board. Point out that the prefix *geo-* means "Earth" and *stationary* means "standing still." Ask students to explain how this information can help them better understand the meaning of *geostationary orbit*.

- Write the term *remote sensing* on the board. Explain that the word *remote* means "far away" or "distant." Offer the example of a remote control.

- Point out that the prefix *micro-* means "small," so *microgravity* means "very little gravity." Explain that when astronauts feel almost weightless in space, they are experiencing microgravity.

↻ Comprehensible Input

Vocabulary in Context: Picture It!

1. **Say the Term** Say each term slowly, artificially stressing each syllable. Have students repeat. Then say the term more naturally and have students repeat.

2. **Introduce Word Meaning** Connect each term to the visual that illustrates it.

3. **Demonstrate** Use gestures and visuals to demonstrate each term. If time permits, let students experiment with balloons to feel the thrust. Invite them to explain the relationship between the direction that the balloon travels and the direction that the escaping air travels. Remind them that a similar process thrusts rockets into space.

4. **Apply** After each term has been discussed, have students demonstrate understanding with Talk About It.

Talk About It

Guide Discussion Before students start their independent discussion, check for understanding with the following sentence starters:

1. *Speed in a given direction is . . .* (velocity).

2. *The force that moves a rocket is . . .* (thrust).

3. *An object that orbits Earth is a . . .* (satellite).

4. *The condition of feeling weightless is called . . .* (microgravity).

5. *A place with no air is a . . .* (vacuum).

RTI Response to Intervention

If students have difficulty pronouncing or spelling the word *vacuum* with two *u*'s . . .

Then draw a vacuum cleaner on the board. Have students say the familiar word. Then label it, explaining the unusual spelling.

Your Turn

Guide Discussion Encourage students to use the visuals for support. Circulate among the pairs, correcting any misunderstandings.

Exploring Space

↻ Language Production

Do You Understand?

Comprehension Support Before students start the activity, have a few students explain in their own words the purpose of each of the technologies.

Model Demonstrate how students can prepare to make their drawings. Say, *I know that a space station is a place that orbits Earth. People can live and work on a space station. I will want to make sure that my drawing shows people.*

Talk About It

Guide Discussion For the terms *space shuttle, space station,* and *space probe,* encourage students to remove the word *space* and then think about the meanings of the remaining words.

Your Turn

Guide Discussion Encourage the whole class to share their comparisons. Make sure that students understand that the gases that give a rocket thrust come from the burning of rocket fuel.

In Other Words

Model Read the sentence aloud for students. Then ask, *What is another way to say this? What is another word, or words, for* benefits? Have students take turns reading the sentence aloud, choosing one of the yellow-highlighted words to fill in the space each time. Then have students suggest their own sentences that use the word *benefit* or *benefits* as a verb.

Do You Understand?

Draw a line from each term to its definition. One has been done for you.

Term	Definition
space spinoff	a large satellite on which people can live for a long time
velocity	getting information about objects in space by using space probes
thrust	something that was developed for space but can also be used on Earth
remote sensing	the force that moves a rocket forward
space station	describes speed and direction

Talk About It
Complete the sentences.

① Two types of spacecraft that do not carry people are . . . space probes and rovers.
② A large satellite where people live is called a . . . space station.
③ Robots that explore other planets are called . . . rovers.
④ To blast off into space, spacecraft use . . . rockets, thrust.

Your Turn
Talk to a partner about the way rockets help spacecraft blast off. Then talk about the balloon activity you observed at the start of the lesson. Compare what is similar or different about the two events.

→ **In Other Words** →

Exploration of space	benefits	people.
	helps	
	does good things for	

Leveled Language Proficiency

Students at each proficiency level should be able to perform the following tasks.

Listening/Speaking

Early Beginner/Beginner Use pictures or gestures to respond to oral questions about space exploration. Name pictures using single words or simple phrases.

Early Intermediate Use a bilingual dictionary to clarify meanings of words heard. Using phrases or simple sentences, orally describe objects used to explore space.

Intermediate Identify objects or terms based on oral descriptions. Participate in discussions about technologies used to explore space using appropriate and adequate words and phrases.

Advanced/Transitioning Summarize information that is heard in a class discussion about space exploration. Support a conclusion by orally listing facts and details.

Your Turn

Look at the three pictures. On the lines below each picture, write what the term means.

rocket
This pushes out gas in one direction and the spacecraft goes in the other direction.

space probe
a spacecraft that can collect data, but does not have people on board

rover
a robot that gets information in space

Talk and Write About It 💬 ✏️
Work with a partner. Complete the statements about space exploration.

1. Outer space is a vacuum because _it has almost no matter_ .
2. In a geostationary orbit, a satellite _stays above the same point on Earth as both move in the same direction_ .
3. A rocket works by _pushing out gas in one direction to move in another direction_ .
4. A space spinoff is _a space invention that is used on Earth_ .

Produce Language
What are some ways that people learn about space? Write a few sentences using the vocabulary terms.

_____
_____
_____
_____
_____

Exploring Space **89**

Leveled Language Proficiency

Students at each proficiency level should be able to perform the following tasks.

Reading/Writing

Early Beginner/Beginner Match pictures and words. Label images of objects used to explore space.

Early Intermediate Sort words into categories. List technologies used for space exploration.

Intermediate Follow written directions to complete a task. Write a simple description of how a satellite with a geostationary orbit travels around Earth.

Advanced/Transitioning Infer from descriptions in text how rockets and various spacecraft move and work. Write comparisons of how objects in this lesson are alike and different.

↻ Assess Understanding

Your Turn

Model Before students begin the activity, invite a few volunteers to explain in their own words space probes, rockets, and rovers.

Talk and Write About It

On Their Own Begin by reviewing the Big Question from the first page of the lesson. Have students explain some of the ways people use space spinoffs, such as scratch-resistant lenses, joystick controllers, freeze-dried foods, and other technologies commonly used on Earth.

Produce Language

On Their Own Discuss with students some of the ways that scientists use technology to learn about space. List key ideas on the board for students to refer to when writing their sentences.

Wrap Up

Table Talk Have students reread the Big Question as a way to reflect on what they learned. Encourage students to build fluency by reading their writing in groups or to the class.

✔ **Learned** and applied vocabulary related to space exploration

✔ **Spoken** statements about various ways people use technology that was first used in space

✔ **Written** statements about how people learn about space

Lesson 23

The Sun and the Solar System

Vocabulary geocentric, heliocentric, ellipse, solar system, astronomical unit, planet, dwarf planet, planetesimal, corona, solar wind, sunspot, solar flare, terrestrial planet, gas giant, asteroid belt, asteroid, comet, coma, nucleus

Materials KWL chart, plastic foam balls, diagram of the solar system

 Science Background

- The solar system formed about 4.6 billion years ago from a cloud of hydrogen, helium, rock, ice, and other materials.

- The inner planets—Mercury, Venus, Earth, and Mars—are small and dense and have rocky surfaces.

- The outer planets—Jupiter, Saturn, Uranus, and Neptune—are much larger than Earth and do not have solid surfaces.

Frontload the Lesson

 What are the characteristics of the sun?

Talk About It

Build Background Model for students how to ask questions about how well you know a term. Say, *I know what a comet is. I am going to put that in the* Know *column. I don't know what a solar flare is. I am going to put that in the* Want *column.* Explain to students that they will not fill in the third column until the end of the lesson.

Content and Language

Predict

Model Read the objectives aloud. Read them again, having students chorally read with you.

Guide Discussion Ask students to use their own words to describe the objectives to a partner.

The Sun and the Solar System

 Big Question What are the characteristics of the sun and the solar system?

You will . . .
- Identify the sun as the center of the solar system.
- Describe characteristics of the sun and the solar system.
- Learn and use terms related to the sun and the solar system.

Talk About It

Look at the terms in the Picture It box. Listen as your teacher reads each term aloud.

1. Write terms you **know** well in the **Know** column.
2. Write terms you **want** to know more about in the **Want** column.
3. Later, you will write terms you **learned** in class in the **Learned** column.

Know	Want	Learned

Predict
Look at the Big Question and the "You will . . ." statements at the top of the page. Describe what you think you are going to learn in this lesson.

I think I am going to learn about . . .

Leveled Instruction

Early Beginner/Beginner Beginners should partner with students of higher language proficiency to complete activities. Advanced students can orally ask beginners whether or not they know each term and help them complete the KWL chart.

Early Intermediate Provide sentence frames for students to help them construct answers to questions about the sun and solar system. Encourage them to refer to the Picture It box to complete activities.

Intermediate Students should work with little assistance. They should be able to read the terms well enough to determine how well they know them.

Advanced/Transitioning These students should work with students of lower-level language proficiency. Expect detailed explanations about terms related to the sun and the solar system.

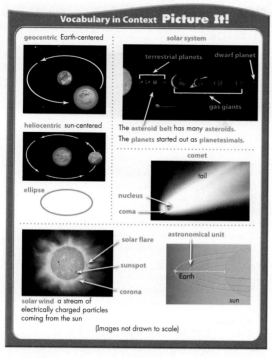

Vocabulary in Context Picture It!

geocentric Earth-centered

solar system
terrestrial planets   dwarf planet
gas giants

heliocentric sun-centered

The asteroid belt has many asteroids.
The planets started out as planetesimals.

comet
tail

ellipse
nucleus
coma

solar flare
astronomical unit
sunspot
Earth
corona
sun
solar wind a stream of
electrically charged particles
coming from the sun

(Images not drawn to scale)

Your Turn
Talk with a partner about the terms in the Picture It box. Choose one term
that you are not sure about. Talk with your partner about the term. See if
you can figure out what it means.

The Sun and the Solar System   **91**

Academic Vocabulary

- Write the terms *heliocentric* and *geocentric* on
  the board. Underline *helio-* and *geo-*. Explain that
  helio- comes from the Greek word that means
  "sun," and that *geo-* comes from the Greek word
  for Earth. Have students discuss how to use the
  -centric parts of the word to better understand
  the meaning of the terms. Emphasize that the
  geocentric model of the solar system is not correct.

- Explain that the word *corona* means "crown" in
  Spanish, and that the word comes from a Latin
  word. Have students discuss how the sun's corona
  is like a crown.

- Students may be familiar with the word *belt* as an
  article of clothing. Explain that just as a belt goes
  around someone's body, the asteroid belt goes
  around the sun.

- Have students share any vocabulary terms they
  recognize as cognates of words in their first
  languages.

↻ Comprehensible Input

Vocabulary in Context: Picture It!

1. **Say the Term** Say each term slowly, artificially
   stressing each syllable. Have students repeat.
   Then say the term more naturally and have
   students repeat.

2. **Introduce Word Meaning** Connect each term
   to the visual that illustrates it.

3. **Demonstrate** Use gestures and visuals to
   demonstrate each term.

4. **Apply** After each term has been discussed,
   have students demonstrate understanding with
   Talk About It.

Talk About It

Guide Discussion Before students start their
independent discussion, check for understanding
with the following sentence starters:

1. *The model of the solar system that places Earth
   at its center is . . .* (geocentric).

2. *The model of the solar system that places the
   sun at its center is . . .* (heliocentric).

3. *Most asteroids orbit the sun in the . . .*
   (asteroid belt).

4. *The average distance between Earth and the
   sun is one . . .* (astronomical unit).

5. *The shape of each planet's orbit is an . . .*
   (ellipse).

R T I Response to Intervention

If students have difficulty distinguishing the words
comet and *coma* . . .

Then review the pronunciations of the words,
emphasizing the first syllables. To check students'
understanding, have them write the words on
cards and then hold up the appropriate word as
you ask questions about each one.

Your Turn

Guide Discussion Call on volunteers to share
what they discussed with the rest of the class.

The Sun and the Solar System

Language Production

Do You Understand?

Comprehension Support Before students start the activity, invite volunteers to list features of the sun. List the terms on the board for students to use as a word bank. Point out to students that the sun is the center of the solar system.

Model Demonstrate how students can use Picture It for support. Say, *I know that the dark areas on the sun have a special name. I am going to look back at the Picture It box for help in figuring out what these dark areas are called.*

Talk About It

Guide Discussion Read the sentences aloud with students. Encourage students to look back at the diagram of the sun they completed for support.

Your Turn

Guide Discussion Have volunteers share their lists of words that describe the sun. List the words on the board. Ask students to explain what makes the sun a unique object in the solar system.

A Closer Look

On Their Own Encourage students to work in pairs to complete this word study activity. Then have them discuss the differences in the alternate meanings.

Do You Understand?

Look at the picture of the sun. Use the terms in the box to label the sun's features.

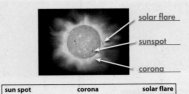

- solar flare
- sunspot
- corona

| sun spot | corona | solar flare |

Talk About It
Talk with a partner. Complete the sentences.

1. Dark areas on the sun are called . . . sunspots.
2. Giant eruptions on the sun cause . . . solar flares.
3. The sun's outer ring, or halo, is its . . . corona.
4. Pluto is not really a planet. Instead, it is a . . . dwarf planet.
5. Streams of charged particles from the sun are . . . solar winds.
6. A small, rocky object that orbits the sun in the asteroid belt is called an . . . asteroid.
7. Planets and other objects in the solar system formed from small bodies are called . . . planetesimals.
8. The solid inner core of a comet is called the . . . nucleus.
9. The fuzzy outer layer of a comet is called the . . . coma.

Your Turn
Work with a partner. Discuss some of the sun's characteristics.

A Closer Look

Multiple Meanings Many of the terms in this lesson include words with multiple meanings. For instance, the terms *belt, coma,* and *nucleus* have more than one meaning. Use a dictionary to find at least two meanings for each of these words.

Leveled Language Proficiency

Students at each proficiency level should be able to perform the following tasks.

Listening/Speaking

Early Beginner/Beginner Point to pictures of objects in the solar system in response to oral questions. Orally express agreement or disagreement with a statement.

Early Intermediate Classify and sort objects or visuals based on oral directions. Answer *what, where, why* questions about objects in the solar system.

Intermediate Identify main ideas of oral discussions. Orally summarize a description of some of the objects in the solar system.

Advanced/Transitioning Follow complex oral directions to complete activities. Explain, using complete and complex sentences, the difference between the geocentric and heliocentric models of the solar system and explain which one is accurate.

Your Turn
Draw a diagram of the solar system.
Include as many details as you can think of.
Write at least five labels to show different objects found in the solar system.

Drawing of the solar system should include drawings and labels for at least five of the following: planet, dwarf planet, terrestrial planet, gas giant, asteroid, and asteroid belt.

Talk and Write About It 💬 ✏️
Complete the statements about the solar system.

1. A dwarf planet is a <u>tiny planet</u>.
2. A terrestrial planet is one of <u>the four planets closest to the sun</u>.
3. A stream of charged particles from the sun is called a <u>solar flare</u>.
4. The shape of the planets' orbits is an <u>ellipse</u>.
5. The distance from the sun to Earth is one <u>astronomical unit</u>.
6. Two parts of a comet are the <u>Accept any two of: nucleus, coma, and tail</u>.

Produce Language
Write about some parts of the solar system. Use description words and comparison words. Use as many vocabulary terms as you can. Then fill in the last column of your Know-Want-Learned chart.

_____
_____
_____
_____
_____

The Sun and the Solar System   **93**

Leveled Language Proficiency

Students at each proficiency level should be able to perform the following tasks.

Reading/Writing

Early Beginner/Beginner Read from a list of words and connect the words to pictorial representations of objects in the solar system. Write a list of words needed to complete a writing task.

Early Intermediate Read descriptions of objects in the solar system and then identify the terms they describe. Write a list of phrases to help complete a writing task.

Intermediate Read descriptions of the sun and solar system, and then circle key terms and phrases in the reading. Use key terms and phrases in complete sentences.

Advanced/Transitioning Read detailed paragraphs about objects in the solar system, and summarize orally or with diagrams. Write a list of key words and phrases; use them as headers for a written summary of lesson topics.

↻ Assess Understanding

Your Turn

Model Before students start the activity, set out several plastic or foam balls or other objects of different sizes. Ask students to help you arrange the objects so they make a working model of the solar system. Encourage students to explain their thinking as they make suggestions.

Talk and Write About It

On Their Own If students are not sure about the names of each planet, point to the planets in a classroom diagram as you name them. Share this mnemonic device to help students remember the sequence: *My Very Eager Mother Just Served Us Nachos.*

Produce Language

On Their Own Before students begin writing, have them form small groups so that they can share their diagrams of the solar system. Encourage students to take turns and point out how their drawings show the way the solar system is organized. As they finish their writing, encourage them to return to their Know-Want-Learned charts and complete the final column. If time allows, you may want to complete the final column as a class.

Wrap Up

Table Talk Have students reread the Big Question and discuss it as a way to reflect on what they learned. Encourage students to build fluency by reading their writing in groups or to the class.

✔ **Learned** and applied vocabulary related to objects in the solar system

✔ **Spoken** statements about features of the sun

✔ **Written** statements about how the solar system is organized

Lesson 24

Telescopes, Stars, and the Universe

Vocabulary electromagnetic radiation, visible light, wavelength, spectrum, telescope, observatory, parallax, universe, light-year, scientific notation, spectrograph, Hertzsprung-Russell diagram, nebula, black hole, galaxy, quasar, big bang theory, dark matter

Science Background

- Telescopes collect and focus light and other forms of electromagnetic radiation.

- A star is born when the contracting gas and dust from a nebula becomes so dense and hot that nuclear fusion starts. After a star runs out of fuel, it becomes a white dwarf, a neutron star, or a black hole.

- According to the big bang theory, the universe formed in an enormous explosion billions of years ago.

⟳ Frontload the Lesson

 How do astronomers learn about distant objects in the universe?

Talk About It

Build Background The images shown are enhanced renderings of data captured by the powerful Hubble telescope. Imaging scientists compile the digital "photographs" of visible light, infrared, and ultraviolet radiation, and add their own coloring to make the pictures as clear and detailed as possible.

⟳ Content and Language

Predict

Model Read the objectives aloud. Repeat the words *universe* and *telescope* while clapping as you say each syllable.

Guide Discussion Encourage students to use the pictures and labels on this page as well as the text to help them make their predictions.

Telescopes, Stars, and the Universe

Big Question How do astronomers learn about distant objects in the universe?

You will . . .
- Describe how scientists use telescopes to study the universe.
- Identify faraway objects in the universe.
- Use terms related to telescopes, stars, and the universe.

Talk About It

Look at the photographs below. These are things found deep in space.

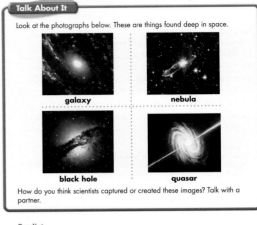

galaxy

nebula

black hole

quasar

How do you think scientists captured or created these images? Talk with a partner.

Predict

Look at the Big Question and the "You will . . ." statements at the top of the page. Describe what you think you are going to learn in this lesson.

I think I am going to learn about . . .

Leveled Instruction

Early Beginner Have students point to pictures and use gestures to answer questions. When students point to a picture, say the term aloud and then write the term on the board.

Beginner Keep a list of key terms on the board for students to refer to when answering questions about the universe.

Early Intermediate/Intermediate After students finish the lesson, have them return to the images on this page and describe the characteristics of these space objects, using as many vocabulary terms as possible.

Advanced/Transitioning Have these students partner with beginner students. Encourage them to model how they think about, talk about, and write about their ideas about the universe.

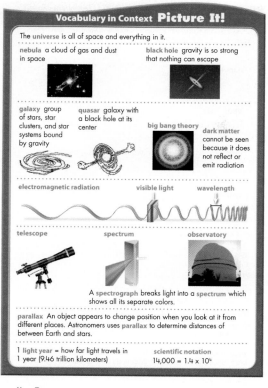

The **universe** is all of space and everything in it.

nebula a cloud of gas and dust in space

black hole gravity is so strong that nothing can escape

galaxy group of stars, star clusters, and star systems bound by gravity

quasar galaxy with a black hole at its center

big bang theory

dark matter cannot be seen because it does not reflect or emit radiation

electromagnetic radiation

visible light

wavelength

telescope

spectrum

observatory

A **spectrograph** breaks light into a **spectrum** which shows all its separate colors.

parallax An object appears to change position when you look at it from different places. Astronomers uses **parallax** to determine distances of between Earth and stars.

1 **light year** = how far light travels in 1 year (9.46 trillion kilometers)

scientific notation
14,000 = 1.4 x 10⁴

Your Turn
Talk with a partner about the pictures in the Picture It box. Choose two terms that you are confused about. Ask if your partner can help explain them.

Telescopes, Stars, and the Universe **95**

Academic Vocabulary

- Write the term *telescope* on the board. Point out that the word-part *tele-* means "from a distance" and *-scope* means "to see."

- Write the compound word *light-year* on the board. Point out the two parts: *light* and *year*. Explain that a light-year is the distance light travels in one year.

- Point out that the term *spectrograph* contains the word-part *-graph*, which means "to write." Have students discuss how this can help them better understand the meaning of the term.

- To demonstrate the meaning of *parallax,* have students hold a finger about two feet in front of their faces. Students should first close their left eye and then close their right eye, and observe how the position of their finger seems to change relative to the background.

↻ Comprehensible Input

Vocabulary in Context: Picture It!

1. **Say the Term** Say each term slowly, artificially stressing each syllable. Have students repeat. Then say the term more naturally and have students repeat.

2. **Introduce Word Meaning** Connect each term to the visual that illustrates it.

3. **Demonstrate** Use gestures and visuals to demonstrate each term.

4. **Apply** After each term has been discussed, have students demonstrate understanding with Talk About It.

Talk About It

Guide Discussion Before students start their independent discussion, check for understanding with the following sentence starters:

1. *All the colors contained in white light form a . . .* (spectrum).

2. *Large telescopes are built into buildings called . . .* (observatories).

3. *All of space makes up the . . .* (universe).

4. *Matter that cannot be seen is . . .* (dark matter).

5. *A tool that helps people see into space is a . . .* (telescope).

6. *A device that breaks light into colors is a . . .* (spectrograph).

RTI Response to Intervention

If students have difficulty reading or decoding the word *wavelength* . . .

Then point out the two parts of the compound word: *wave* and *length*. Explain that a *wavelength* is the "length of one wave."

Your Turn

Guide Discussion Listen in on student conversations and correct any errors. After students have finished talking with their partners, call on a few pairs to share what they learned from each other.

Telescopes, Stars, and the Universe

 # Language Production

Do You Understand?

Comprehension Support Read each term and definition with students. Encourage them to look at the terms and images in the Picture It box.

Model Demonstrate how students can ask themselves questions to help them match terms and definitions. Say, *Is a nebula a huge group of stars? No, it isn't. Is it a large cloud of gas and dust? Yes. So I draw a line from nebula to its definition.*

Talk About It

Guide Discussion Read the sentences aloud with students as they work together to complete each one.

Your Turn

Guide Discussion Make sure that students understand that certain objects in the universe, such as dark matter and black holes, do not emit light and therefore cannot be seen with telescopes that collect light.

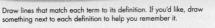

Do You Understand?

Draw lines that match each term to its definition. If you'd like, draw something next to each definition to help you remember it.

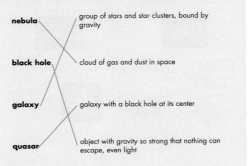

nebula — group of stars and star clusters, bound by gravity

black hole — cloud of gas and dust in space

galaxy — galaxy with a black hole at its center

quasar — object with gravity so strong that nothing can escape, even light

Talk About It
Complete the sentences.

1. Nothing can escape the pull of a . . . black hole.
2. A building that has telescopes built into it is called an . . . observatory.
3. Stars begin their lives as parts of . . . galaxy.
4. Matter in the universe that does not give off radiation is called . . . dark matter.
5. Some stars seem to move when viewed from different places. This is called . . . parallax.

Your Turn
Work with a partner. Talk about things in the universe that you might be able to see with a telescope.

Leveled Language Proficiency

Students at each proficiency level should be able to perform the following tasks.

Listening/Speaking

Early Beginner/Beginner Gesture or point in response to oral directions. Ask simple information questions about visuals that show objects in the universe.

Early Intermediate Answer spoken questions using their own words. Respond to questions about black holes and quasars using short phrases or simple sentences.

Intermediate Engage in a game that involves listening to vocabulary terms and then explaining their meaning. Participate in limited discussions with phrases and simple sentences about black holes and quasars.

Advanced/Transitioning Follow multiple-step oral directions. Define black holes and quasars and describe the special characteristics of each.

Your Turn
Write words and/or draw pictures to tell about each term.

scientific notation	light-year	spectrograph
sample: 2,400 = 2.4×10^3	how far light travels in 1 year	sample: a device that breaks light into colors
big bang explosion, beginning of our universe	telescope a tool for seeing things far away	galaxy sample: huge group of stars bound together by gravity

Talk and Write About It
Complete the statements about space.

1. A light-year is _the distance light travels in one year_.
2. A spectrograph separates _light into colors_.
3. To determine how far away a star is, astronomers may use _parallax_.
4. Telescopes are used to _see faraway objects_.
5. The numbers 5.8×10^7 are written in _scientific notation_.
6. Visible light is one type of _electromagnetic radiation_.
7. Light you can see is called _visible light_.

Produce Language
Explain three things that astronomers do to learn about the universe. Use as many vocabulary terms as you can.

1. _____
   _____
2. _____
   _____
3. _____
   _____

Telescopes, Stars, and the Universe **97**

Leveled Language Proficiency

Students at each proficiency level should be able to perform the following tasks.

Reading/Writing

Early Beginner/Beginner Read one- or two-word labels on visuals related to the universe. Write words and phrases related to pictures in the lesson.

Early Intermediate Use context clues and visuals to infer the meaning of captions. Write explanations of discoveries about the universe using multiple sentences in a logical order.

Intermediate Use reading strategies such as text structure to help understand what they read. Write details and examples to describe discoveries about the universe.

Advanced/Transitioning Make inferences while reading about discoveries about the universe. Write coherent sentences telling what scientists do to learn about space.

Assess Understanding

Your Turn

Model As students complete the activity, prompt student thinking with questions such as *What is a light-year? What do you think the big bang looked like? What is electromagnetic radiation?* After students have completed the activity, have volunteers share some of the words and images they included in their grid.

Talk and Write About It

On Their Own Call on volunteers to use their own words to define or give examples of some of the terms from the lesson.

Produce Language

On Their Own Before writing, brainstorm with students some of the things that astronomers have learned about the universe. Model scanning back through the lesson to find ideas. List key terms and phrases on the board. Encourage students to use the terms and phrases as they complete the sentences.

Wrap Up

Table Talk Have students review the Big Question and use it to reflect on what they learned. Encourage students to build fluency by reading their writing in groups or to the class.

✔ **Learned** and applied vocabulary related to the exploration of the universe

✔ **Spoken** statements about objects and systems in the universe

✔ **Written** statements about scientific ideas about space

EARTH SCIENCE STUDENT BOOK RESOURCES

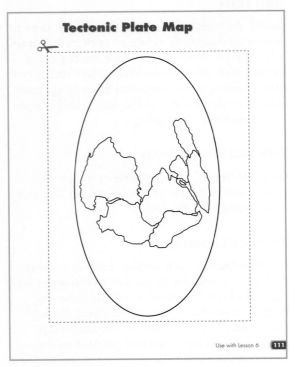

page 111

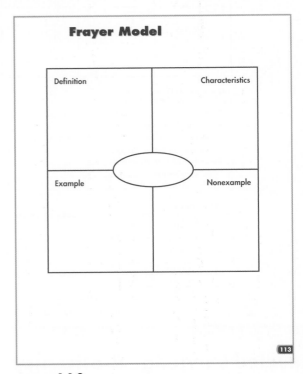

page 113

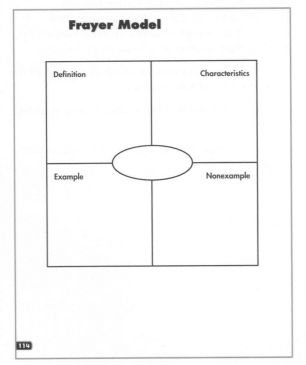

page 114

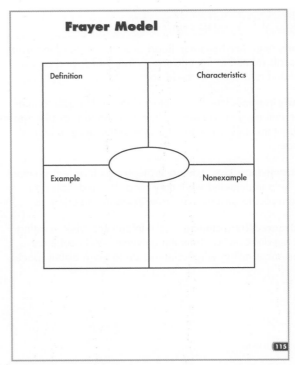

page 115

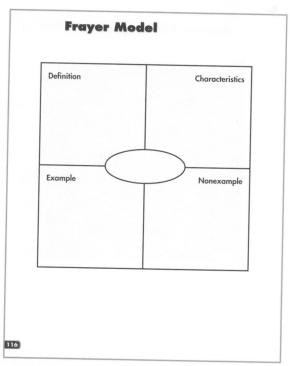

page 116

page 117

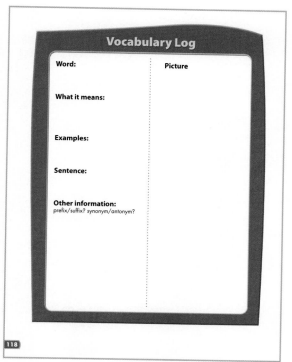

page 118

page 119

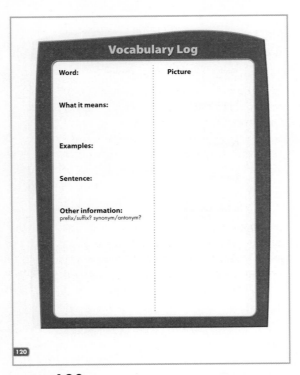

page 120

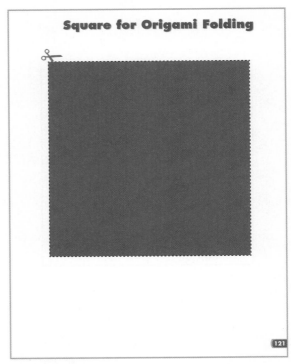

page 121

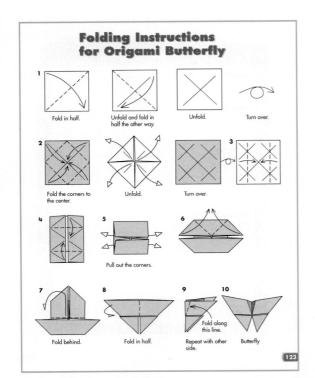

page 123

CREDITS

Illustrations

2, 3, 4, 7, 8, 31, 67, 69 Greg Harris; **3, 8, 9, 15, 24, 38, 39, 43, 50, 58, 59, 81, 98, 99, 100, 103, 105** Kenneth Batelman; **5, 83, 87** Nathan Jarvis; **6, 46, 47, 82** Laurie O'Keefe; **7, 39, 55, 91, 98, 102, 104** Precision Graphics; **7, 32, 67, 71, 83, 91, 92, 94, 95** Stephen Durke; **7, 53** Studio Liddell; **8, 11, 13, 16, 26, 44, 50, 52, 59, 60, 63, 66, 79, 80, 83, 84, 85, 87, 91, 98, 102, 104** Rob Schuster; **17** Robert Hynes; **23, 27, 47, 55, 56** John Edwards; **31, 33, 55** Steve McEntee; **35, 36, 37, 43, 71, 72, 74, 75, 76** Joe LeMonnier; **51** Kevin Jones; **51** Rich McMahon; **51** Ted Smykal; **59, 104, 105** Peter Bull; **63** Theresa Sakno; **86, 87** Adam Benton; **87, 89** Paul Rivoche; **87, 104** Robin Boyer; **123** Reproduced with permission by Dover Publications from Easy Origami by John Montroll, October 1992./©Dover Publications.

Photographs

Every effort has been made to secure permission and provide appropriate credit for photographic material. The publisher deeply regrets any omission and pledges to correct errors called to its attention in subsequent editions.

Unless otherwise acknowledged, all photographs are the property of Pearson Education, Inc.

Photo locators denoted as follows: Top (T), Center (C), Bottom (B), Left (L), Right (R), Background (Bkgd)

Cover

Origami "Snowflakes" designed and folded by Brian Chan, in handmade Origamido® paper by Richard L. Alexander and Michael G. LaFosse.

7 Stockbyte/Thinkstock; **10** Goddard Space Flight Center Scientific Visualization Studio/NASA; **12** Goddard Space Flight Center Scientific Visualization Studio/NASA; **14** (BC) DK Images, Florea Marius Catalin/iStockphoto, Rehlik/Fotolia, ste72/Fotolia; **15** (BL) ©DK Images, andy koehler/Fotolia, (BR, BC) Colin Keates/Courtesy of the Natural History Museum, London/©DK Images, (TR) DK Images, Florea Marius Catalin/iStockphoto, ste72/Fotolia, Zee/Fotolia; **18** Andreas Einsiedel/©DK Images; **19** (C) DK Images, Ionescu Bogdan/Fotolia, Jim Parkin/Fotolia, michal81/Fotolia; **20** michal812/Fotolia; **35** Jupiterimages/Getty Images/Thinkstock; **42** photka/Fotolia; **46** Ralf Kraft/Fotolia, Tonda/Fotolia; **63** Galyna Andrushko/Fotolia; **64** Galyna Andrushko/Fotolia; **70** Chris White/Fotolia, Hemera Technologies/Thinkstock, George Doyle/Thinkstock/Getty Images, tataram/Fotolia; **72** ©Linda Bucklin/Shutterstock; **73** Chris White/Fotolia, tataram/Fotolia; **75** Julius/Fotolia, Jupiterimages/Getty Images/Thinkstock; **79** ©Corbis/Jupiter Images; **87** NASA; **94** Hubble/NASA, NASA; **95** Comstock/Thinkstock, Hubble/NASA, Paul Huizenga/Fotolia; **98** EuToch/Fotolia; **100** Zedcor Wholly Owned/Getty Images/Thinkstock; **103** Terex/Dreamstime LLC, Britvich/Dreamstime LLC, Chiyacat/Dreamstime LLC.

CONTENTS

Appendix: STEM Topics

STEM lessons appear, following the Physical Science lessons.

Lesson 2

Introduction to Living Things

Vocabulary organism, cell, unicellular, multicellular, metabolism, development, homeostasis, binomial nomenclature, genus, species, prokaryote, nucleus, eukaryote, evolution, asexual reproduction, sexual reproduction

Materials building blocks, cup with water, pictures of different organisms' stages of development

 Science Background

- All living things are made of cells, contain DNA, use energy, respond to their surroundings, and grow, develop, and reproduce.
- All living things are classified into groups. The levels of classification are domain, kingdom, phylum, class, order, family, genus, and species.

↻ Frontload the Lesson

What are common characteristics of all living things?

Talk About It

Build Background Explain to students that *organisms* are living things. *Characteristics* are traits or features that show something's character or nature.

↻ Content and Language

Predict

Model Read the Big Question and the objectives aloud. Model using key words to make one prediction about the lesson.

Guide Discussion Ask students to say the objectives with you. Have them discuss what the objectives mean to them.

 Big Question What are the common characteristics of all living things?

You will . . .
- Understand that all living things are made of cells, use energy, respond to their surroundings, and reproduce.
- Know that living things are classified into groups based on group characteristics.
- Use science terms to compare and contrast living things.

Talk About It

Circle the pictures that show living things.

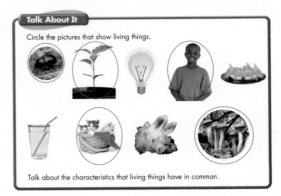

Talk about the characteristics that living things have in common.

Predict
Look at the Big Question and the "You will . . ." statements at the top of the page. Describe what you think you are going to learn in this lesson.

I think I am going to learn about . . .

6   Lesson 2

Leveled Instruction

Early Beginner Have the students repeat the terms *living* or *not living* as you point to each picture. Ask students to do this on their own after several repetitions.

Beginner Provide sentence frames for students to help them construct answers to the questions. Example: *This___ is a living organism. This ___ is not a living organism.*

Early Intermediate/Intermediate Ask students to explain their answers to questions about living organisms, providing help as needed.

Advanced/Transitioning Ask these students to use complete, complex sentences to describe the characteristics of living organisms.

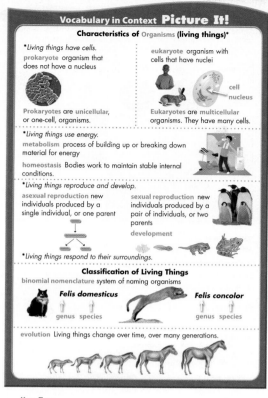

Vocabulary in Context Picture It!

Characteristics of Organisms (living things)*

*Living things have cells.
prokaryote organism that does not have a nucleus

eukaryote organism with cells that have nuclei

cell nucleus

Prokaryotes are unicellular, or one-cell, organisms.

Eukaryotes are multicellular organisms. They have many cells.

*Living things use energy.
metabolism process of building up or breaking down material for energy
homeostasis Bodies work to maintain stable internal conditions.

*Living things reproduce and develop.
asexual reproduction new individuals produced by a single individual, or one parent

sexual reproduction new individuals produced by a pair of individuals, or two parents

development

*Living things respond to their surroundings.

Classification of Living Things
binomial nomenclature system of naming organisms

Felis domesticus
genus species

Felis concolor
genus species

evolution Living things change over time, over many generations.

Your Turn
Explain what you know about the characteristics of living things. Give examples.

Introduction to Living Things **7**

Academic Vocabulary

- Tell students that classification comes from the word *classify*, which means "to arrange according to shared characteristics." *Classification* is the process by which things are organized by the characteristics they have.

- Write the words *binomial nomenclature* on the board. Underline the root word *nom* in both words and explain that *nom* is a Latin word that means "name." The words *binomial* and *nomenclature* both refer to the naming of something. The scientific system of naming living things is called *binomial nomenclature*.

- Explain that the word *karyo* is a Greek word meaning "kernel or nut" and refers to the nucleus of a cell. Since the prefix *pro-* means "before," the word *prokaryotes* means "before the nucleus."

- Review the prefixes *uni-, multi-, a-, bi-, pro-,* and *eu-* with students. *Uni-* means "one," *multi-* means "many," *a-* means "without," *bi-* means "two," and *eu-* means "good" or "true."

↻ Comprehensible Input

Vocabulary in Context: Picture It!

1. **Say the Term** Say each term slowly, artificially stressing each syllable. Have students repeat. Then say the term more naturally and have students repeat.

2. **Introduce Word Meaning** Connect each term to the visual that illustrates it.

3. **Demonstrate** Use gestures and visuals to demonstrate the terms.

4. **Apply** After all of the terms have been discussed, have students demonstrate understanding with Talk About It.

Talk About It

Guide Discussion Check for understanding with the following sentence starters:

1. *The major part of the cell, which directs its activities, is called the . . .* (nucleus).

2. *Organisms with cells that have a nucleus are called . . .* (eukaryotes).

3. *An organism that doesn't have a nucleus is called a . . .* (prokaryote).

4. *The process that organisms use to get energy is . . .* (metabolism).

5. *People drink water when they have been exercising, to maintain . . .* (homeostasis).

6. *The naming system for organisms is called . . .* (binomial nomenclature).

RTI Response to Intervention

If students have difficulty understanding the meaning of the term *homeostasis* . . .

Then explain that the prefix *homeo-* means "same" and *stasis* means "stillness." Bodies want to keep their internal conditions the same as usual—still, or stable.

Your Turn

Guide Discussion Ask students to use the Picture It box terms to discuss the characteristics of living things. Give examples to help guide the discussion.

Introduction to Living Things

↻ Language Production

Do You Understand?

Comprehension Support Before students start the activity, review the root words and prefixes in the chart and the terms in the Picture It box. Remind students that each of these terms describes something related to living things.

Model Read the instructions and follow the chart with your finger from the prefix and root words to show the box in which the first word should be written. After students complete the activity, ask them to consider the words *binomial* and *asexual.* Guide a discussion of the prefixes *bi-* and *a-*, meaning "two" and "absence of."

Talk About It

Guide Discussion Read the statements aloud with students. Then have them work in pairs to complete the sentences. As you discuss the terms, word parts, and definitions, refer back to the Picture It box. Have student pairs search for other terms that combine prefixes and root words. Then, if time allows, have student pairs extend the activity by hunting through their science textbooks for other terms they know or can find containing the same word parts.

Your Turn

Guide Discussion Listen to students as they explain the meanings of the prefixes, root words, and vocabulary terms. Help them to relate these terms to specific living things by giving examples of each, such as bacteria being prokaryotes and therefore also unicellular organisms. Extend the activity by having student pairs search for additional examples of each term by looking through their science textbook.

In Other Words

Model Read the example sentence aloud for students and have them repeat it. Then ask, *What is another way to say this? What is another word, or words, for* characteristics? Have students take turns reading the sentence aloud, choosing one of the yellow-highlighted words to fill in the space each time. Then have students suggest their own sentences that use the word *characteristics.*

Do You Understand?

Prefixes and root words can combine to make a word. Find the correct box to write each vocabulary term that describes living things.

Prefix \ Root	uni- (one) 	multi- (many)	pro- (before)	eu- (true)
cell 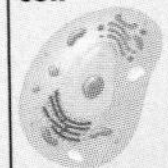	unicellular	multicellular		
karyo (nucleus) 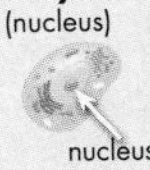			prokaryote	eukaryote

Talk About It

Use the terms from the chart above to complete the sentences.

1. The prefix meaning "one" and the root word *cell* form the word . . . unicellular.
2. The prefix meaning "many" and the root word *cell* form the word . . . multicellular.
3. The prefix meaning "before" and the root *karyo*, meaning "nucleus," form . . . prokaryote.
4. The prefix meaning "true" and the root *karyo* form . . . eukaryote.

Your Turn

Explain to a partner what each of these terms means: *unicellular, multicellular, prokaryote,* and *eukaryote.*

In Other Words ➡

All living things share some	characteristics	in common.
	traits	
	attributes	

8 Lesson 2

Leveled Language Proficiency

Students at each proficiency level should be able to perform the following tasks.

Listening/Speaking

Early Beginner/Beginner Repeat vocabulary terms correctly and identify the prefix and root word in each term.

Early Intermediate Use hand gestures and short phrases to respond to oral questions about living organisms. Explain vocabulary terms orally, using short phrases and simple sentences.

Intermediate Understand spoken descriptions of organisms from different species and genus. Explain orally, in complete sentences, vocabulary terms relating to living things.

Advanced/Transitioning Understand a discussion about binominal nomenclature. Use complete and complex sentences to explain vocabulary terms, prefixes, and root words and relate them to examples of living things.

Look at the animals and their scientific names. Circle the part of the animal's name that tells its genus. Underline the part of the animal's name that tells its species.

Felis domesticus   Felis concolor   Felis marmorata

What characteristics do the animals have in common? What characteristics are different? Discuss with a partner.

Talk and Write About It

Complete the statements about how scientists classify living things.

1. The binomial nomenclature system gives each organism a <u>two part scientific name</u>

2. The first part of an organism's scientific name is the <u>genus</u>.

3. The second part of an organism's scientific name is the <u>species</u>.

4. The characteristics that organisms in the genus *Felis* share are <u>fur, four legs, retractable claws, sharp hunter's teeth, whiskers</u>.

5. The characteristics that are different for each species shown are <u>size, fur color and markings, length of fur</u>

Produce Language

Write what you learned about living things in this lesson. Use as many vocabulary terms as you can.

_____

_____

_____

_____

_____

Introduction to Living Things   **9**

Leveled Language Proficiency

Students at each proficiency level should be able to perform the following tasks.

Reading/Writing

Early Beginner/Beginner Read words and parts of words that are used to describe the characteristics of living things. Write characteristics of living things.

Early Intermediate Read simple phrases and recognize words and word roots relating to the characteristics of living things. Write short phrases to describe the characteristics of living things.

Intermediate Read and comprehend phrases and terms related to the characteristics of living things. Write a description of the characteristics of living things using key vocabulary.

Advanced/Transitioning Read aloud sentences related to the characteristics of living things. Write complete and complex sentences, using examples, describing the characteristics of living things.

↻ Assess Understanding

Your Turn

Model Read instructions aloud to students. Tell students the meanings of each of the scientific names in Latin: *concolor* means "the same color," *domesticus* means "of the house," and *marmorata* means "marble." *Felis* comes from the word *felidae*, which refers to the cat family. Encourage group discussion about the question, *How does binomial nomenclature help scientists classify living things?*

Talk and Write About It

On Their Own Provide help in reading each of the sentences, and encourage students to talk about the similarities and differences in the characteristics of each species.

Produce Language

On Their Own Have students reread the Big Question at the beginning of the lesson if they need a topic or focus to get started. Then have them write about what they've learned, using pictures and sentences in the lesson for support. Encourage students to post their writing around the room, and give students time to read each other's work.

Wrap Up

Table Talk Have students reflect on what they learned. Encourage students to build fluency by reading their writing in groups or to the class.

✔ **Learned** and applied vocabulary related to the characteristics of living things

✔ **Read** statements about the characteristics of living things

✔ **Heard** statements about the characteristics of living things

Cell Structure and Function

Vocabulary cell, cell wall, ribosomes, endoplasmic reticulum, nucleus, cytoplasm, Golgi apparatus, cell membrane, vacuole, mitochondria, chloroplast, lysosomes, cell theory, microscope

Materials green, yellow, and red pencils; microscope; chart paper

Science Background

- The cell theory states that cells are the basic units of structure and function in living things. All living things are composed of cells, and all cells come from other cells.

- Each kind of cell structure has a specific function.

- In multicellular organisms, cells are organized into tissues, organs, and organ systems.

Frontload the Lesson

What is the structure of a cell?

Talk About It

Build Background Read the first sentence to students, and then point out that living things may be *unicellular* or *multicellular*. Define each term for students and then have them guess the number of cells found in each organism. Point out that the picture on the right shows a tiny unicellular organism that can be seen under a microscope.

Content and Language

Predict

Model Read the Big Question and the objectives aloud and have students repeat after you.

Guide Discussion Ask students to read the objectives with you. Then have them predict what they will learn about cells.

Cell Structure and Function

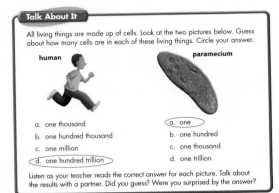

Big Question What is the structure of a cell?

You will . . .
- Identify cells as the basic units of living things.
- Label the different parts of a cell.
- Use terms to talk about the functions of cell parts.

Talk About It

All living things are made up of cells. Look at the two pictures below. Guess about how many cells are in each of these living things. Circle your answer.

human

a. one thousand
b. one hundred thousand
c. one million
d. one hundred trillion

paramecium

a. one
b. one hundred
c. one thousand
d. one trillion

Listen as your teacher reads the correct answer for each picture. Talk about the results with a partner. Did you guess? Were you surprised by the answer?

Predict
Look at the Big Question and the "You will . . ." statements at the top of the page. Describe what you think you are going to learn in this lesson.

I think I am going to learn about . . .

10 Lesson 3

Leveled Instruction

Early Beginner/Beginner Have students trace the cells into their notebooks. Then have them label the cells with the vocabulary terms using color codes. Have them highlight the terms that are clear to them in green, the ones that are somewhat unclear in yellow, and those that are very unclear in pink. Look at students' codes and modify instruction to assist them with the terms and concepts that are most challenging.

Early Intermediate/Intermediate Encourage students to create a personal dictionary in their notes in which they summarize the meaning of each term in their own words. Have students share their summaries with the class, and write the most accurate responses for each term on a piece of chart paper for the whole class to see. Leave the list up to be used as a reference during the lesson.

Advanced/Transitioning Partner these students with beginning students and have them model how to structure more detailed descriptions of cell parts and their functions.

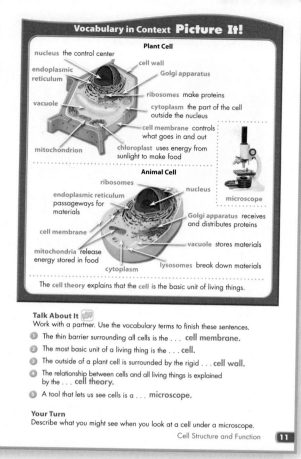

Vocabulary in Context **Picture It!**

Plant Cell

nucleus the control center

cell wall

endoplasmic reticulum

Golgi apparatus

ribosomes make proteins

vacuole

cytoplasm the part of the cell outside the nucleus

cell membrane controls what goes in and out

mitochondrion

chloroplast uses energy from sunlight to make food

Animal Cell

ribosomes

endoplasmic reticulum passageways for materials

nucleus

microscope

cell membrane

Golgi apparatus receives and distributes proteins

mitochondria release energy stored in food

vacuole stores materials

cytoplasm

lysosomes break down materials

The cell theory explains that the cell is the basic unit of living things.

Talk About It

Work with a partner. Use the vocabulary terms to finish these sentences.

1. The thin barrier surrounding all cells is the . . . cell membrane.
2. The most basic unit of a living thing is the . . . cell.
3. The outside of a plant cell is surrounded by the rigid . . . cell wall.
4. The relationship between cells and all living things is explained by the . . . cell theory.
5. A tool that lets us see cells is a . . . microscope.

Your Turn

Describe what you might see when you look at a cell under a microscope.

Cell Structure and Function **11**

Academic Vocabulary

- Explain that the word *mitochondria* is a plural form, and that the singular form is *mitochondrion*. Point out the different labels on the cell drawings. Use the labels as a springboard for teaching plural and singular subject-verb agreement. Have students identify singular and plural terms and list them in a 2-column chart. Supply the missing plural/singular form. Then have students practice simple subject-verb sentences with each.

- Point out the use of the prefixes *micro-*, *cyto-*, and *endo-* in the lesson. Use this table to help students break down the meanings of these words.

Word Part	Meaning	Word
micro	small	microscope
scop	look	
cyto	cell	cytoplasm endoplasmic
endo	inner or within	
plasm	formative material	

- Remind students of the way the word *theory* is used in science. In common usage, the word *theory* means a hunch or an idea. Explain that in science, a *theory* is an explanation of something that has been observed and tested. A *theory* must have extensive evidence to back it up.

↻ Comprehensible Input

Vocabulary in Context: Picture It!

1. **Say the Term** Say each term slowly, artificially stressing each syllable. Have students repeat. Then say the term more naturally and have students repeat.

2. **Introduce Word Meaning** Connect each term to the visual that illustrates it.

3. **Demonstrate** Use gestures and visuals to demonstrate. For example:

   - Display large drawings of a plant cell and an animal cell. Explain the function of each cell part. For example say, *A plant cell has a cell wall. Look at the walls of our classroom. They are hard. They give the classroom its shape. They protect us. The cell wall does the same thing for a plant cell.*

   - Point to a microscope and say, *I cannot study cells without a microscope. Why? Cells are too small to see just with my eye.*

4. **Apply** After each term has been discussed, have students demonstrate understanding with Talk About It.

Talk About It

Guide Discussion Read the sentence starters aloud for students. Remind them to use the words in the Picture It box to answer the questions.

R T I Response to Intervention

If students have difficulty pronouncing the terms *mitochondria* and *chloroplast*, . . .

Then point out that they both have a *ch* that makes a hard *k* sound. Give examples of words containing a hard *ch* that would be more familiar to students, such as *chemical, chrome, echo, character,* or the name *Michael*.

Your Turn

Guide Discussion If possible, allow students to study an object under a microscope and then discuss their responses. Otherwise, refer them to the drawing of the plant cell in the Picture It box and point out that the cell cannot be seen without a microscope.

Cell Structure and Function

↻ Language Production

Do You Understand?

Comprehension Support Before students start the activity, review the vocabulary terms found in the chart. Write each term on the board. Then ask students questions to help review the function of each structure. For example say, *Which part of the cell controls the cell's activities?*

Model Demonstrate how students can ask themselves questions to help them do the activity. Say, *What type of cell has a tough outer layer? Is there a nucleus in both animal cells and plant cells?*

Talk About It

Guide Discussion Read the sentences aloud with students as they work together to complete the items.

Your Turn

Guide Discussion Listen to student discussions as students compare their charts. Help them correct any mistakes or misunderstandings as needed.

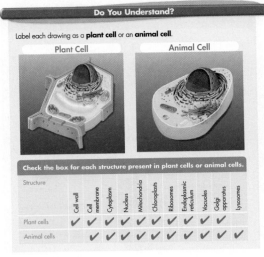

Do You Understand?

Label each drawing as a **plant cell** or an **animal cell**.

Plant Cell   Animal Cell

Check the box for each structure present in plant cells or animal cells.

Structure	Cell wall	Cell membrane	Cytoplasm	Nucleus	Mitochondria	Chloroplasts	Ribosomes	Endoplasmic reticulum	Vacuoles	Golgi apparatus	Lysosomes
Plant cells	✓	✓	✓	✓	✓	✓	✓	✓	✓	✓	
Animal cells		✓	✓	✓	✓		✓	✓	✓	✓	✓

Talk About It 🖳
Complete the sentences.

1. Both plant cells and animal cells are surrounded by a . . . cell membrane.
2. Water, food, and other materials are stored in . . . vacuoles.
3. Animal cells are not surrounded by a . . . cell wall.
4. The control center of a cell is the . . . nucleus.
5. The part of the cell outside the nucleus is called the . . . cytoplasm.
6. The part of a plant cell that makes food using energy from sunlight is the . . . chloroplast.

Your Turn
Work with a partner. Compare your charts. Talk about the structures that are found in both animal cells and plant cells. Then talk about the structures that are found only in plant cells.

Leveled Language Proficiency

Students at each proficiency level should be able to perform the following tasks.

Listening/Speaking

Early Beginner/Beginner Point to the parts of the cell upon hearing them read aloud. Use a word or a short spoken phrase along with a visual aid to respond to questions about cell structure.

Early Intermediate Answer spoken questions about cell structure when a visual aid is provided. Use a visual aid to tell about cell structure with short spoken phrases or simple sentences.

Intermediate Respond to oral questions about the functions of different parts of the cell with some repetition. Use complete spoken sentences to compare the features of plant cells and animal cells.

Advanced/Transitioning Respond to oral explanations of cell theory and structure without assistance or repetition. Explain, using complete and complex spoken sentences, how each part of the cell functions.

Your Turn
Look at the cells below. Label each as a **plant cell** or an **animal cell.**
Then, label each cell using the words from the box.

cell membrane	cell wall	chloroplast
cytoplasm	mitochondria	nucleus

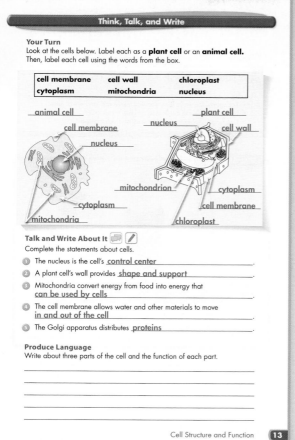

animal cell
cell membrane
nucleus
cytoplasm
mitochondria

plant cell
nucleus
cell wall
mitochondrion
cytoplasm
cell membrane
chloroplast

Talk and Write About It
Complete the statements about cells.

1. The nucleus is the cell's control center .
2. A plant cell's wall provides shape and support .
3. Mitochondria convert energy from food into energy that can be used by cells .
4. The cell membrane allows water and other materials to move in and out of the cell .
5. The Golgi apparatus distributes proteins .

Produce Language
Write about three parts of the cell and the function of each part.

_____
_____
_____
_____
_____

Cell Structure and Function   **13**

Leveled Language Proficiency

Students at each proficiency level should be able to perform the following tasks.

Reading/Writing

Early Beginner/Beginner Locate words that describe cells and cell features. Draw and label pictures to show cell structure.

Early Intermediate Read independently to find references to cell structure. Write short phrases to describe some of the structures found in cells.

Intermediate Use text to identify the differences between plant and animal cells. Write a description of cell functions using complete sentences.

Advanced/Transitioning Summarize text about cell structure and cell theory. Write a paragraph describing the function of the nucleus, cell membrane, cell walls, mitochondria, and chloroplasts.

 # Assess Understanding

Your Turn

Model Draw a simplified cell on the board to show students how to use leader lines and labels. Review with students the difference between a *cell wall* and a *cell membrane*. Encourage students to refer to the drawings on the previous pages for guidance. As an extension, students may want to use colored pencils to color each cell to differentiate the parts.

Talk and Write About It

On Their Own Have partners read and complete each sentence orally. Then have students write their responses individually.

Produce Language

On Their Own After the writing activity, provide an opportunity for students to read what they have written to a partner. Encourage students to listen to their partner and to ask one follow-up question. Then have students pick new partners one or two more times, explaining to the new partner one thing they learned form the previous partner's writing.

Wrap Up

Table Talk Have students review the Big Question to reflect on what they learned. Encourage students to build fluency by reading their writing in groups or to the class.

✔ **Learned** and applied vocabulary related to cell structure and cell theory

✔ **Spoken** statements about the differences between a cell wall and a cell membrane, and what types of cells have these structures

✔ **Written** statements comparing features of animal cells and plant cells

Lesson 4

Cell Chemistry and Transport

Vocabulary diffusion, osmosis, passive transport, active transport, selectively permeable

Materials clear plastic cups; food coloring; medicine droppers; permeable cloth; cup of water; jelly; sand; paper clips

Science Background

- The cell membrane acts as a barrier between the inside of the cell and the outside environment.

- Diffusion and osmosis are forms of *passive transport*: the materials move from a higher concentration to a lower concentration without the need for energy. Osmosis is the diffusion of water. Movement of materials from a lower concentration to a higher concentration is called *active transport*. This process requires energy.

⟳ Frontload the Lesson

How do materials move into and out of a cell?

Talk About It

Build Background Distribute materials to groups for the activity. Review safety guidelines. Tell students that they will demonstrate *diffusion*. Explain that *diffusion* happens when a material moves from where there is more of it to where there is less.

⟳ Content and Language

Predict

Model Lead students in a class brainstorm about ways to predict the topic of a given reading.

Guide Discussion Have students repeat the Big Question and each objective after you state it. Then have them make their predictions.

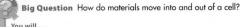

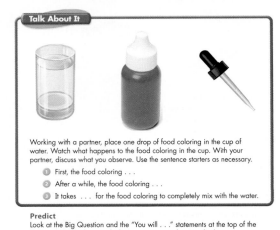

Big Question How do materials move into and out of a cell?

You will . . .
- Recognize the ways that materials move into and out of cells.
- Learn how the cell controls what enters and leaves.
- Use terms related to cell chemistry and cell transport.

Talk About It

Working with a partner, place one drop of food coloring in the cup of water. Watch what happens to the food coloring in the cup. With your partner, discuss what you observe. Use the sentence starters as necessary.

1. First, the food coloring . . .
2. After a while, the food coloring . . .
3. It takes . . . for the food coloring to completely mix with the water.

Predict
Look at the Big Question and the "You will . . ." statements at the top of the page. Describe what you think you are going to learn in this lesson.

I think I am going to learn about . . .

Leveled Instruction

Early Beginner Have students point to pictures or vocabulary terms as you read the words aloud. Students may benefit from reviewing some basic science terms. Be sure they understand terms such as: *materials, controls, enters,* and *leaves.* Give brief examples or demonstrations of these terms.

Beginner Reinforce learning by having students write any new terms on index cards to practice reading aloud or to hold up as answers to questions.

Early Intermediate/Intermediate Activate prior knowledge for students, by having them copy the terms on cards and sort the cards by most to least familiar. Encourage intermediate to advanced students to create glossaries, posters, or bulletin boards by illustrating the terms and/or adding definitions.

Advanced/Transitioning As you move through the lesson activities, encourage these students to act as student-experts, presenting one or more of the demonstrations or explanations.

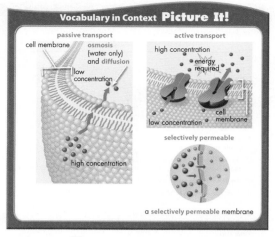

passive transport

cell membrane

osmosis (water only) and diffusion

low concentration

high concentration

active transport

high concentration

energy required

cell membrane

low concentration

selectively permeable

a selectively permeable membrane

Talk About It

Work with a partner. Use the terms in the box above to complete the sentences.

1. Only certain substances can cross a membrane that is . . . selectively permeable.

2. Substances move from an area of higher concentration to an area of lower concentration by . . . diffusion.

3. Some materials can move across a cell membrane without using energy. This is called . . .passive transport.

4. Water moves across a cell membrane by the process of . . .osmosis.

5. Some materials must use energy in order to cross a cell membrane. This is called . . .active transport.

Your Turn

With a partner, talk about the different ways you could show what the vocabulary terms mean. Work together to create simple hand signals or other clues that will help you remember each term.

Academic Vocabulary

- Point out that several terms in this lesson contain suffixes. For example, *diffusion, permeable* and *passive, active,* and *selectively,* all have suffixes that students can separate from a base word to help determine the new word's meaning.

- Remind students that a suffix often is a clue to the word's part of speech. For example, *-ion* signals the noun form of a word. *Diffuse* is a verb meaning "to spread out." *Diffusion* is a noun meaning "the process during which something spreads." The suffix *-able* signals an adjective. The verb *permeate* means "to enter and pass through a porous substance or membrane"; the adjective *permeable* indicates something that is capable of being permeated.

- Point out that *active* and *passive* are antonyms. Remind students that antonyms are words that are the opposite of each other. In science, the term *active* indicates something that requires energy. In contrast, *passive* refers to something that doesn't use energy. Make sure students understand that *passive,* in this context, does not mean there is inactivity. It simply means the activity does not require an input of energy.

↻ Comprehensible Input

Vocabulary in Context: Picture It!

1. **Say the Term** Say each term slowly, artificially stressing each syllable. Have students repeat. Then say the term more naturally and have students repeat.

2. **Introduce Word Meaning** Connect each term to the visual that illustrates it.

3. **Demonstrate** Use gestures and visuals to demonstrate each term.

   - For the terms *osmosis, diffusion,* and *passive transport,* draw up the four corners of a permeable cloth to make a bowl-like area. Say, *This cloth is like a cell.* Hold the cloth bowl over a bucket and pour a cup of water into the cloth to demonstrate passive transport, such as diffusion and osmosis.

   - Next, pour jelly on the cloth. Ask students to note that the substance doesn't pass through without pushing on it or using energy. Say, *This is what happens in active transport.*

   - Now, pour some water with sand and paper clips. Say, *This cloth is selectively permeable. It allows only some substances to go through.*

4. **Apply** After all of the terms have been discussed, have students demonstrate understanding with Talk About It.

Talk About It

Guide Discussion Ask students to use the vocabulary terms and gestures to describe each picture in the Picture It box.

RTI Response to Intervention

If students have difficulty saying the term *selectively permeable* . . .

Then Point out that the different *e*'s in in this term make several sounds. Emphasize the schwa (unstressed vowel), short vowel, silent vowel, *r*-controlled and long vowels.

Your Turn

Guide Discussion Have students demonstrate the signals or clues they think up. Call on a different student pair for each term.

Cell Chemistry and Transport

↻ Language Production

Do You Understand?

Comprehension Support Point out the features of the three diagrams. Explain that the colored circles indicate molecules of a substance and that in each case, the concentration of the substance (the number of molecules) is higher on one side of the membrane than on the other side.

Model Before students start the activity, have several students stand in a circle with two students in the middle of the circle. Explain that the students forming the circle are the "cell membrane." Have the rest of the students stand outside the circle. Point out that there are more students outside the circle than inside. Then allow one or two of the students on the outside to pass into the circle. Explain that this is *passive transport*. Point out that there are still more students outside the circle than inside the circle. Then have the students inside the circle pass out of the circle with the help of a student in the "cell membrane." Tell students this demonstrates *active transport*.

Talk About It

Guide Discussion Read the sentence starters aloud with students as they work together to complete the sentences.

Your Turn

Guide Discussion Listen to student discussions as they compare the three processes. Help them correct any mistakes or misunderstandings as needed.

A Closer Look

On Their Own Write the word *transport* on the board. Draw a slash between the syllables to emphasize the two roots that make up the word. Then write the roots separately. Ask, *What does the root* trans- *mean? What does* -port *mean?* Encourage students to read the other sample words. As they read each word, write it on the board, separating the syllables. Model defining the first word. Say, *The root* trans- *means "across." Then I see the root* plant, *so this word must mean "carry or move something from one place to another—across—to a new place."*

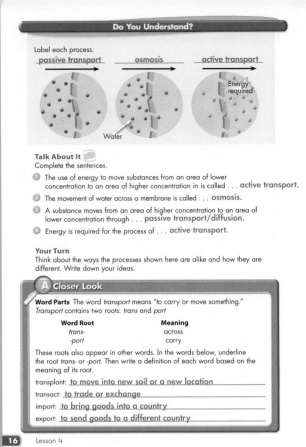

Do You Understand?

Label each process.

passive transport → osmosis → active transport

Energy required

Water

Talk About It
Complete the sentences.

1. The use of energy to move substances from an area of lower concentration to an area of higher concentration in is called . . . **active transport.**

2. The movement of water across a membrane is called . . . **osmosis.**

3. A substance moves from an area of higher concentration to an area of lower concentration through . . . **passive transport/diffusion.**

4. Energy is required for the process of . . . **active transport.**

Your Turn
Think about the ways the processes shown here are alike and how they are different. Write down your ideas.

A Closer Look

Word Parts The word *transport* means "to carry or move something." *Transport* contains two roots: *trans* and *port*

Word Root	Meaning
trans-	across
-port	carry

These roots also appear in other words. In the words below, underline the root *trans-* or *-port*. Then write a definition of each word based on the meaning of its root.

transplant: to move into new soil or a new location

transact: to trade or exchange

import: to bring goods into a country

export: to send goods to a different country

16   Lesson 4

Leveled Language Proficiency

Students at each proficiency level should be able to perform the following tasks.

Listening/Speaking

Early Beginner/Beginner Gesture or point to diagrams in response to oral instructions. Answer questions about cell transport using single words or short spoken phrases.

Early Intermediate/Intermediate Follow oral instructions to complete cell diagrams with minimal help. Answer questions about cell transport using short spoken phrases or simple sentences.

Advanced/Transitioning Participate fully in a discussion about cell transport, using complete, complex sentences.

Your Turn

Now draw your own diagram to show one type of materials transport that takes place in cells.

1. Use colors, symbols, and labels in your diagram.

2. Be sure that your diagram includes a cell membrane and materials on both sides of the membrane.

Answers should resemble one of the cell transport diagrams shown in the lesson.

Talk and Write About It

Trade diagrams with a partner. Read each other's diagrams and discuss what you see. Then complete the following sentence starters to describe your diagram.

1. My diagram shows . . .

2. In this type of transport, materials . . .

Answers will vary, depending on students' drawings.

3. In my diagram, the cell membrane . . .

Produce Language

Write sentences to explain the different ways materials move into and out of cells. Use as many vocabulary terms as you can.

_____

_____

_____

_____

Cell Chemistry and Transport   **17**

Assess Understanding

Your Turn

Model Read the instructions aloud for the students. Point out the features of the other diagrams in the lesson—the cell membrane, the arrows that indicate the direction of movement, and so on. On the board, draw the diagram of osmosis from the previous page, and use this to model how to draw the item.

Talk and Write About It

On Their Own Encourage student pairs to ask each other questions and ask for further help with their diagram if they need it.

Produce Language

On Their Own Have student pairs write about the different ways that materials are transported across cell membranes. Have those who wish to share their writing add it to a class bulletin board.

Wrap Up

Table Talk Have students reread the Big Question at the beginning of the lesson. Use this as a discussion starter for small groups to reflect on what they learned. Encourage students to build fluency by reading their writing in groups or to the class.

✔ **Learned** and applied vocabulary related to cell transport and DNA

✔ **Read** statements about how materials move across cell membranes

✔ **Written** statements about the forms of cell transport they learned about in this lesson

---

Leveled Language Proficiency

Students at each proficiency level should be able to perform the following tasks.

Reading/Writing

Early Beginner/Beginner Read labels on cell diagrams. Show understanding of diagrams by adding missing labels.

Early Intermediate/Intermediate Read sentences about cell transport. Demonstrate understanding by writing words and phrases to correctly complete sentences about cell transport.

Advanced/Transitioning Read a diagram of cell transport and ask questions to clarify understanding. Write complete sentences that compare and contrast the different methods of transport in cells.

Cell Processes and Energy

Vocabulary photosynthesis, cellular respiration, fermentation, autotroph, heterotroph, cell cycle, interphase, replication, mitosis, chromosome, cytokinesis

Materials several colors of modeling clay

 Science Background

- The body breaks down nutrients to release the sugars in them. The cells then break down the sugars (glucose) in the presence of oxygen, releasing energy. This process —*cellular respiration*—occurs in both autotrophs and heterotrophs. *Fermentation* is a similar process that takes place in the absence of oxygen.

- The regular sequence of growth and division in cells is called *the cell cycle*. It consists of three main stages: interphase, mitosis, and cytokinesis.

 ## Frontload the Lesson

How do living things get energy?

Talk About It

Build Background Explain that when the hawk eats the rabbit, most of the energy stored in the rabbit's body is transferred to the hawk.

 ## Content and Language

Predict

Model Read the objectives aloud. As you read, write key terms on the board.

Guide Discussion Have students read the Big Question aloud. Ask students to predict what they might learn based on what they discussed.

Cell Processes and Energy

 Big Question How do living things get energy?

You will . . .
- Find out how organisms get and use energy.
- Recognize that plants get energy differently from how animals do.
- Learn how cells divide and multiply.
- Use words and terms related to cell processes and energy.

Talk About It

Look at the drawing. Think about what you know about how living things get food and energy. Talk with a partner using the sentence starters below.

1. A hawk gets energy by eating . . .
2. A rabbit gets energy by eating . . .
3. Grass gets energy through the . . .

Predict
Look at the Big Question and the "You will . . ." statements at the top of the page. Describe what you think you are going to learn in this lesson.

   I think I am going to learn about . . .

Leveled Instruction

Early Beginner/Beginner Have beginners work with more advanced students. The advanced students can help beginners draw their arrows.

Early Intermediate Encourage students to use the images in the Picture It box to guide them as they work on the diagram here. They may also benefit from explanations about how plants and animals get energy.

Intermediate Students should be able to work with little assistance on the diagram. They should be able to understand and respond to questions about energy using complete sentences.

Advanced/Transitioning Pair these students with students of lower-level language proficiency. Students should be able to respond to complex questions about energy transfer using complete sentences.

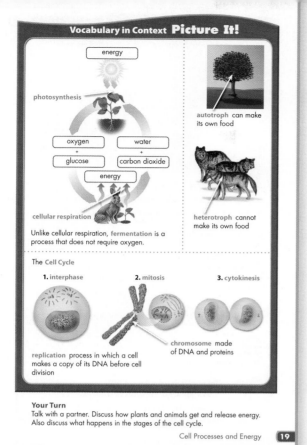

Vocabulary in Context Picture It!

energy

photosynthesis

autotroph can make its own food

oxygen + glucose

water + carbon dioxide

energy

cellular respiration

heterotroph cannot make its own food

Unlike cellular respiration, **fermentation** is a process that does not require oxygen.

The Cell Cycle

1. interphase   2. mitosis   3. cytokinesis

replication process in which a cell makes a copy of its DNA before cell division

chromosome made of DNA and proteins

Your Turn
Talk with a partner. Discuss how plants and animals get and release energy. Also discuss what happens in the stages of the cell cycle.

Cell Processes and Energy   **19**

Academic Vocabulary

- Point out that some of the vocabulary terms in this lesson have related word forms that represent different parts of speech.

Word	Part of Speech
cell	noun
cellular	adjective
divide	verb
division	noun
replicate	verb
replication	noun

- The word *photosynthesis* contains two roots that are clues to its meaning:
  photo- means "light"
  -synthesis means "to put together"

- The word *cycle* is used here to indicate a sequence of events that is repeated regularly. Point out that students may be familiar with this use of the word in science (water cycle, rock cycle). In other contexts, however, the word has other meanings, as in the words *bicycle* and *motorcycle*. Ask volunteers to tell the meaning of *cycle* in these words (wheel). Point out the connection in the two meanings.

↻ Comprehensible Input

Vocabulary in Context: Picture It!

1. **Say the Term** Say each term slowly, artificially stressing each syllable. Have students repeat. Then say the term more naturally and have students repeat.

2. **Introduce Word Meaning** Connect each term to the visual that illustrates it.

3. **Demonstrate** Use gestures and visuals to demonstrate each term.

4. **Apply** After all of the terms have been discussed, have students demonstrate understanding with Talk About It.

Talk About It

Guide Discussion Ask students to use the Picture It box terms to compare how plants and animals get food and to describe the main events of the cell cycle.

1. *The cell grows and divides in a sequence of steps known as the . . .* (cell cycle).

2. *The stage of the cell cycle where the cell divides into two daughter cells is called . . .* (cytokinesis).

3. *The cell makes an exact copy of its DNA during . . .* (replication).

4. *Inside the nucleus, DNA and proteins form structures called . . .* (chromosomes).

5. *Sugars break down and release energy without using oxygen during . . .* (fermentation).

RTI Response to Intervention

If students have difficulty saying the word *cytokinesis . . .*

Then have them practice the sounds that make up each syllable. Point out that the *c* sounds like an *s;* the *y* sounds like an *i;* and the *e* is a long vowel sound.

Your Turn

Guide Discussion Ask students to use sequence words such as *first, second,* and *last* to explain the stages of the cell cycle.

Cell Processes and Energy

↻ Language Production

Do You Understand?

Comprehension Support Before students start the activity, review the following terms in the Picture It box: *carbon dioxide, water, oxygen, glucose,* and *energy*. Make sure students understand these terms before they begin their work.

Model Direct students to turn back to the Picture It box. Point to the sun and the word *energy* in that diagram. Trace the arrow from the sun to the diagram. Point to the picture of the plants. Then point to the terms *carbon dioxide* and *water*. Say, *Plants combine carbon dioxide and water using energy from sunlight.* Continue to trace your finger along the path toward the terms *glucose* and *oxygen* and say, *The products of this are glucose and oxygen.*

Then remark that the diagram here shows the same thing. Ask students to suggest words to write on the diagram and locations for each label.

Talk About It

Guide Discussion Read the sentences aloud with students as they work together to complete them.

Your Turn

Guide Discussion Listen to students as they discuss the processes. Help them correct any mistakes or misunderstandings as needed.

A Closer Look

On Their Own Have students work in pairs to complete this word study activity. You may want to review the homophones *sell* and *cell* to be sure students know the difference. Explain that the dictionary gives at least seven common meanings for *cell*, and that each is related to the word's original meaning "a small room." Encourage students to use a dictionary to look up the different meanings of *cell* and its origin. Students may want to extend the activity by discussing the meaning of *cell* as "a small mobile telephone" and researching the technology behind *cellular phones.*

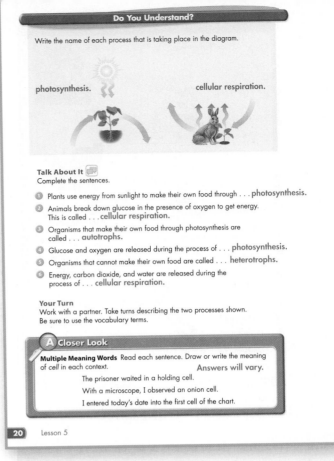

Do You Understand?

Write the name of each process that is taking place in the diagram.

photosynthesis.   cellular respiration.

Talk About It
Complete the sentences.

1. Plants use energy from sunlight to make their own food through . . . photosynthesis.
2. Animals break down glucose in the presence of oxygen to get energy. This is called . . . cellular respiration.
3. Organisms that make their own food through photosynthesis are called . . . autotrophs.
4. Glucose and oxygen are released during the process of . . . photosynthesis.
5. Organisms that cannot make their own food are called . . . heterotrophs.
6. Energy, carbon dioxide, and water are released during the process of . . . cellular respiration.

Your Turn
Work with a partner. Take turns describing the two processes shown. Be sure to use the vocabulary terms.

A Closer Look

Multiple Meaning Words Read each sentence. Draw or write the meaning of *cell* in each context. **Answers will vary.**

The prisoner waited in a holding cell.

With a microscope, I observed an onion cell.

I entered today's date into the first cell of the chart.

Leveled Language Proficiency

Students at each proficiency level should be able to perform the following tasks.

Listening/Speaking

Early Beginner/Beginner Point to images and diagrams as more advanced students explain them. Use sentence frames to orally describe cell processes.

Early Intermediate Trace the stages of the cell cycle as the teacher describes them. Tell about photosynthesis using short spoken phrases or simple sentences.

Intermediate Comprehend questions that the teacher or other students ask about the cell cycle. Use complete sentences to orally describe photosynthesis and cellular respiration.

Advanced/Transitioning Ask questions to clarify understanding about the cell cycle and cell processes. Use complete and complex sentences to describe and compare photosynthesis and cellular respiration.

Think, Talk, and Write

Your Turn

Write the names of the stage of the cell cycle.

interphase   mitosis   cytokinesis

Talk and Write About It

Complete the statements about cell processes and energy.

1 Cytokinesis is what happens when cytoplasm divides, making <u>two identical cells</u>.

2 During interphase, DNA is <u>copied or replicated</u>.

3 When replication is finished, the cell has <u>made a copy of its DNA</u>.

4 The process of mitosis is what happens when the cell begins to <u>divide</u>.

5 The cell cycle is <u>the stages of growth and division that a cell goes through</u>.

Produce Language

Write about how different kinds of organisms get energy. Describe how cells grow and divide. Use as many vocabulary terms as you can.

_____

_____

_____

_____

_____

_____

_____

Cell Processes and Energy **21**

Leveled Language Proficiency

Students at each proficiency level should be able to perform the following tasks.

Reading/Writing

Early Beginner/Beginner Working with a more advanced student, locate words that describe the stages of the cell cycle. Write single words or short phrases about the cell cycle.

Early Intermediate Read and use short sentences to discuss energy diagrams and labels with a partner. Write short sentences about the stages of the cell cycle.

Intermediate Read and use full sentences to discuss cell diagrams with a partner. Write complete sentences about the cell cycle.

Advanced/Transitioning Understand written sentences about the stages of the cell cycle. Write complete sentences to describe the diagram and the sequence of events involved in the cell cycle.

↻ Assess Understanding

Your Turn

Model Draw a simple cycle on the board. Label three stages as *A, B,* and *C.* Explain that for the cycle to work, the stages must take place in that order. That is, you cannot get to *B* until you have reached *A,* and you can't get from *A* to *C* without going through *B.*

Talk and Write About It

On Their Own Encourage students to talk about the stages of the cell cycle. If students know the names of the four phases of mitosis (prophase, metaphase, anaphase, and telophase), have them write this information on their diagrams.

Produce Language

On Their Own Have students write what they have learned about the cell cycle and about cell energy. Offer opportunities for students to read aloud from what they have written. Encourage students to ask each other questions and to answer them.

Wrap Up

Table Talk Have students reread the Big Question as a way to reflect on what they learned. Encourage students to build fluency by reading their writing in groups or to the class.

✔ **Learned** and applied vocabulary related to photosynthesis, cellular respiration, and the cell cycle

✔ **Heard** statements about how cells get and use energy

✔ **Written** statements about the three stages of the cell cycle and about photosynthesis and cellular respiration

Lesson 6

Genetics

Vocabulary trait, gene, heredity, genetics, genotype, phenotype, dominant allele, recessive allele, homozygous, heterozygous, Punnett square, probability

Materials vocabulary cards

 Science Background

- An organism's traits are controlled by the alleles the organism inherits from its parents. Some alleles are dominant and other alleles are recessive.

- There are few examples of traits controlled by a single gene with dominant/recessive alleles. Most traits are the result of more complex patterns of inheritance.

- A Punnett square is a graphic organizer that can be used as a tool to calculate the probability of outcomes of a particular cross, or match up, of two parents.

Frontload the Lesson

What determines the characteristics that living things inherit from their parents?

Talk About It

Build Background Have students write the words on index cards. Read each word aloud as students sort them into three piles. Model responses.

Content and Language

Predict

Model Read the Big Question and the objectives aloud. Paraphrase the Big Question in a few different ways, checking for student understanding by asking for examples.

Guide Discussion Encourage students to use the lesson title and the Big Question as they make their predictions about what they will learn.

Genetics

 Big Question What determines the characteristics that living things inherit from their parents?

You will . . .
- Compare different traits.
- Learn how some traits are passed from parent to offspring.
- Understand and use key words related to genetics.

Talk About It

Look at the terms in the Picture It box on the next page.

Write each term on an index card as your teacher reads it. Place each card in one of three piles.

Pile 1: I know what this term means.

Pile 2: I have heard this term, but am not sure how it is used in science.

Pile 3: I have not heard of this term.

| gene | genetics | genotype |

Now explain your piles to a partner. Use these sentence starters.

1. I know that . . . means . . .
2. I have heard of . . .
3. I don't know what the term . . . means.

Predict

Look at the Big Question and the "You will . . ." statements at the top of the page. Describe what you think you are going to learn in this lesson.

I think I am going to learn about . . .

Leveled Instruction

Early Beginner/Beginner Ask students to point to images or hold up cards as a way to answer questions or complete sentences.

Early Intermediate/Intermediate Generate conversation by asking students to discuss the difference between traits they were born with and traits they acquired or learned. Invite students to decide whether a trait such as height, which develops later in life, is *inherited* or acquired.

Advanced/Transitioning Partner these students with beginning students. Have them work together to come up with answers to the discussion questions.

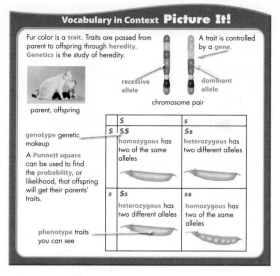

Vocabulary in Context **Picture It!**

Fur color is a **trait**. Traits are passed from parent to offspring through **heredity**. **Genetics** is the study of heredity.

A trait is controlled by a **gene**.

recessive allele

dominant allele

chromosome pair

parent, offspring

genotype genetic makeup

A Punnett square can be used to find the **probability**, or likelihood, that offspring will get their parents' traits.

	S	*s*
S	**SS** homozygous has two of the same alleles	**Ss** heterozygous has two different alleles
s	**Ss** heterozygous has two different alleles	**ss** homozygous has two of the same alleles

phenotype traits you can see

Talk About It

Use the words in the Picture It box to finish the sentences.

1. A genotype is either homozygous or . . . **heterozygous.**
2. *Ww* or *ww* is an example of a . . . **genotype.**
3. A gene controls a . . . **trait.**
4. The study of heredity is called . . . **genetics.**
5. Your hair color is part of your . . . **phenotype.**
6. A chart that shows the probability that offspring will inherit a trait is a . . . **Punnett square.**

Your Turn

Talk with a partner about the vocabulary terms above. Which pairs of terms are antonyms, words that have meanings opposite from one another?

Genetics **23**

Academic Vocabulary

- Help students practice using academic vocabulary by brainstorming some near synonyms for the word *trait. (characteristic, quality, feature)* As students discuss heredity, have them use as many of these terms as they can.

- Several idioms are used to discuss heredity. If necessary explain the term *idiom* as "a casual or common figure of speech." Then brainstorm some idioms used to mean "inherit." List phrases such as *passed down, handed down, passed along, spitting image,* and "she has her mother's . . ." on the board. Share examples of each, and have student pairs use the terms in conversation.

- The idiom "It runs in the family" is often used to describe heredity. Have students define the word *run.* Explain that *run* has a different meaning in this idiom. It roughly means "persists" or "continues." Ask students for examples of traits that might "run in the family."

- *Cognates* are words that have the same or similar roots and meanings in two languages. Have students share any vocabulary terms they recognize as cognates to words in their first languages. Most of the terms in this lesson have cognates in Spanish.

↻ Comprehensible Input

Vocabulary in Context: Picture It!

1. **Say the Term** Say each term slowly, artificially stressing each syllable. Have students repeat. Then say the term more naturally and have students repeat.

2. **Introduce Word Meaning** Connect each term to the visual that illustrates it.

3. **Demonstrate** Use gestures and visuals to demonstrate each term. For example:

   - Write *Bb* on the board. Ask students if this shows a *phenotype* or a *genotype.* Repeat the correct term: *genotype.*

   - Point to the genotype on the board. Ask students if it is a *heterozygous* or a *homozygous* genotype. Repeat the correct term: *heterozygous.*

   - Have students repeat after you, as you point to each allele: *dominant allele, recessive allele.*

4. **Apply** After all of the terms have been discussed, have students demonstrate understanding with Talk About It.

Talk About It

Guide Discussion Read the directions chorally with students and have them work with their partners to complete the sentences.

RTI Response to Intervention

If students have difficulty pronouncing the word *phenotype* . . .

Then remind students that the letter combination ph is usually pronounced with an *f* sound.

Your Turn

Guide Discussion Encourage students to use the definitions of the terms to explain why they chose each pair of opposites.

Language Production

Do You Understand?

Comprehension Support Have students look through the cards and ask any questions they may have. Pick one card to do as an example with the class. Then have students continue on their own.

Model Demonstrate how students can make sentences out of each term to describe the picture or phrase on the card. For example, the card with *Yy* represents the term *heterozygous*. This could be turned into the sentence *Yy is an example of a heterozygous genotype.* Use the same card as an example here as you used above in Comprehension Support.

Talk About It

Guide Discussion Read the statements aloud with students as they work together to complete the sentences.

Your Turn

Guide Discussion Listen to student discussions as they compare their answers. Help them correct any mistakes or misunderstandings as needed. Then ask students to quiz each other, using the cards as flashcards.

A Closer Look

On Their Own Have students work in pairs to complete this word study activity. Ask if they can come up with another example sentence for each homophone. Then ask them for other examples of homophones—words that sound the same but are spelled differently. *(Examples: prey, pray; their, there,* and *they're; I, eye; here, hear)*

Cut out the genetics cards in the Resources section of the book. On the back of each card, write the correct term. Choose terms from the word box below.

dominant allele	heredity	Punnett square
gene	heterozygous	recessive allele
genetics	homozygous	trait
genotype	phenotype	

Talk About It
Complete the sentences.

1. You can see a phenotype but you cannot see a . . . **genotype.**
2. The genotype *AA* or *aa* is . . . **homozygous.**
3. The genotype *Aa* is . . . **heterozygous.**
4. Probabilities of inheritance can be shown with a . . . **Punnett square.**

Your Turn
Work with a partner. Compare your answers to the Do You Understand activity. Then take turns using the cards as flashcards. Show each picture and have your partner say the correct term.

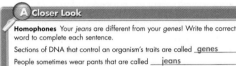

A Closer Look

Homophones Your *jeans* are different from your *genes!* Write the correct word to complete each sentence.

Sections of DNA that control an organism's traits are called __genes__ .

People sometimes wear pants that are called __jeans__ .

Leveled Language Proficiency

Students at each proficiency level should be able to perform the following tasks.

Listening/Speaking

Early Beginner/Beginner Respond to questions about genetics by pointing to the correct card. Read terms from cards aloud to answer questions.

Early Intermediate Follow oral instructions to identify illustrated terms represented in print. Use simple spoken sentences to respond to questions about what is shown in an illustration, diagram, or graphic organizer.

Intermediate Understand oral definitions of the genetics vocabulary terms. Use complete sentences to describe the terms and concepts represented in illustrations and text.

Advanced/Transitioning Understand and respond to spoken comparisons between different genetics terms. Use complete and complex spoken sentences to compare and contrast terms related to genetics.

Fill in the Punnett square below by describing the phenotype or drawing a picture.

S = smooth pods

s = pinched pods

	S	s
S	**SS** smooth pod	**Ss** smooth pod
s	**Ss** smooth pod	**ss** pinched pod

Talk and Write About It

Talk to a partner about your Punnett square. Then complete the statements about genetics.

1. Three of the offspring from the cross above will have a phenotype of ___smooth pods___

2. The number of offspring from the cross above that will have a genotype of pinched pod is ___one___

3. In the cross above, the genotypes of the parents are both ___Ss___

4. If an offspring inherits a dominant allele, then ___the trait will always show up___

5. In order for a recessive trait to show, then the offspring must inherit ___two of the recessive alleles___

Produce Language

In the cross above, how do the phenotypes and genotypes of the offspring compare to the phenotypes and genotypes of the parents? Write a few sentences explaining your answer.

_____

_____

_____

_____

Genetics **25**

Leveled Language Proficiency

Students at each proficiency level should be able to perform the following tasks.

Reading/Writing

Early Beginner/Beginner Choose the correct genetics term for each cut-out card. Write the correct term to identify each term represented in the Punnett square.

Early Intermediate Match short phrases with the correct genetics term. Write short phrases to describe aspects of heredity.

Intermediate Compare responses to questions about genetics. Write a complete definition for the different vocabulary terms.

Advanced/Transitioning Read aloud sentences that describe genetics and heredity. Write a brief explanation for why offspring look different from parents.

Assess Understanding

Your Turn

Model Encourage students to explain the information on the page, using complete sentences. For example, the activity shows S = smooth pods. Write model sentences on the board and read them for the class. For example, write *The letter S represents smooth pods.* More advanced speakers could construct more complex sentences, such as *The letter S stands for the dominant allele, which makes smooth pods.*

Talk and Write About It

On Their Own Encourage student groups to talk about the information from the Punnett square. Ask, *Which trait are we focusing on in this cross? What do the parents look like for this trait? What percentage of the offspring will have smooth pods? What percentage will have pinched pods?*

Produce Language

On Their Own First have students write an answer to the question. Then have students discuss their answers in pairs. Finally, lead a discussion with the whole class to address the Big Question, *What determines the characteristics that living things inherit from their parents?*

Wrap Up

Table Talk Have students reflect on what they learned. Encourage students to build fluency by reading their writing in groups or to the class.

✔ **Learned** and applied vocabulary related to genetics

✔ **Heard** statements about how traits are passed from parent to offspring

✔ **Written** statements about genetics and heredity

DNA: The Code of Life

Vocabulary nitrogen bases, DNA replication, messenger RNA, transfer RNA, mutation, cancer, tumor, chemotherapy, ribosome, protein, amino acids

Science Background

- DNA carries genetic information about an organism. A DNA molecule is double-stranded; the strands are connected by pairs of nitrogen bases. The four kinds of bases are guanine (G), adenine (A), thymine (T), and cytosine (C). Guanine always pairs with cytosine, and thymine pairs with adenine.

- Protein synthesis is a process in which the cell uses information from a gene on a chromosome to produce a specific protein.

- Mutations in DNA can cause a gene to produce an incorrect protein.

Frontload the Lesson

What does DNA do?

Talk About It

Build Background Talk about the word *code* with students. Be sure they understand what a bar code and a ZIP code are.

Content and Language

Predict

Model Read the Big Question and the objectives aloud. As students repeat after you, correct any mispronunciations they may make.

Guide Discussion Encourage students to use the Big Question, the objectives, and the lesson title as they make their predictions.

Big Question What does DNA do?

You will . . .
- Learn about DNA and the genetic code.
- Recognize the relationship between DNA, RNA, and proteins.
- Understand how cancer is related to DNA.
- Use terms related to DNA and the genetic code.

Talk About It

A code is a system of signals or symbols. Each signal or symbol gives information about something. Here are two kinds of codes that you may have seen.

10 Green Street
My Town, MA 01010

Sarah Student
4 Elm Street
Anytown, CA 91919

bar code   ZIP code

Where have you seen these codes? What do these codes tell you? What do you think a code in your genes might tell your body?

Predict
Look at the Big Question and the "You will . . ." statements at the top of the page. Describe what you think you are going to learn in this lesson.

I think I am going to learn about . . .

26   Lesson 7

Leveled Instruction

Early Beginner Ask students to point to vocabulary terms about DNA as you read them aloud.

Beginner Students should respond to simple questions about codes and DNA using single words and short phrases.

Early Intermediate/Intermediate Students should answer questions about DNA using short sentences (early intermediate) or full sentences with some detail (intermediate).

Advanced/Transitioning Ask questions about DNA and codes using complex sentences. Students should answer questions using complex sentences that include some detail.

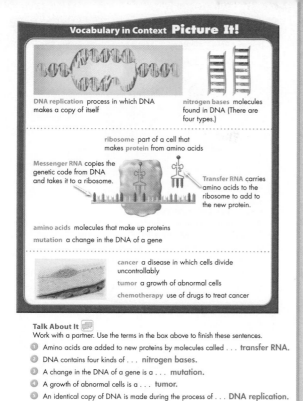

Vocabulary in Context **Picture It!**

DNA replication process in which DNA makes a copy of itself

nitrogen bases molecules found in DNA (There are four types.)

ribosome part of a cell that makes protein from amino acids

Messenger RNA copies the genetic code from DNA and takes it to a ribosome.

Transfer RNA carries amino acids to the ribosome to add to the new protein.

amino acids molecules that make up proteins

mutation a change in the DNA of a gene

cancer a disease in which cells divide uncontrollably

tumor a growth of abnormal cells

chemotherapy use of drugs to treat cancer

Talk About It
Work with a partner. Use the terms in the box above to finish these sentences.

1. Amino acids are added to new proteins by molecules called . . . **transfer RNA.**
2. DNA contains four kinds of . . . **nitrogen bases.**
3. A change in the DNA of a gene is a . . . **mutation.**
4. A growth of abnormal cells is a . . . **tumor.**
5. An identical copy of DNA is made during the process of . . . **DNA replication.**

Your Turn
Talk with a partner about how nitrogen bases pair up in DNA.

DNA: The Code of Life **27**

Academic Vocabulary

- Point out that *base* has both scientific and everyday meanings. In science, it can be a category of chemical. The word also refers to the bottom of a structure, the objects at the four corners of a baseball infield, or the main point of an idea.

- The term *type* is a multiple-meaning word that may confuse students. Explain that it is often used to mean a kind of thing: one *type* of nitrogen base. We also talk about the *type*, or the lettering in printing, such as the type in a book. The verb *type* means "to key in information," such as typing a report.

- Point out that the word *chemotherapy* actually refers to any kind of drug used as a medicine, but in common usage, it usually designates drugs used to treat cancer. Tell students that the word part *chemo-* in *chemotherapy* means "chemical." Most medicines are made of chemicals.

- Cognates are words that have the same or similar roots and meanings in two languages. Have students share any vocabulary terms they recognize as cognates to words in their first languages. For example, the Spanish words for *mutation* and *cancer* are *mutación* and *cáncer*.

↻ Comprehensible Input

Vocabulary in Context: Picture It!

1. **Say the Term** Say each term slowly, artificially stressing each syllable. Have students repeat. Then say the term more naturally and have students repeat.

2. **Introduce Word Meaning** Connect each term to the visual that illustrates it.

3. **Demonstrate** Use gestures and visuals to demonstrate each term. For example:

   - When teaching *nitrogen bases*, write G, A, T, and C on the board and have students locate the letters on the picture in their books. Then explain that these letters stand for the names of the four types of nitrogen bases: *Adenine, Cytosine, Guanine, Thymine.* Emphasize that students don't need to learn or remember the names, as they will only be using the one-letter abbreviations.

   - For *messenger RNA,* act out the role of a messenger. Bring a "message" to a student.

4. **Apply** After all of the terms have been discussed, have students demonstrate understanding with Talk About It.

Talk About It

Guide Discussion Have students work with a partner to complete the statements. Remind them to refer to the Picture It box above for help.

RTI Response to Intervention

If students have trouble pronouncing the terms *nitrogen* and *messenger* . . .

Then explain that the *g* in both terms is pronounced like a *j.* Say each word slowly and have students repeat.

Your Turn

Guide Discussion Ask volunteers to explain in their own words why the order of nitrogen bases in a gene is important. Give students time to plan their answers.

DNA: The Code of Life

↻ Language Production

Do You Understand?

Comprehension Support Begin by asking students to compare this diagram to the similar diagram in Picture It. Help them see that the diagram on this page, unlike the one in the Picture It box, includes a partially synthesized protein molecule.

Model To help students label the diagram, begin by saying, *I know that proteins are long-chain molecules, and that proteins are made on ribosomes. I see the long-chain molecule in the picture, so I can label it* "new protein."

Talk About It

Guide Discussion Read the sentences aloud with students. Then have students work in pairs to complete each one.

Your Turn

Guide Discussion Listen to student discussions as they talk about the steps in protein synthesis. Point out the connection to the Big Question. Help them correct mistakes or misunderstandings.

In Other Words

Model Read the example sentence aloud for students and have them repeat it. Then ask, *What is another way to say this? What is another word or words for* specific? Have students take turns reading the sentence aloud, choosing one of the yellow-highlighted words to fill in the space each time. Then have students suggest their own sentences that include the word *specific*.

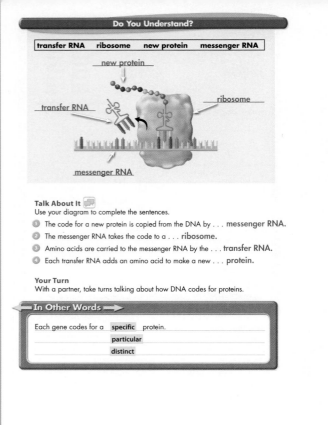

Do You Understand?

| transfer RNA | ribosome | new protein | messenger RNA |

new protein

transfer RNA

ribosome

messenger RNA

Talk About It
Use your diagram to complete the sentences.
1. The code for a new protein is copied from the DNA by . . . messenger RNA.
2. The messenger RNA takes the code to a . . . ribosome.
3. Amino acids are carried to the messenger RNA by the . . . transfer RNA.
4. Each transfer RNA adds an amino acid to make a new . . . protein.

Your Turn
With a partner, take turns talking about how DNA codes for proteins.

→ In Other Words →

Each gene codes for a | specific | protein.
| particular |
| distinct |

28 Lesson 7

Leveled Language Proficiency

Students at each proficiency level should be able to perform the following tasks.

Listening/Speaking

Early Beginner Gesture, point, and use some single words to identify different aspects of DNA diagrams in response to oral directions. Answer simple *yes/no* questions about DNA.

Beginner Follow simple oral directions to identify information in a DNA table. Ask and answer questions about DNA with single words and short phrases.

Early Intermediate/ Intermediate Answer questions and participate in discussions about mutations using full sentences.

Advanced/Transitioning Respond to spoken questions and orally summarize information about DNA and cancer using complex sentences.

Your Turn

The first DNA piece shows the correct order of nitrogen bases for a gene. The others have mutations. Draw arrows to show where the mutations occur.

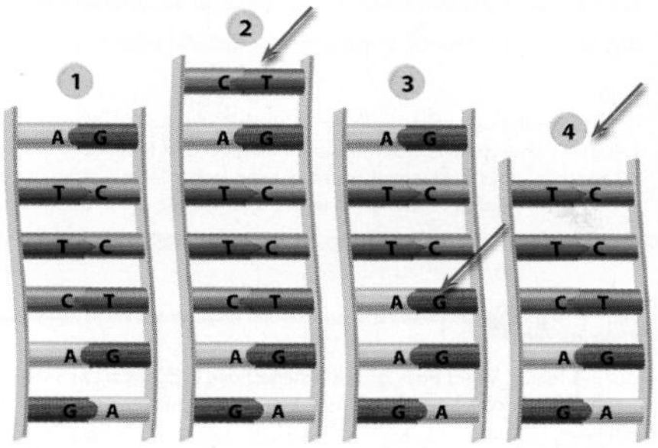

Describe the different mutations with a partner. Use the terms *DNA* and *nitrogen bases*.

Talk and Write About It

Complete these statements about mutations.

1. Any change in the DNA of a gene is called a _mutation_.
2. Some mutations happen when DNA is making a copy of itself during _DNA replication_.
3. Harmful mutations can cause the disease _cancer_.
4. Uncontrolled cell division in cancer can cause growth of a _tumor_.

Produce Language

Write what you learned about DNA. Use as many key terms as you can.

_____
_____
_____
_____
_____
_____

Leveled Language Proficiency

Students at each proficiency level should be able to perform the following tasks.

Reading/Writing

Early Beginner/Beginner Identify written words associated with illustrations. Write lists of words and phrases to describe protein synthesis, mutations, and cancer.

Early Intermediate Read and understand simple sentences. Write simple sentences about protein synthesis, mutations, and cancer.

Intermediate Comprehend material written in full sentences. Describe protein synthesis, mutations, and cancer in short paragraphs using full sentences.

Advanced/Transitioning Read and understand material written in full sentences and arranged in multiple paragraphs. Describe the connection between protein synthesis, mutations, and cancer in detail using complete sentences.

↻ Assess Understanding

Your Turn

Model Read the instructions aloud with students. As you read, point to the DNA drawings so that students understand what they are comparing.

Talk and Write About It

On Their Own Encourage student groups to talk about the three types of DNA mutations shown here. (Illustration *2* shows an added base pair; *3* shows a replaced base pair; and in *4*, a base pair has been deleted.) Then have students discuss and complete the sentences.

Produce Language

On Their Own Have students both write and talk about the genetic code and making proteins. Encourage them to also talk and write about how a DNA mutation will produce an abnormal protein, which in some cases can lead to cancer.

Wrap Up

Table Talk Have students reflect on the Big Question and what they learned. Encourage students to build fluency by reading their writing in groups or to the class.

✔ **Learned** and applied vocabulary related to the genetic code, DNA replication, protein synthesis, and cancer

✔ **Heard** statements about messenger RNA, transfer RNA, and protein synthesis

✔ **Read** statements about DNA replication, mutations, and cancer

Human Genetics and Gene Technologies

Vocabulary sex chromosomes, sex-linked gene, carrier, genetic disorder, pedigree, selective breeding, clone, genetic engineering, genome, inbreeding, hybridization

Materials picture of your own family or another family

Science Background

- The sex chromosomes carry genes that determine gender, as well as genes for other traits. Color blindness and hemophilia are sex-linked traits.

- Genetic disorders can be caused by mutations in genes or by changes in chromosomes.

Human Genetics and Gene Technologies

 Big Question How can people use genetic information?

You will . . .
- Describe the ways that traits are inherited.
- Discuss how genetic disorders are inherited and treated.
- List some ways that scientists use genetic technology.
- Use terms related to human genetics and genetic technology.

Talk About It

Look at this family. What traits do the parents have in common with their children? Draw arrows from the parents' traits to the children's traits that are the same.

Talk with a partner about the ways that family members can look like each other.

Predict

Look at the Big Question and the "You will . . ." statements at the top of the page. Describe what you think you are going to learn in this lesson.

I think I am going to learn about . . .

30 Lesson 8

Frontload the Lesson

 How can people use genetic information?

Talk About It

Build Background Ask students whether they have ever planted seeds collected from mature plants. How did the offspring resemble the parent plants? Explain that some similarities between parents and offspring are passed on by genes.

Content and Language

Predict

Model Read the Big Question and the objectives aloud. As students repeat after you, correct any mispronunciations they may make.

Guide Discussion Encourage students to use the Big Question and the lesson title as they make their predictions.

Leveled Instruction

Early Beginner Ask students to point to vocabulary terms as you say each term aloud. To respond to questions, have students point to pictures.

Beginner Students should respond to simple questions about sex-linked genes and genetic disorders using single words and short phrases.

Early Intermediate/Intermediate Students should answer questions about sex-linked genes and genetic disorders using short sentences (early intermediate) or complete sentences with some detail (intermediate).

Advanced/Transitioning Ask questions about sex-linked inheritance and genetic disorders using complex sentences. Students should answer questions using complex sentences that include some detail.

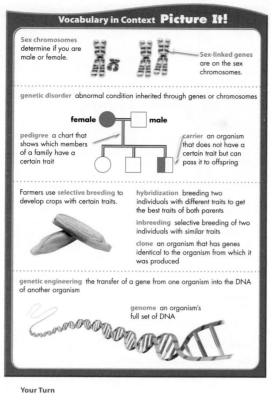

Vocabulary in Context Picture It!

Sex chromosomes determine if you are male or female.

Sex-linked genes are on the sex chromosomes.

genetic disorder abnormal condition inherited through genes or chromosomes

female ● ⚬ □ male

pedigree a chart that shows which members of a family have a certain trait

carrier an organism that does not have a certain trait but can pass it to offspring

Farmers use selective breeding to develop crops with certain traits.

hybridization breeding two individuals with different traits to get the best traits of both parents

inbreeding selective breeding of two individuals with similar traits

clone an organism that has genes identical to the organism from which it was produced

genetic engineering the transfer of a gene from one organism into the DNA of another organism

genome an organism's full set of DNA

Your Turn
Talk with a partner about how traits are passed from parent to offspring. Use as many vocabulary terms as you can.

Human Genetics and Gene Technologies **31**

Academic Vocabulary

- Point out that *carrier* comes from the word *carry*. Its basic meaning is "someone who carries something" or "something used to carry something." Relate this meaning to the definition of the term *carrier* in genetics.

- Explain that *pedigree* can also be the line of ancestors of a purebred animal, such as a horse or a dog.

- Students may mistakenly associate the word *sex* in the terms *sex chromosome* and *sex-linked gene* with the mating act. If necessary, emphasize that here—and in most scientific discussions—the word *sex* is just a synonym for gender. Just like the words *age* and *height,* it names a characteristic. Allow students to substitute the word *gender,* if helpful.

- Cognates are words that have the same or similar roots and meanings in two languages. Have students share any vocabulary terms they recognize as cognates to words in their first languages.

↻ Comprehensible Input

Vocabulary in Context: Picture It!

1. **Say the Term** Say each term slowly, artificially stressing each syllable. Have students repeat. Then say the term more naturally and have students repeat.

2. **Introduce Word Meaning** Connect each term to the visual that illustrates it.

3. **Demonstrate** Use gestures and visuals to demonstrate each term.

4. **Apply** After all of the terms have been discussed, have students demonstrate understanding with Talk About It.

Talk About It

Guide Discussion Before students start their independent discussion, check for understanding with the following sentence starters:

1. *Genes that determine if a person is male or female are found on the . . .* (sex chromosomes)

2. *An organism's full set of DNA is its . . .* (genome)

3. *To produce crops with certain traits, farmers use . . .* (selective breeding)

4. *An organism that has exactly the same genes as its parent is called a . . .* (clone)

5. *Genes found on the sex chromosomes are called . . .* (sex-linked genes)

R T I Response to Intervention

If students have trouble saying the term *genetic engineering,* . . .

Then have them practice the sounds that form each syllable. Write the syllables on the board and point to each one as you pronounce it.

Your Turn

Guide Discussion Encourage students to refer back to the family shown in the first Talk About It as they discuss genetic inheritance.

Human Genetics and Gene Technologies

Language Production

Do You Understand?

Comprehension Support Before students start the activity, briefly review what a pedigree chart is and how individuals are arranged on it. Point out the horizontal line connecting a male and female that indicates parents, and the vertical line and bracket that connect parents to children.

Model Demonstrate to students how to interpret the pedigree chart. For example, refer them to the pedigree in Picture It. Ask questions such as, *What represents a male? What represents a female? What shows an organism that is a carrier?*

Talk About It

Guide Discussion Read the sentence starters aloud with students as they work to complete the sentences.

Your Turn

Guide Discussion Listen to student discussions as they talk about the pedigree chart. Point out the connection to the Big Question. Correct any mistakes or misunderstandings as needed.

In Other Words

Model Read the example sentence aloud for students and have them repeat it. Then ask, *What is another way to say this? What is another word, or words, for identify?* Have students take turns reading the sentence aloud, choosing one of the yellow-highlighted words to fill in the space each time. Then have students suggest their own sentences for using the word *identify*.

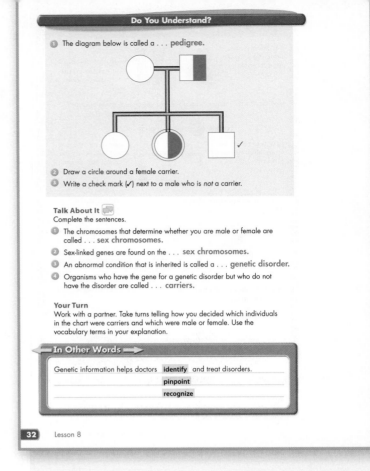

Do You Understand?

1. The diagram below is called a . . . pedigree.

2. Draw a circle around a female carrier.
3. Write a check mark (✓) next to a male who is *not* a carrier.

Talk About It
Complete the sentences.
1. The chromosomes that determine whether you are male or female are called . . . sex chromosomes.
2. Sex-linked genes are found on the . . . sex chromosomes.
3. An abnormal condition that is inherited is called a . . . genetic disorder.
4. Organisms who have the gene for a genetic disorder but who do not have the disorder are called . . . carriers.

Your Turn
Work with a partner. Take turns telling how you decided which individuals in the chart were carriers and which were male or female. Use the vocabulary terms in your explanation.

In Other Words

Genetic information helps doctors | identify | and treat disorders.
pinpoint
recognize

32 Lesson 8

Leveled Language Proficiency

Students at each proficiency level should be able to perform the following tasks.

Listening/Speaking

Early Beginner Gesture and point to locations on a pedigree chart to respond to simple oral directions. Answer simple questions by pointing to a chart and saying single words.

Beginner Follow simple oral directions to identify individuals in a pedigree chart. Ask and answer questions with single words and short phrases.

Early Intermediate/ Intermediate Follow oral directions expressed in complete sentences to identify individuals in a pedigree chart. Answer questions and participate in discussions using complete sentences.

Advanced/Transitioning Follow oral directions expressed in complex sentences. Use complex sentences to answer questions and explain the patterns in a pedigree chart.

Your Turn

Draw lines to match the terms with their definitions.

clone	used for centuries to develop crops with certain traits
selective breeding	the transfer of a gene from one organism into another organism
genome	organism with the exact same genes as the parent from which it was produced
genetic engineering	an organism's full set of DNA

Talk and Write About It

Complete the following statements.

1. Two kinds of selective breeding are <u>inbreeding and hybridization</u>.
2. All the DNA in an organism makes up its <u>genome</u>
3. Genetic disorders can be caused by changes in the structure of either <u>chromosomes or genes</u>
4. An animal that is an exact genetic copy of its parent is a <u>clone</u>.

Produce Language

Write about some ways that scientists use genetic technology. Use as many vocabulary terms as you can.

_____
_____
_____
_____
_____
_____
_____
_____

Leveled Language Proficiency

Students at each proficiency level should be able to perform the following tasks.

Reading/Writing

Early Beginner/Beginner Identify some written words associated with a pedigree chart. Write lists of words and phrases to describe sex-linked genes and genetic disorders.

Early Intermediate Read and understand simple sentences about genes. Write simple sentences about sex-linked genes and genetic disorders.

Intermediate Read and understand information about genes written in complete sentences. Describe sex-linked genes and genetic disorders in a short paragraph using complete sentences.

Advanced/Transitioning Read and understand material about genes written in complete sentences and organized in multiple paragraphs. Write explanations of the connection between sex-linked genes and genetic disorders in detail using complete sentences.

↻ Assess Understanding

Your Turn

Model Read the terms and definitions with students. If necessary model finding a match by process of elimination, or model self-correcting a wrong answer by testing it out against the information in the Picture It box.

Talk and Write About It

On Their Own Have partners take turns reading and completing each sentence aloud. Then have each student write the missing term.

Produce Language

On Their Own Encourage brainstorming by having students work in pairs to look back through the lesson, starting with the Big Question. Have student pairs both write and talk about what they have learned. After the writing activity, invite students to read what they have written aloud to the class.

Wrap Up

Table Talk Have students reflect on the Big Question and what they learned. Encourage students to build fluency by reading their writing in groups or to the class.

✔ **Learned** and applied vocabulary related to genes and chromosomes

✔ **Spoken** statements about sex-linked genes and genetic disorders

✔ **Written** statements about genetic information and technology

Lesson 9

Change Over Time

Vocabulary species, variation, adaptation, evolution, natural selection, fossil, homologous structures, gradualism, punctuated equilibrium

Materials cutout sheets Evolution Cards (Student Book, Resources section)

Science Background

- Evidence that indicates that organisms have changed over time includes the following: fossils; the geographic distribution of living and fossil organisms; embryological development; body structures, including homologous structures and vestigial structures; and, at the molecular level, homologous molecules and the universal genetic code.

- A new species can form when a group of individuals is isolated long enough to evolve traits that are different from the rest of the species. The two groups can no longer mate and reproduce.

Frontload the Lesson

How do living things change over time?

Talk About It

Build Background Ask students to think about different breeds of dogs. Point out that all dogs belong to the same species. Just as dogs are all different, so are members of other species.

Content and Language

Predict

Model Read the Big Question and the objectives aloud. As students repeat after you, correct any mispronunciations that students make.

Guide Discussion Encourage students to use the lesson title and the Big Question as they make their predictions about what they will learn.

 Big Question How do living things change over time?

You will . . .
- Discuss differences among living things.
- Describe how living things change over time.
- Understand and use key terms related to evolution.

Talk About It

Look at the five plants. Living things of one type can still have variety. Do you think these are all the same kind of plant?

Arabidopsis thaliana plants

Discuss the following questions with a partner.

1. Compare and contrast the individual plants. What similarities and differences do you see?
2. What are some similarities and differences among dogs you have seen?

Predict
Look at the Big Question and the "You will . . ." statements at the top of the page. Describe what you think you are going to learn in this lesson.

I think I am going to learn about . . .

34 Lesson 9

Leveled Instruction

Early Beginner Ask students to point to the different plant parts (leaf, flower, stalk). Prompt students to point out differences with questions such as *Which plant is shortest?*

Beginner Have students point to the different parts of the plant. Ask students to point to several differences they see among the plants.

Early Intermediate/Intermediate Ask intermediate students to tell you about the differences they observe. Have them explain which differences might be favorable traits.

Advanced/Transitioning In pairs, have advanced students discuss their answers to the Talk About It questions. Invite students to compare an *adaptation* and a *variation*.

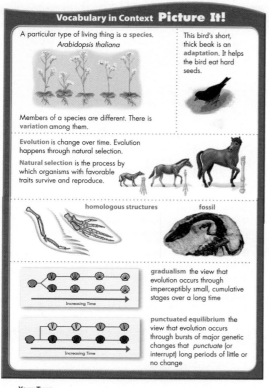

Vocabulary in Context **Picture It!**

A particular type of living thing is a **species**.
Arabidopsis thaliana

This bird's short, thick beak is an **adaptation**. It helps the bird eat hard seeds.

Members of a species are different. There is **variation** among them.

Evolution is change over time. Evolution happens through natural selection.

Natural selection is the process by which organisms with favorable traits survive and reproduce.

homologous structures   fossil

gradualism the view that evolution occurs through imperceptibly small, cumulative stages over a long time

Increasing Time

punctuated equilibrium the view that evolution occurs through bursts of major genetic changes that *punctuate* (or interrupt) long periods of little or no change

Increasing Time

Your Turn
Talk with a partner about the vocabulary terms above. Describe what each picture shows. Try to use each term in a sentence.

Change Over Time **35**

Academic Vocabulary

- In common use, the word *variation* means "differences." In science, *variation* refers specifically to differences in heritable traits among members of one species.

- Review the term *punctuated equilibrium* with students. Ask students to think about how punctuation interrupts sentences. Explain that, similar to punctuation, *punctuated equilibrium* is a pattern of evolution in which long, stable periods of no change are interrupted by brief, rapid periods of change.

- Cognates have the same (or similar) roots and meanings in two languages. Have students share any vocabulary terms they recognize as cognates to words in their first languages. Many of the terms in this lesson have cognates in Spanish. For example, the Spanish word for *evolution* is "evolución" and the Spanish word for *adaptation* is "adaptación."

↻ Comprehensible Input

Vocabulary in Context: Picture It!

1. **Say the Term** Say each term slowly, artificially stressing each syllable. Have students repeat. Then say the term more naturally and have students repeat.

2. **Introduce Word Meaning** Connect each term to the visual that illustrates it.

3. **Demonstrate** Use gestures and visuals to demonstrate each term.

4. **Apply** After all of the terms have been discussed, have students demonstrate understanding with Talk About It.

Talk About It

Guide Discussion Before students start their independent discussion, check for understanding with the following sentence starters:

1. *Evolution happens through a process called . . .* (natural selection.)

2. *A rabbit's front leg and a bird's wing are examples of . . .* (homologous structures.)

3. *The view that evolution occurs slowly and steadily is called . . .* (gradualism.)

4. *Differences among members of a species are called . . .* (variations.)

RTI Response to Intervention

If students have difficulty pronouncing the words *evolution, adaptation,* or *variation . . .*

Then point out that all three words have the same number of syllables, and all are pronounced with emphasis on the third syllable. Repeat these words, syllable by syllable.

Your Turn

Guide Discussion Assign one term to a pair of students, and have each pair share sentences using the term.

Change Over Time

↻ Language Production

Do You Understand?

Comprehension Support Ask students to locate and cut out the Evolution Cards in the Resources section at the back of the Student Book. Have students look through the cards and ask any questions.

Model If desired, students can complete this activity as if it were a memory matching game. Have students make their own definition cards, the same size as the picture-cards. Then have them place the cards face down. In pairs, each student takes a turn flipping over two cards. If the cards match (image + definition), the student removes the cards from the set. If the cards do not match, the student turns the cards face down again.

Talk About It

Guide Discussion To help students complete the sentences, read each statement aloud together, while everyone holds up the correct pair of cards.

Your Turn

Guide Discussion Listen to student discussions as they compare their pairs of cards. Help them correct any mistakes or misunderstandings, as needed.

In Other Words

Model Read the example sentence aloud for students and have them repeat it. Then ask, *What is another way to say this? What is another word, or words, for the verb* to contrast? Have students take turns reading the sentence aloud, choosing one of the yellow-highlighted phrases to fill in the space each time. Then have students suggest their own sentences for using the word *contrast* as a verb. Point out that in the academic term *compare and contrast,* the verb *to contrast* means "to find differences among or between," while the verb *to compare* means "to find similarities."

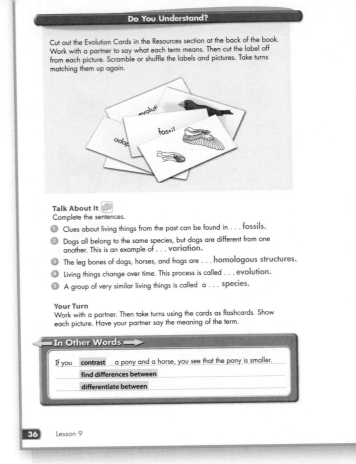

Talk About It 💬
Complete the sentences.
1. Clues about living things from the past can be found in . . . fossils.
2. Dogs all belong to the same species, but dogs are different from one another. This is an example of . . . variation.
3. The leg bones of dogs, horses, and frogs are . . . homologous structures.
4. Living things change over time. This process is called . . . evolution.
5. A group of very similar living things is called a . . . species.

Your Turn
Work with a partner. Then take turns using the cards as flashcards. Show each picture. Have your partner say the meaning of the term.

▶ In Other Words ▶

If you	contrast	a pony and a horse, you see that the pony is smaller.
	find differences between	
	differentiate between	

Leveled Language Proficiency

Students at each proficiency level should be able to perform the following tasks.

Listening/Speaking

Early Beginner/Beginner Hold up a card with the correct term or picture in response to oral questions. Read aloud terms that correctly match illustrations of science concepts.

Early Intermediate Follow oral instructions to identify terms or images. Use simple sentences to describe the illustrations of concepts related to evolution.

Intermediate Listen to and summarize oral definitions of terms related to evolution. Use complete sentences to describe the terms and concepts represented on each of the cards.

Advanced/Transitioning Listen to and summarize complete and complex explanations of the vocabulary terms and how the terms relate to each other. Talk about additional examples to explain concepts relating to evolution.

Your Turn

Draw a line to connect each picture with the correct term.

punctuated equilibrium

fossil

gradualism

homologous structures

Talk and Write About It

Complete the statements about evolution.

1. Natural selection occurs when <u>living things with favorable traits survive and reproduce offspring</u>.
2. Fossils give evidence for evolution because <u>they show how life forms have changed over time</u>.
3. Homologous structures are <u>body parts that correspond in different species, such as the front limb bones of a bird, a horse, and</u> a frog.
4. Lions have sharp teeth. This adaptation helps a lion to <u>eat its prey</u>.
5. Evolution is the process in which <u>how a species changes over time</u>.

Produce Language

Write about how a species changes over time. Tell how evolution and natural selection are related.

_____
_____
_____
_____

Change Over Time   **37**

Leveled Language Proficiency

Students at each proficiency level should be able to perform the following tasks.

Reading/Writing

Early Beginner/Beginner Choose the correct term for an illustration of a science concept. Answer questions about evolution by writing the correct term.

Early Intermediate Read through the lesson to find references to a particular term. Write short phrases about evolution and natural selection.

Intermediate Comprehend phrases that describe terms related to evolution, adaptation, and natural selection. Write a brief definition of each term.

Advanced/Transitioning Read grade-level science textbooks that provide evidence for evolution and related concepts. Write complete sentences describing the relationship between evolution and natural selection.

Assess Understanding

Your Turn

Model Encourage students to describe each image using complete sentences and the appropriate vocabulary terms. Invite volunteers to provide sentences. Write the sentences on the board and read them to the class.

Talk and Write About It

On Their Own Encourage student groups to talk about the pictures from Your Turn. Ask, *What does the picture show? How does it show . . . ?*

Produce Language

On Their Own First, have students write an explanation. Then, have student pairs discuss their answers. Finally, lead a discussion with the whole class to address the Big Question, *How do living things change over time?*

Wrap Up

Table Talk Have students reflect on what they learned. Encourage students to build fluency by reading their writing in groups or to the class.

✔ **Learned** and applied vocabulary related to how species change

✔ **Spoken** statements about evolution and natural selection

✔ **Written** statements about adaptation and variation

Lesson 10

Populations and Communities

Vocabulary habitat, biotic factor, abiotic factor, organism, population, immigration, emigration, limiting factor, community, ecosystem, ecology, birth rate, death rate, population density, carrying capacity

Materials pictures of different ecosystems and habitats, pictures of various organisms, pictures of baby animals, pictures of limiting factors (such as floods)

 Science Background

- An organism gets the things it needs to live, grow, and reproduce from its environment.

- The levels within an ecosystem are *organism*, *population*, and *community*.

Populations and Communities

 Big Question How is an ecosystem organized?

You will . . .
- Explain that a habitat provides everything an organism needs to live.
- Describe how populations in an ecosystem can change.
- Use vocabulary terms to describe the levels of organization in an ecosystem.

Talk About It

A *habitat* is an environment that provides the things an organism needs to live, grow, and reproduce. What does this habitat provide? Circle the things that help the organisms live.

Which of the things you have circled are living? Which are not living?

Predict
Look at the Big Question and the "You will . . ." statements at the top of the page. Describe what you think you are going to learn in this lesson.

I think I am going to learn about . . .

38   Lesson 10

Frontload the Lesson

 How is an ecosystem organized?

Talk About It

Build Background Define unfamiliar words such as *environment*, *organism*, and *reproduce*. As students complete the activity, prompt them to think about the living things and nonliving things that are needed to support life, such as food from plants and animals, water, shelter, sunlight, air, and soil.

Content and Language

Predict

Model Read the objectives aloud. Ask students to repeat after you. Correct any mispronunciations they make.

Guide Discussion Ask students to reread the objectives. Encourage them to use the sentence starter to say what they think they will learn.

Leveled Instruction

Early Beginner Have students repeat the term *habitat* and the name of each element of the habitat that supports life, as you prompt by pointing to each picture.

Beginner/Early Intermediate Provide sentence frames for students to help them organize their answers. Example: *An organism needs ___ to live.*

Intermediate Ask students to explain their answers to questions about habitats, providing help as needed.

Advanced/Transitioning Ask these students to use complete, compound sentences to talk about other types of habitats in the natural world.

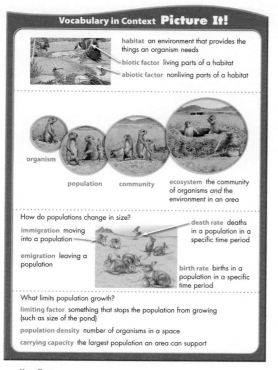

Academic Vocabulary

- The word *factor* refers to a condition or circumstance that contributes to a specific result, such as the limitation of population size.

- Explain that in the words *biotic* and *abiotic,* the root word *bio-* means "life," and the prefix *a-* means "without" or "not."

- In the word *ecosystem,* the prefix *eco-* means "habitat" or "environment," and comes from the Latin word *oeco-,* meaning "household" or "house." The word *system* means "an interdependent group that forms a whole." It may help Spanish speakers to note that the word *habitat* is similar to the Spanish *habitar,* meaning "to inhabit, or to live in or at (a certain place)."

- Explain that the suffix *-ology* means "the study of." So *ecology* means "the study of interrelationships between organisms and their environment. Have students brainstorm other "*-ology*" words they know or have heard.

- The word *density* is used in physical science to refer to the mass of material in a certain amount of space, or volume. In the term *population density, density* is used to refer to the number of individuals in a specific, defined area.

↻ Comprehensible Input

Vocabulary in Context: Picture It!

1. **Say the Term** Say each term slowly, artificially stressing each syllable. Have students repeat. Then say the term more naturally and have students repeat.

2. **Introduce Word Meaning** Connect each term to the visual that illustrates it.

3. **Demonstrate** Use gestures and visuals to demonstrate each term.

4. **Apply** After each term has been discussed, have students demonstrate understanding with Talk About It.

Talk About It

Guide Discussion Before students start their independent discussion, check for understanding with the following sentence starters:

1. *The nonliving parts of a habitat are called . . .* (abiotic factors).

2. *All the members of one species in an area make up a . . .* (population).

3. *Organisms and their environment make up an . . .* (ecosystem).

4. *Movement of individuals into a population's area is called . . .* (immigration).

5. *Movement of individuals out of a population's area is called . . .* (emigration).

6. *Something that stops a population from growing is called a . . .* (limiting factor).

7. *The largest population an area can support is called its . . .* (carrying capacity).

R T I Response to Intervention

If students have difficulty understanding the meaning of the term *limiting factor . . .*

Then review the concept with more examples of how climate, space, food, or water supply can limit population growth.

Your Turn

Guide Discussion Ask students to use the Picture It terms to discuss populations, communities, and the way an ecosystem is organized.

Populations and Communities

 Language Production

Do You Understand?

Comprehension Support Before students start the activity, review the picture definitions of *organism, population, community,* and *ecosystem* in the Picture It box. Remind students of the many organisms and ecosystems there are on Earth. It may help students to choose a local ecosystem, or even to visit one. If students have lived in other parts of the world, expand the discussion by encouraging students to share about any ecosystems they've observed.

Model Read the instructions aloud and allow students to complete each drawing before going on to the next instruction. Give verbal cues such as, *Remember that a community has many different populations* and *Don't forget abiotic factors in the environment you are drawing.* You may refer students back to the habitat picture at the beginning of the lesson.

Talk About It

Guide Discussion As students complete the sentences, reinforce the relationships between the vocabulary terms. Have students work with partners to compare their completed sentences. Then, have volunteers read the completed sentences aloud. As students read have them point out an example in their ecosystem drawing to make sure that the student understands the concept.

Your Turn

Guide Discussion You may wish to provide pictures of ecosystems found on Earth and the organisms, populations, and communities found in each, as well as the abiotic factors that are part of the environment. Have students plan and write their oral responses before sharing with a partner.

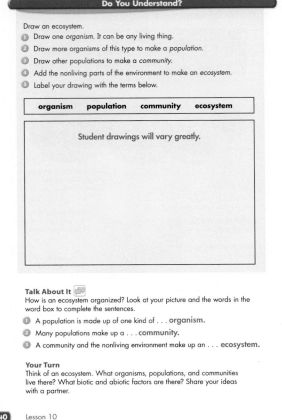

Do You Understand?

Draw an ecosystem.
1. Draw one *organism*. It can be any living thing.
2. Draw more organisms of this type to make a *population.*
3. Draw other populations to make a *community.*
4. Add the nonliving parts of the environment to make an *ecosystem.*
5. Label your drawing with the terms below.

organism	population	community	ecosystem

Student drawings will vary greatly.

Talk About It
How is an ecosystem organized? Look at your picture and the words in the word box to complete the sentences.
1. A population is made up of one kind of . . . organism.
2. Many populations make up a . . . community.
3. A community and the nonliving environment make up an . . . ecosystem.

Your Turn
Think of an ecosystem. What organisms, populations, and communities live there? What biotic and abiotic factors are there? Share your ideas with a partner.

40 Lesson 10

Leveled Language Proficiency

Students at each proficiency level should be able to perform the following tasks.

Listening/Speaking

Early Beginner/Beginner Identify related pictures as a response to oral directions. Say one or two words, or short phrases, to describe biotic and abiotic factors in an ecosystem.

Early Intermediate Respond to oral directions with teacher guidance. Explain the vocabulary terms, relating how an ecosystem is organized using short phrases and simple sentences.

Intermediate Follow oral directions with little to no help. Explain the vocabulary terms, and describe how birth rates and death rates affect populations.

Advanced/Transitioning Follow oral directions independently and give assistance to beginning students. Explain how populations, communities, and ecosystems are related, and orally identify biotic and abiotic factors found there.

Think, Talk, and Write

Your Turn

How do populations change in size? Write the correct word on each line.

| immigration | emigration | birth rate | death rate |

death rate

immigration

emigration

birth rate

Talk and Write About It

Complete the statements about populations.

① Some limiting factors for a fish population might include <u>the size of the pond;</u> <u>the amount of food; the amount of water; the temperature of t</u>he water

② To figure out the population density of the fish in the pond, you must know <u>the number of fish and the size of the pond</u>

③ The carrying capacity of the pond for the fish is the greatest number of <u>the largest number of fish it can support</u>

④ Populations can get bigger through <u>immigration, having a birth</u> <u>rate that is greater than the death rate</u>

⑤ Populations can get smaller through <u>emigration, a death rate greater</u> <u>than the birth rate</u>

Produce Language

Write about ways that populations in an ecosystem can change. Give an example. Use as many vocabulary terms as you can.

_____
_____
_____
_____
_____

Leveled Language Proficiency

Students at each proficiency level should be able to perform the following tasks.

Reading/Writing

Early Beginner/Beginner Identify words that are used to describe populations and communities, and how ecosystems are organized. Write words to label illustrations showing levels in an ecosystem.

Early Intermediate Read simple phrases, and recognize words relating to populations and communities. Write short phrases to describe ecosystems.

Intermediate Read and comprehend phrases and terms related to populations and communities. Write a description of the way populations change size and how ecosystems are organized.

Advanced/Transitioning Read and respond to sentences related to populations and communities. Write complete and compound sentences, using examples, describing the way populations change size and what limits population growth.

↻ Assess Understanding

Your Turn

Model Review the diagram and terms in the Picture It box before students complete the activity. Extend the discussion, by having students answer the question aloud in complete sentences, as they point to parts of the picture for reference.

Talk and Write About It

On Their Own Provide help in reading each of the sentences and encourage students to think about all possible answers as they complete the sentences.

Produce Language

On Their Own Have student pairs both write and talk about what they've learned about populations and communities, using lesson elements for support. Encourage them to discuss population growth and limits, and how an ecosystem is organized, using as many vocabulary terms as possible.

Wrap Up

Table Talk Have students reflect on what they learned. Encourage students to build fluency by reading their writing in groups or to the class.

✔ **Learned** and applied vocabulary related to populations and communities

✔ **Spoken** statements about limiting factors and population density

✔ **Written** statements about biotic and abiotic factors in an ecosystem

Lesson 11

Interaction and Change in Ecosystems

Vocabulary niche, predation, competition, symbiosis, mutualism, commensalism, parasitism, succession, primary succession, pioneer species, secondary succession

Materials pictures of predators and prey; pictures that show symbiotic relationships

Science Background

- Three types of symbiotic relationships are mutualism, commensalism, and parasitism.

- Primary succession is the series of changes that occur in an area where no soil or organisms exist. Secondary succession is the series of changes that occur where the ecosystem has been disturbed, but where soil and organisms still exist.

Frontload the Lesson

What interactions and changes take place in ecosystems?

Talk About It

Build Background Define background words, such as *interactions, organisms,* and *habitat*. Focus students' attention on interactions in the illustration by asking questions such as, *What does the squirrel eat? Where does this food come from?* Emphasize that the plants are living things, and that they make food from air and sunlight.

Content and Language

Predict

Model Read the Big Question and the objectives aloud and have students repeat after you. Correct any mispronunciations they make.

Guide Discussion Ask students to say the objectives with you. Have them use the Talk About It to predict what they will learn.

Interaction and Change in Ecosystems

 Big Question What interactions and changes take place in an ecosystem?

You will . . .
- Identify the different types of interactions among organisms in an ecosystem.
- Discuss how ecosystems develop and change.
- Use key terms to describe interactions and changes in ecosystems.

Talk About It

Look at the picture below. Find the living things in the picture. Where do they live? Do they eat? Do other living things eat them? How do they get food? Talk about it with a partner.

Predict
Look at the Big Question and the "You will . . ." statements at the top of the page. Describe what you think you are going to learn in this lesson.

I think I am going to learn about . . .

Lesson 11

Leveled Instruction

Early Beginner After you have introduced the terms in Picture It, point to the illustrations, one at a time, and ask volunteers to say the correct term.

Beginner/Early Intermediate Provide sentence frames to help students respond to the illustration on this page. For example, say *This squirrel eats ____. This squirrel lives ____.* Be sure students name some plants as living things, such as the trees and grass. Explain that plants make their own food from air and sunlight.

Intermediate These students should be able to work fairly independently. Ask students to describe interactions in a small ecosystem that they are familiar with.

Advanced/Transitioning Ask these students to speak and write complete, compound sentences as they complete activities about interactions and changes in ecosystems.

Vocabulary in Context Picture It!

niche an organism's role in an environment

competition

predation

symbiosis a relationship where two species live together and one or both benefit

Types of Symbiosis

mutualism Both species benefit.

parasitism One benefits, but the other is harmed.

commensalism One species benefits, and the other is not harmed.

succession changes in a community over time
Primary succession begins in an area with no soil or organisms.

pioneer species the first species to come to an area

Secondary succession takes place in an area where there are organisms and soil.

Your Turn
Talk with a partner. Explain the interactions shown in the pictures.

Interaction and Change in Ecosystems **43**

Academic Vocabulary

- Explain the difference between the homophones *prey* and *pray*. *Prey* is what a predator eats; *pray* is a verb meaning "to make a plea for something."

- *Competition* comes from the Latin *competere*, meaning "to strive for" or "to contend for." The words *compete* and *competitor* come from the same root.

- The term *mutualism* comes from the word *mutual*, meaning "directed toward each other." *Mutualism* is used to refer to the relationship in which each organism helps the other.

- The term *commensalism* comes from the Latin words *com-* (together) and *mensa* (table). It means "coming together."

- The term *parasitism* comes from *para-* (alongside) and *sitos* (food). It means "eating at another's table," or "eating from another organism." Point out the organisms living on the fish.

- Review the academic terms *primary* and *secondary* with students. The word *primary* in *primary succession* means "first." The word *secondary* in *secondary succession* means "second." Have students brainstorm other phrases or sentences that use these words. (*primary colors, secondary colors; primary election, secondary reason,* and so on)

↻ Comprehensible Input

Vocabulary in Context: Picture It!

1. **Say the Term** Say each term slowly, artificially stressing each syllable. Have students repeat. Then say the term more naturally and have students repeat.

2. **Introduce Word Meaning** Connect each term to the visual that illustrates it.

3. **Demonstrate** Use gestures and visuals to demonstrate each term.

4. **Apply** After each term has been discussed, have students demonstrate understanding with Talk About It.

Talk About It

Guide Discussion Before students start their independent discussion, check for understanding with the following sentence starters:

1. *An organism's role in its habitat is its . . .* (niche.)

2. *A relationship in which one organism kills another for food is called . . .* (predation.)

3. *The struggle between animals for resources such as food is called . . .* (competition.)

4. *Mutualism and parasitism are types of . . .* (symbiosis.)

5. *The series of changes that occur in an area with no soil or organisms is called . . .* (primary succession.)

RTI Response to Intervention

If students confuse the term *succession* with the word *secession* . . .

Then explain that *succession* refers to the order or sequence of events. Write the verbs *secede* and *succeed* on the board, pronouncing them slowly and discussing their meanings. Then do the same with *succession* and *secession*.

Your Turn

Guide Discussion Ask students to discuss interactions between organisms that take place in an ecosystem. Point out details in the pictured examples and provide any of your own pictures to help guide the discussion.

Interaction and Change in Ecosystems

↻ Language Production

Do You Understand?

Comprehension Support Before students begin the activity, review the terms *succession, primary succession, secondary succession, and pioneer species.* Remind students of the sequence in which each type of succession occurs.

Model Read the instructions aloud, and encourage students to complete the activity as independently as possible.

Talk About It

Guide Discussion Read the sentence starters aloud with students as they complete the sentences. Encourage students to infer how interactions between organisms change as succession proceeds. (For example, as the ecosystem becomes more complex, it provides a greater variety of food, allowing a greater variety of animals to populate the area.)

Your Turn

Guide Discussion Give each group time to read its lists aloud to the class. You may want to make a master list on the board. Encourage students to talk about the events that set succession in motion—for example, natural disasters such as volcanic eruptions, and human activities such as clear-cutting.

Do You Understand?

Number the pictures in the correct sequence. Label the set *primary succession* or *secondary succession.*

secondary succession

Talk About It
Talk to a partner. Look at the pictures. Use key terms to complete the sentences.

1. Change to a community over time is called . . . **succession.**
2. Farming, hurricanes, and wildfires are examples of disturbances that lead to . . . **secondary succession.**
3. In an environment with no soil, the first species to enter is called a . . . **pioneer species.**

Your Turn
With a group, list ways an ecosystem can change. Think about the land, plants, animals, climate, and changes made by humans. Share your list with the class.

44   Lesson 11

Leveled Language Proficiency

Students at each proficiency level should be able to perform the following tasks.

Listening/Speaking

Early Beginner/Beginner Point to appropriate pictures as a response to oral directions. Identify the sequence of events in succession orally, using the sequence words *first, second,* and *third.*

Early Intermediate Sequence and label pictures with minimal verbal cues. Explain the vocabulary terms aloud, relating the changes that take place in ecosystems.

Intermediate Follow oral directions with little to no help. Use complete spoken sentences to compare and contrast primary and secondary succession.

Advanced/Transitioning Follow oral directions and complete tasks independently. Use complete and complex sentences to orally describe interactions and changes in ecosystems.

Your Turn

What interactions are taking place in this community? Label each using a word from the word box.

predation	competition	symbiosis
mutualism	commensalism	parasitism

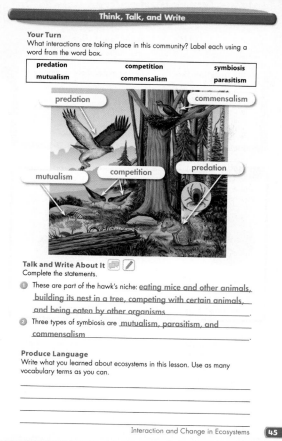

predation

commensalism

mutualism   competition   predation

Talk and Write About It
Complete the statements.

1. These are part of the hawk's niche: _eating mice and other animals, building its nest in a tree, competing with certain animals, and being eaten by other organisms_.

2. Three types of symbiosis are _mutualism, parasitism, and commensalism_.

Produce Language
Write what you learned about ecosystems in this lesson. Use as many vocabulary terms as you can.

_____

_____

_____

_____

Interaction and Change in Ecosystems   45

Leveled Language Proficiency

Students at each proficiency level should be able to perform the following tasks.

Reading/Writing

Early Beginner/Beginner Place word cards with correct pictures to show predation and competition. Write single words or short phrases to describe interactions.

Early Intermediate Read simple phrases and recognize words relating to symbiosis. Write short phrases to describe types of symbiosis.

Intermediate Read and comprehend phrases and terms related to succession in ecosystems. Using complete sentences, write a description of succession in ecosystems and provide examples.

Advanced/Transitioning Read paragraphs related to mutualism, commensalism, and parasitism. Write grammatically correct, complete sentences to describe each type of symbiosis.

↻ Assess Understanding

Your Turn

Model Review the terms *niche, predation, competition, symbiosis, mutualism, commensalism, parasitism,* and *succession* in the Picture It box before students complete the activity.

Talk and Write About It

On Their Own Provide help reading the sentences, and encourage students to think about all of the possible answers as they complete the sentences. You might have students collaborate on describing the niches of different organisms, such as mosses, snails, frogs, and so forth. Make sure that students do not confuse the terms *habitat* and *niche*.

Produce Language

On Their Own Have student groups both write and talk about what they've learned about the changes and interactions that take place in ecosystems. Encourage them to use as many vocabulary terms as possible.

Wrap Up

Table Talk Have students reread the Big Question and discuss answers with a partner in order to reflect on what they learned. Encourage students to build fluency by reading their writing in groups or to the class.

✔ **Learned** and applied vocabulary related to interaction and change in ecosystems

✔ **Spoken** statements about roles of organisms in ecosystems

✔ **Written** statements about ways two species can live together so that one benefits

Lesson 12

Ecosystems and Biomes

Vocabulary producer, consumer, herbivore, carnivore, omnivore, scavenger, decomposer, food chain, food web, energy pyramid, biome, climate, desert, rain forest, grassland, deciduous forest, boreal forest, tundra, biogeography

Materials pictures of various consumers and producers

Science Background

- Each organism in an ecosystem is a producer, a consumer, or a decomposer.

- In an energy pyramid, the most energy is available at the producer level. Each higher level has less energy available than the level below it.

- The six major biomes are desert, rain forest, grassland, deciduous forest, boreal forest, and tundra.

Frontload the Lesson

How do energy and matter move through ecosystems?

Talk About It

Build Background Read aloud the directions and discuss the concept of a *food chain*. Make sure that students understand that a food chain is a diagram that shows the transfer of energy as well as the transfer of matter.

Content and Language

Predict

Model Read the Big Question and the objectives aloud. As students repeat after you, correct any mispronunciations. Refer to the pictures in the lesson to help define *biomes*.

Guide Discussion Ask students to say the objectives with you. Have them use the sentence starter to say what they think they will learn.

Ecosystems and Biomes

Big Question How do energy and matter move through ecosystems?

You will . . .
- Construct diagrams to show how energy moves through ecosystems in food chains and food webs.
- Describe how matter cycles through ecosystems.
- Use vocabulary terms to describe ecosystems and biomes.

Talk About It

A food chain shows which organisms eat which other organisms. Discuss the following food chain with a partner. Use the questions below.

1. What animal provides food for the boy?
2. What plant starts the food chain?
3. Why is the cow between the grass and the boy in this diagram?

Predict
Look at the Big Question and the "You will . . ." statements at the top of the page. Describe what you think you are going to learn in this lesson.

I think I am going to learn about . . .

Leveled Instruction

Early Beginner To help students understand the use of the terms *chain* and *web* in *food chain* and *food web*, show them pictures of a common metal chain and a spider web, and relate these pictures to the structure of food-chain and food-web diagrams.

Beginner/Early Intermediate Provide sentence frames for students as they point to each picture in sequence. For example: *This food chain begins with the plant ___ . Then the ___ eats the ___. Next, the ___ eats the ___.*

Intermediate These students should be able to work fairly independently. Ask students to give examples of plants and animals in biomes they know about, such as a rain-forest biome or desert biome.

Advanced/Transitioning Have students identify examples of plants and animals in different biomes, such as in the rain forest, and explain in complex sentences how these organisms can form a food chain.

Vocabulary in Context **Picture It!**

consumer

A food web is made up of many food chains.

producer

Each level of an energy pyramid has less energy available than the one below it.

herbivore

carnivore

scavenger

decomposer   omnivore

A **biome** is a group of ecosystems with similar **climates** and organisms.

Earth has six major **biomes** each of which appears in North America, as shown on the map.

Biogeography is the study of where organisms live and how they got there.

■ Desert   ■ Deciduous forest
■ Rain forest   ■ Boreal forest
■ Grassland   ■ Tundra

Your Turn
Use the vocabulary terms to explain to a partner what a food chain, a food web, and an energy pyramid show.

Ecosystems and Biomes **47**

Academic Vocabulary

- The words *herbivore, carnivore,* and *omnivore* share the suffix, *-vore,* which means "devouring" or "eating." *Carni-* comes from a root meaning "flesh," so *carnivore* means "flesh-eating." *Herbi-* comes from *herb,* a type of plant. So *herbivore* means "plant-eating." *Omni-* comes from the Latin word *omnis,* meaning "all," so the word *omnivore* means "to eat everything."

- The words *producer, consumer, scavenger,* and *decomposer* share the suffix *-er,* meaning "one who." This makes their meanings "one who produces," "one who consumes," "one who scavenges," and "one who decomposes."

- Explain through gestures and drawings the meanings of each verb. Then give examples of *decomposing* (leaves in a compost pile), *scavenging* (crows eating roadkill), and *producing* (plants making food).

- Cognates are words in different languages that have the same roots and similar spellings. For example, the Spanish word for *herbivore* is *herbívoro.* Invite students to share any cognates for the terms in this lesson.

↻ Comprehensible Input

Vocabulary in Context: Picture It!

1. **Say the Term** Say each term slowly, artificially stressing each syllable. Have students repeat. Then say the term more naturally and have students repeat.

2. **Introduce Word Meaning** Connect each term to the visual that illustrates it.

3. **Demonstrate** Use gestures and visuals to demonstrate each term.

4. **Apply** After each term has been discussed, have students demonstrate understanding with Talk About It.

Talk About It

Guide Discussion Before students start their independent discussion, check for understanding with the following sentence starters:

1. *A diagram that shows an animal eating a plant, and then the animal being eaten by another animal is called a . . .* (food chain.)

2. *Plants make their own food. They are called . . .* (producers.)

3. *Organisms that eat others are called . . .* (consumers.)

4. *An animal that eats plants is an . . .* (herbivore.)

5. *An animal that eats animals is a . . .* (carnivore.)

6. *A diagram that shows energy levels in a food chain is called an . . .* (energy pyramid.)

7. *A group of ecosystems with similar climates and organisms is a . . .* (biome.)

RTI Response to Intervention

If students have difficulty understanding the meaning of the term *energy pyramid . . .*

Then draw a pyramid and point out that the bottom level is broadest and each successive level is narrower, showing how energy is lost in every step of the food web.

Your Turn

Guide Discussion Ask students to use the Picture It! terms to discuss the types of biomes and the ways energy moves through ecosystems. Give examples to help guide the discussion.

Ecosystems and Biomes

↻ Language Production

Do You Understand?

Comprehension Support Before students start the activity, use the Picture It box to review the food web and related vocabulary. Remind students of what the terms *herbivore, carnivore, omnivore, and scavenger* mean.

Model Read the instructions aloud. Allow students to complete the activity as independently as possible.

Talk About It

Guide Discussion Read the statements aloud with students as they work to complete the sentences. As you discuss the terms and their definitions, refer back to the diagram of a food web. Explain that food chains and food webs always start with producers. (You might point out that almost all producers are plants or photosynthetic microorganisms. In a very few cases, chemosynthetic microorganisms are at the base of a food chain. Chemosynthetic organisms synthesize food molecules in processes that do not depend on light to supply energy.)

Your Turn

Guide Discussion Listen to student discussions and correct any mistakes or misunderstandings as needed. Encourage students to use the vocabulary terms in their discussions.

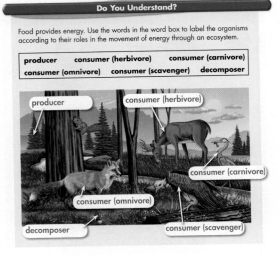

Do You Understand?

Food provides energy. Use the words in the word box to label the organisms according to their roles in the movement of energy through an ecosystem.

| producer | consumer (herbivore) | consumer (carnivore) |
| consumer (omnivore) | consumer (scavenger) | decomposer |

Talk About It 💬
Complete the sentences.

1. A diagram that shows the amount of energy that moves from one level to another in a food web is called an . . . energy pyramid.
2. Organisms that break down dead organisms and wastes are called . . . decomposers.
3. Organisms that make their own food are called . . . producers.
4. Four types of consumers are . . . herbivores, carnivores, omnivores, and scavengers.
5. A consumer that eats both plants and animals is called an . . . omnivore.

Your Turn
Work with a partner. Talk about the picture. Tell how energy moves through the ecosystem.

48   Lesson 12

Leveled Language Proficiency

Students at each proficiency level should be able to perform the following tasks.

Listening/Speaking

Early Beginner/Beginner Identify pictures and repeat vocabulary terms as a response to oral directions. Use short words to describe food chains.

Early Intermediate In response to simple oral questions, identify illustrations of organisms as producers, consumers, or decomposers.

Intermediate Follow oral directions with little to no help. Orally explain the sequence of events in a food chain and the types of organisms found in a food chain.

Advanced/Transitioning Follow oral directions and complete tasks independently. Fluently participate in class discussions that explain the relationship between the levels in an energy pyramid.

Think, Talk, and Write

Your Turn

Write the name of each biome under its picture. Then write one type of plant found in that biome.

desert biome	rain-forest biome	grassland biome

desert biome — sample: cactus

grassland biome — sample: grass

rain-forest biome — Sample: moss

Talk and Write About It

Work with a partner. Complete these sentences about Earth's biomes.

1. Each of the six major biomes has different _climates and organisms_

2. One plant that lives in desert biomes is a _cactus (answers may vary)_

3. The climate of a tropical rain forest is _warm and humid_

4. Where I live, the climate is _Answers will vary._

Produce Language

Write your description of one of the biomes pictured above. Use as many vocabulary terms as you can.

_____

_____

_____

_____

_____

A Closer Look

Look at the word **biogeography.** Underline the word parts *bio-*, *geo-*, and *-graph-*. What does each word part mean?

Ecosystems and Biomes **49**

Leveled Language Proficiency

Students at each proficiency level should be able to perform the following tasks.

Reading/Writing

Early Beginner/Beginner Identify, read, and write the term *biome*. Label pictures of different biomes.

Early Intermediate Read and write the term *biome* and use it in simple phrases. Write short phrases to describe the plants and animals found in several biomes.

Intermediate Read and comprehend simple sentences related to ecosystems. Using complete written sentences, differentiate between producers, consumers, and decomposers.

Advanced/Transitioning Read simple articles in popular magazines about ecosystems. Write summaries of these articles.

Assess Understanding

Your Turn

Model Read the instructions and review the term *biome* before students complete the activity. Relate biomes to ecosystems by reminding students that the climate in each biome determines the plants and animals that can live in the ecosystems within it.

Talk and Write About It

On Their Own Provide help reading each of the sentences, and encourage students to think about all possible answers as they complete the sentences. Circulate among pairs of students, listening as they complete the sentences. Correct any misconceptions.

Produce Language

On Their Own Have students review the Big Question. Invite student groups to both write and talk about what they've learned about biomes and ecosystems, and the ways energy and matter move through ecosystems. Encourage students to use as many vocabulary terms as possible.

A Closer Look

Model Read the text aloud and underline the word parts *bio-*, *geo-*, and *-graph-* in the term *biogeography*. Then say, Bio- *means "life."* Geo- *means "Earth."* -Graph- *means "having to do with writing."* The term *biogeography* means "the study of where on Earth living organisms are found." Discuss how plants might spread from one continent to another.

Wrap Up

Table Talk Have students reflect on what they learned. Encourage students to build fluency by reading their writing in groups or to the class.

✔ **Learned** and applied vocabulary related to how energy moves through ecosystems

✔ **Spoken** statements about biomes and ecosystems

✔ **Written** statements about how matter cycles through ecosystems

Lesson 13

Resources and Biodiversity

Vocabulary environmental science, nonrenewable resource, renewable resource, natural resource, sustainable use, extinction, conservation, pollution, ecological footprint, clear-cutting, selective cutting, biodiversity, endangered species, threatened species

Materials images of: pollution, renewable resources, and nonrenewable resources

Science Background

- Natural resources include organisms, water, sunlight, minerals, air, and any parts of Earth that humans use for survival and for industrial development.

- Forests can be renewable resources if new trees are planted to replace trees that are cut. Fisheries can provide a sustainable yield if people limit fishing, adjust fishing methods, develop aquaculture techniques, and find new resources.

Frontload the Lesson

How do people use Earth's resources?

Talk About It

Build Background Model drawing and writing about things that you did yesterday and the natural resources you use in daily life.

Content and Language

Predict

Model Read the Big Question and the objectives aloud. Focus on key terms in the objectives, such as *environment* and *resources*.

Guide Discussion If students have diffuiculty making a prediction, have them focus on the second "You will . . ." statement. Do a word web together for the word *environment*.

Resources and Biodiversity

 Big Question How do people use Earth's resources?

You will . . .
- Distinguish between renewable and nonrenewable resources.
- Identify actions that are more or less harmful to the environment.
- Use terms related to resource use.

Talk About It

Draw pictures or write about four things you did yesterday.

Review your pictures and words. What are some resources, such as cloth, wood, gas, or electricity, that you used yesterday? What resources do you use most days?

    Yesterday, I used . . .

    Most days, I use . . .

Predict
Look at the Big Question and the "You will . . ." statements at the top of the page. Describe what you think you are going to learn in this lesson.

    I think I am going to learn about . . .

50 Lesson 13

Leveled Instruction

Early Beginner Have students work with a partner who speaks the beginners' first language but is more advanced in English. Encourage the students to discuss the pictures in the first language. The advanced student can then say the terms in English and have the beginner repeat the English terms.

Beginner Have students work with a more advanced partner to construct a Venn diagram comparing categories, such as renewable and nonrenewable resources.

Early Intermediate/Intermediate Have students use short sentences and simple phrases to differentiate between the terms *threatened, endangered,* and *extinct.*

Advanced/Transitioning Ask students to orally describe in detail how several of their daily activities relate to resource use. Then encourage students to write a description of how they might conserve one or more of those resources.

Vocabulary in Context Picture It!

A person who studies environmental science might learn about natural resources, animal habitats, or endangered species.

natural resources anything people use that comes from the environment

Renewable resources are always available or can be replaced quickly.

Nonrenewable resources cannot be replaced easily or quickly.

sustainable use

conservation

pollution

clear-cutting

selective cutting

biodiversity the range of different species in an area

The resources you use and the waste you cause are your **ecological footprint**.

extinct None of these organisms are alive anymore.

endangered species in danger of becoming extinct

threatened species could become endangered

Your Turn
Talk with a partner about extinct species, endangered species, and threatened species. Draw a picture for each term.

Resources and Biodiversity **51**

Academic Vocabulary

- Point out the meanings of the word parts in the term *biodiversity*: "life" and "many kinds." Talk about how the combined word parts mean "many kinds of life."

- Write the term *endangered species* on the board and underline *danger*. Ask students how endangered species can be in danger. Repeat with *threatened species* and *threat*.

- Point out the base words in some of the lesson terms, such as *pollute* for *pollution* and *conserve* for *conservation*. Discuss with students how identifying the base word can help them understand the meaning of a vocabulary term.

↻ Comprehensible Input

Vocabulary in Context: Picture It!

1. **Say the Term** Say each term slowly, artificially stressing each syllable. Have students repeat. Then say the term more naturally and have students repeat.

2. **Introduce Word Meaning** Connect each term to the visual that illustrates it.

3. **Demonstrate** Use gestures and visuals to demonstrate each term.

4. **Apply** After each term has been discussed, have students demonstrate understanding with Talk About It.

Talk About It

Guide Discussion Before students start their independent discussion, check for understanding with the following sentence starters:

1. *Something from the environment that people use is a . . .* (natural resource).

2. *A place with a wide range of species has great . . .* (biodiversity).

3. *An endangered species is at risk of becoming . . .* (extinct).

4. *A species that may become endangered is called a . . .* (threatened species).

5. *Smoke in the air is an example of . . .* (pollution).

6. *The food and fuels you use and the waste you throw away are part of your . . .* (ecological footprint).

RTI Response to Intervention

If students have difficulty with the words *renewable* and *nonrenewable* . . .

Then break the terms into their meaningful parts and discuss the meaning of each part. For example, a *re-new-able resource* is a "resource that can be made new again."

Your Turn

Guide Discussion Ask students guiding questions, such as *What is an extinct species? Which species is at more risk: an endangered species or a threatened species?*

Resources and Biodiversity

↻ Language Production

Do You Understand?

Comprehension Support Before students start the activity, describe the difference between renewable and nonrenewable resources and give an example of each. Then have students provide additional examples.

Model Demonstrate how students can ask themselves questions to help them complete the activity. Say, *Is gasoline a type of fuel that will be gone after it has been used up, or is it easily replaced, like wind or sun?*

Talk About It

Guide Discussion Check that students can complete the sentences correctly. Talk with students about some of the ways they can reduce their use of nonrenewable resources and increase their use of renewable resources.

Your Turn

Guide Discussion Listen to and encourage student discussions. Clarify discussion points as they arise. Pass around images of renewable resources, such as the sun, trees, and water, and images of nonrenewable resources, such as coal, oil, and metals. Discuss how renewable resources can be replenished, but nonrenewable resources will be gone if people use up the existing reserves.

A Closer Look

On Their Own Have students work in pairs to complete this word study activity. Help them with pronunciation of *extinction*. Then have them suggest new examples of words with the *-tion* ending. To reinforce understanding, they may also brainstorm a list of living things that have met with extinction.

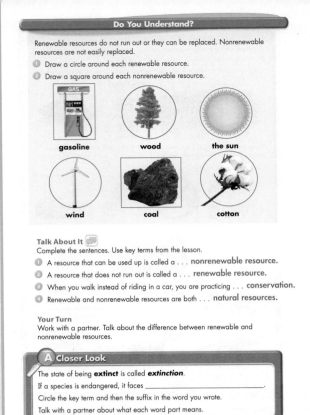

Do You Understand?

Renewable resources do not run out or they can be replaced. Nonrenewable resources are not easily replaced.

1. Draw a circle around each renewable resource.
2. Draw a square around each nonrenewable resource.

gasoline   wood   the sun
wind   coal   cotton

Talk About It
Complete the sentences. Use key terms from the lesson.

1. A resource that can be used up is called a . . . nonrenewable resource.
2. A resource that does not run out is called a . . . renewable resource.
3. When you walk instead of riding in a car, you are practicing . . . conservation.
4. Renewable and nonrenewable resources are both . . . natural resources.

Your Turn
Work with a partner. Talk about the difference between renewable and nonrenewable resources.

A Closer Look

The state of being **extinct** is called *extinction*.
If a species is endangered, it faces _____.
Circle the key term and then the suffix in the word you wrote.
Talk with a partner about what each word part means.

Leveled Language Proficiency

Students at each proficiency level should be able to perform the following tasks.

Listening/Speaking

Early Beginner/Beginner When orally asked to identify renewable and nonrenewable resources, respond by using pictures, actions, or objects. Ask and respond to simple questions about familiar content.

Early Intermediate Use beginning and bilingual dictionaries to clarify meanings of words heard in class. Respond with phrases and short sentences to questions about resources.

Intermediate Determine the meanings of words heard in class based on prefixes and suffixes. Use simple spoken sentences to identify characteristics of resources.

Advanced/Transitioning Use dictionaries, thesauruses, and other resources to clarify meanings of spoken words. Orally rephrase ideas and thoughts to explain the difference between renewable and nonrenewable resources.

Your Turn

Draw a line from the term in the left column to its meaning in the right column.

Term	Meaning
① endangered species	could become endangered in the near future
② extinct	dirty water, air, or land
③ threatened species	cutting down only a few trees
④ sustainable use	cutting down all the trees in an area
⑤ pollution	in danger of becoming extinct soon
⑥ selective cutting	using a resource carefully, so the resource doesn't run out
⑦ clear-cutting	There are no living members of this species.

Talk and Write About It

Complete the statements about how people use resources.

① The difference between clear-cutting and selective cutting is _____
   clear-cutting removes all trees; selective cutting leaves some trees

② Practicing conservation means _____
   using resources carefully so they aren't used up

③ Pollution contaminates or harms many parts of the environment, including:
   on land, in the air, or in water _____.

④ Some examples of natural resources are _____
   gas, coal, wind, trees/wood, sunlight, water _____.

Produce Language

Write about ways that you can help make your ecological footprint smaller.

_____

_____

_____

_____

_____

_____

Resources and Biodiversity **53**

Leveled Language Proficiency

Students at each proficiency level should be able to perform the following tasks.

Reading/Writing

Early Beginner/Beginner Match key terms with associated images and examples. Draw and label illustrations to show ways to conserve resources.

Early Intermediate Use illustrations and context clues to understand textbook explanations about conserving resources. Write a short paragraph that lists ways people can reduce their ecological footprint.

Intermediate Apply word analysis strategies to determine the meanings of unfamiliar terms. Write multiple paragraphs about ways people can reduce their ecological footprint.

Advanced/Transitioning Research and present information about the origins and roots of English words related to natural resources and conservation. Write multiple paragraphs about resource use and choose words based on audience.

↻ Assess Understanding

Your Turn

Model Have students work in pairs to complete this activity. Encourage them to refer to the Picture It box and to the glossaries in their textbooks. Check that students understand the difference between threatened and endangered species.

Talk and Write About It

On Their Own Before students begin writing, go through each of the terms in the Your Turn activity. Describe examples aloud and show pictures. Make sure students understand the meanings of the terms.

Produce Language

On Their Own Before they write, refer students to the Big Question and conduct a class discussion in which students supply answers. Then have a few volunteers share ideas about ways they can reduce their ecological footprint. Write key words and phrases on the board for students to use as support.

Wrap Up

Table Talk Have students reflect on what they learned. Encourage students to build fluency by reading their writing in groups or to the class.

✔ **Learned** and applied vocabulary related to resources and biodiversity

✔ **Heard** statements about renewable and nonrenewable resources

✔ **Read** statements about the risk that some species face

Lesson 14

Viruses, Bacteria, Protists, and Fungi

Vocabulary virus, host, bacteria, decomposer, cytoplasm, flagellum, protist, cilia, algae, fungus, lichen, parasite

Materials rotting wood and unrotted wood (optional)

Science Background

- Viruses are considered nonliving because they lack most of the characteristics of living things. They cannot reproduce on their own. They use host cells to reproduce.

- Bacteria are prokaryotes, so their genetic material is not contained in a nucleus.

- Protists are eukaryotes (organisms with cells that have nuclei) that cannot be classified as animals, plants, or fungi.

- Fungi are eukaryotes that have cell walls and feed by absorbing their food.

Frontload the Lesson

How are living things alike, yet different?

Talk About It

Build Background Make sure that students understand the terms *living* and *nonliving*. If students do not understand the English terms for common objects, provide hints.

Content and Language

Predict

Model Read the Big Question and the objectives aloud. As students repeat after you, correct any mispronunciations that students make.

Guide Discussion Ask students to think about the Talk About It activity and how it might relate to what they will learn.

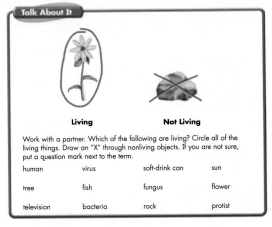

Big Question How are living things alike, yet different?

You will . . .
- Discuss similarities and differences among living things.
- Describe characteristics of viruses, bacteria, protists, and fungi.
- Use terms that describe different types of living things.

Talk About It

Living   Not Living

Work with a partner. Which of the following are living? Circle all of the living things. Draw an "X" through nonliving objects. If you are not sure, put a question mark next to the term.

human	virus	soft-drink can	sun
tree	fish	fungus	flower
television	bacteria	rock	protist

Predict
Look at the Big Question and the "You will . . ." statements at the top of the page. Describe what you think you are going to learn in this lesson.

I think I am going to learn about . . .

54   Lesson 14

Leveled Instruction

Early Beginner Ask students to point to specific words in the list and say *living* or *nonliving*. As students point to words, say each word aloud for them to hear.

Beginner Ask students to find particular items in the list and to say the name of each item aloud. Have students say *It is living* or *It is nonliving*. Help with pronunciation as needed.

Early Intermediate/Intermediate Ask students to explain why they categorized each item as living or nonliving. Ask, *How do you know that _____ is living/nonliving?* Expect students to respond in phrases or complete sentences.

Advanced/Transitioning Partner these students with beginning students to go through the items, comparing answers. Have advanced students model how they structure sentences, such as *A television is not a living thing*.

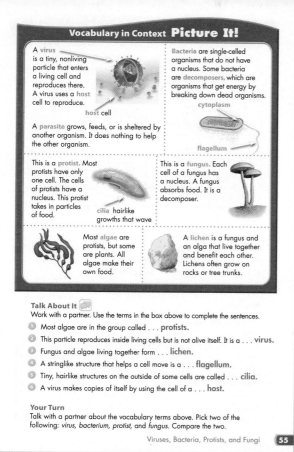

Viruses, Bacteria, Protists, and Fungi 55

Academic Vocabulary

- Explain to students that something that is *nonliving* —such as a television or a plastic bottle—is not alive now and never was alive.

- Some things that were once alive (such as a piece of wood or a dried leaf) may now be *dead* or *no longer living*.

- Describe the meaning of the words *alive* and *not alive*. Note that *alive* is a synonym for *living*, but that *not alive* can refer to something that is *nonliving* or to something that was once alive, but now is not.

- Students may be familiar with the everyday meaning of both the noun and the verb *host*. Encourage them to give examples of the word in an everyday context. Ask partners to compare and contrast the everyday *host* (n.) with *host cell* (adj.). What are some similarities and differences?

- Point out that the term *algae* is a plural form, and that the singular form is *alga*. Explain that *alga* is a Latin word, and that Latin words ending in *a* often form their plural by adding *e*. Refer back to this example when students do the A Closer Look activity, on page 56.

Comprehensible Input

Vocabulary in Context: Picture It!

1. **Say the Term** Say each term slowly, artificially stressing each syllable. Have students repeat. Then say the term more naturally and have students repeat.

2. **Introduce Word Meaning** Connect each term to the visual that illustrates it.

3. **Demonstrate** Use gestures and visuals to demonstrate each term. For example:

   - As you say the word *virus*, model sneezing into a tissue. Tell students that some viruses cause colds.

   - To clarify what decomposers do, you might show students a solid piece of wood and a piece of wood that has rotted.

4. **Apply** After all of the terms have been discussed, have students demonstrate understanding with Talk About It.

Talk About It

Guide Discussion Read the directions chorally with students and have them work with their partners to complete the sentences. Make sure that students understand the difference between flagella and cilia.

RTI Response to Intervention

If students have difficulty with the term *nonliving* . . .

Then give other examples of words with the prefix *non-*, such as *nonsmoking, nonstop, nonsense, nonfiction*. Have students identify the base word for each term (*smoking, stop, sense, fiction*).

Your Turn

Guide Discussion Encourage students to use comparative phrases such as *is similar to* and *is different from*.

Viruses, Bacteria, Protists, and Fungi

↻ Language Production

Do You Understand?

Comprehension Support Have pairs work together to discuss each picture. Then have pairs split up the pictures so that each student talks about two of them.

Model Use a classroom object to demonstrate how students should work through each picture. For example, show a plant. Say, *1. This is a plant. 2. It is alive. 3. It uses sunlight to make its food. It gets water from the soil.* As you give the example, have students follow the numbers on the page, so they see that you are responding to each numbered item.

Talk About It

Guide Discussion Read the sentence starters aloud with students as they work together to complete the sentences. Help students understand the "What Am I?" approach by modeling clues and sentence completion with familiar examples. Say, *I help you tell what time it is. I have numbers on my face. I am a . . .* (clock.)

Your Turn

Guide Discussion Listen to student discussions as they talk about each picture. Help correct pronunciation as needed. Encourage advanced students to elaborate on the characteristics of each pictured item.

A Closer Look

On Their Own Have students work in pairs to complete this word study activity. Give them other examples of words that form their plurals in these ways—for example, *medium/media, cactus/cacti.*

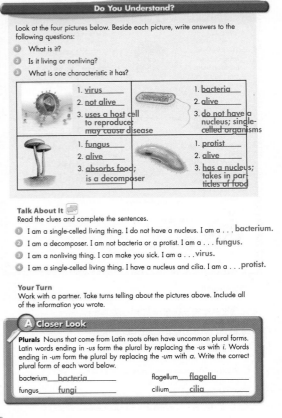

Do You Understand?

Look at the four pictures below. Beside each picture, write answers to the following questions:

1. What is it?
2. Is it living or nonliving?
3. What is one characteristic it has?

1. <u>virus</u> 2. <u>not alive</u> 3. <u>uses a host cell to reproduce; may cause disease</u>	1. <u>bacteria</u> 2. <u>alive</u> 3. <u>do not have a nucleus; single-celled organisms</u>
1. <u>fungus</u> 2. <u>alive</u> 3. <u>absorbs food; is a decomposer</u>	1. <u>protist</u> 2. <u>alive</u> 3. <u>has a nucleus; takes in particles of food</u>

Talk About It 🎧
Read the clues and complete the sentences.

1. I am a single-celled living thing. I do not have a nucleus. I am a . . . bacterium.
2. I am a decomposer. I am not bacteria or a protist. I am a . . . fungus.
3. I am a nonliving thing. I can make you sick. I am a . . . virus.
4. I am a single-celled living thing. I have a nucleus and cilia. I am a . . . protist.

Your Turn
Work with a partner. Take turns telling about the pictures above. Include all of the information you wrote.

> **🔍 A Closer Look**
>
> **Plurals** Nouns that come from Latin roots often have uncommon plural forms. Latin words ending in *-us* form the plural by replacing the *-us* with *i*. Words ending in *-um* form the plural by replacing the *-um* with *a*. Write the correct plural form of each word below.
>
> bacterium <u>bacteria</u>   flagellum <u>flagella</u>
> fungus <u>fungi</u>   cilium <u>cilia</u>

Leveled Language Proficiency

Students at each proficiency level should be able to perform the following tasks.

Listening/Speaking

Early Beginner/Beginner Gesture or point in response to oral questions about the pictures on this page. Use a word or short phrase to respond to questions about a pictured type of organism.

Early Intermediate Use short phrases to respond to oral questions about viruses and hosts. Speak in simple sentences to describe characteristics of bacteria.

Intermediate Understand oral definitions of *virus, bacterium, protist,* and *fungus,* as well as related terms. Use complete spoken sentences to compare and contrast algae, lichens, and fungi.

Advanced/Transitioning Follow oral descriptions of similarities and differences between organisms and viruses. Use complete and complex sentences to orally describe and compare bacteria, protists, and fungi.

Your Turn

Talk about each picture with a partner. Which of the following do you think each picture represents—*virus, bacteria, protist,* or *fungus*? Explain.

virus

bacterium

protist

fungus

Talk and Write About It

Complete the statements about viruses, bacteria, protists, and fungi.

1. One similarity between protists and fungi is <u>both have cells with nuclei</u>
2. Viruses are different from bacteria, protists, and fungi because _____ <u>viruses are not alive</u>.
3. Cilia are different from flagella because <u>cilia are numerous, like hairs on a brush; a flagellum appears as a single tail-like strand</u>
4. One difference between a protist and a bacterium is _____ <u>protists have nuclei but bacteria do not</u>.

Produce Language

Write one interesting thing you have learned about viruses, bacteria, protists, or fungi. Write one question you have.

_____

_____

_____

Viruses, Bacteria, Protists, and Fungi **57**

Leveled Language Proficiency

Students at each proficiency level should be able to perform the following tasks.

Reading/Writing

Early Beginner/Beginner Locate specific words on the lesson pages. Write the correct term to complete sentences about viruses, bacteria, protists, and fungi.

Early Intermediate Read to find references to viruses, bacteria, protists, or fungi. Write short phrases to describe the relationship between a virus and a host.

Intermediate Comprehend written instructions to complete each activity. Use basic but complete sentences in written descriptions of algae, fungi, and lichens.

Advanced/Transitioning Read aloud complete sentences that describe viruses, bacteria, protists, and fungi. Write complex sentences describing similarities and differences among viruses, bacteria, protists, fungi, decomposers, and parasites.

⟳ Assess Understanding

Your Turn

Model Have volunteers describe what is shown in each picture, without using any lesson terms or revealing which term they think the picture represents. Invite other students to add additional details to each description.

Talk and Write About It

On Their Own Encourage student groups to talk about their own experiences with the things shown in the pictures. For example, *Which of these organisms causes colds and flu?* (viruses) *Do you know which kind of organism helps make yogurt?* (bacteria) *Which kind can you sometimes find growing on the ground?* (fungi)

Produce Language

On Their Own First have students write their response. Then have students discuss their answers in pairs. Finally, lead a discussion with the whole class to address the Big Question, *How are living things alike, yet different?*

Wrap Up

Table Talk Have students reflect on what they learned. Encourage students to build fluency by reading their writing in groups or to the class.

✔ **Heard** statements about viruses, bacteria, protists, and fungi

✔ **Spoken** comparisons of viruses, bacteria, protists, and fungi

✔ **Written** statements about the similarities and differences among viruses, bacteria, protists, and fungi

Lesson 15

Plots

Vocabulary chloroplasts, chlorophyll, flower, cone, pollen, pollination, gymnosperms, angiosperms, seeds, phloem, xylem, vascular tissue

Materials index cards, photos of different types of plants

 Science Background

- Nearly all plants are autotrophs (make their own food) and are made of many cells surrounded by cell walls.

- Vascular plants have vascular tissue called *xylem* and *phloem*. This tissue gives the plant its structure, and allows for the transport of food, water, and nutrients.

- Angiosperms and gymnosperms are seed plants. Most gymnosperms have cones in which seeds form. Flowers are the reproductive structures of angiosperms.

Plants

 Big Question What are some characteristics of plants?

You will . . .
- Compare and contrast different types of plants.
- Describe plant structures.
- Understand and use key terms related to plants.

Talk About It

Work with a partner to answer the questions about the pictures.

1. What is happening in this picture?

2. What will happen next in this picture?

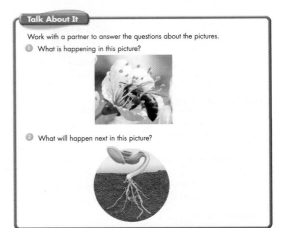

Predict
Look at the Big Question and the "You will . . ." statements at the top of the page. Describe what you think you are going to learn in this lesson.

  I think I am going to learn about . . .

Frontload the Lesson

What are some characteristics of plants?

Talk About It

Build Background To help students answer the first question, point out the bee and ask students what bees carry from one flower to another.

Content and Language

Predict

Model Read the Big Question and the objectives aloud. As students repeat after you, help them with pronunciation.

Guide Discussion Ask students to relate the Talk About It activity on this page to what they will learn.

Leveled Instruction

Early Beginner/Beginner Post a photo or diagram of an angiosperm and a gymnosperm. Give students words on index cards to label basic parts of these plants, such as *stem, leaf,* and so on. As you go through the lesson, have students write key vocabulary terms on index cards to further label the plants.

Early Intermediate/Intermediate Have students identify plants that they are familiar with and categorize them as angiosperms or gymnosperms. Have them create or bring in visuals to display in the classroom.

Advanced/Transitioning Have students create a presentation for their classmates on how plants reproduce. They might choose to do a poster or slide show. Encourage them to use as many key terms as they can.

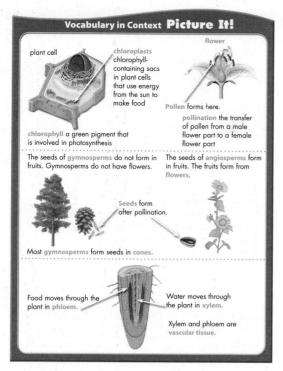

plant cell

chloroplasts chlorophyll-containing sacs in plant cells that use energy from the sun to make food

flower

Pollen forms here.

pollination the transfer of pollen from a male flower part to a female flower part

chlorophyll a green pigment that is involved in photosynthesis

The seeds of gymnosperms do not form in fruits. Gymnosperms do not have flowers.

The seeds of angiosperms form in fruits. The fruits form from flowers.

Seeds form after pollination.

Most gymnosperms form seeds in cones.

Food moves through the plant in phloem.

Water moves through the plant in xylem.

Xylem and phloem are vascular tissue.

Your Turn
Talk to a partner about how plants reproduce. Use as many vocabulary terms as you can.

Academic Vocabulary

- The prefix *chloro-* means "green." *Chloroplasts* are the green cellular structures in which photosynthesis occurs. And *chlorophyll* is the green pigment that gives chloroplasts their color.

- Cognates are words that have the same or similar roots and meanings in two languages. Have students share any vocabulary terms they recognize as cognates to words in their first languages. Most of the terms in this lesson have cognates in Spanish. For example, *polen* is the Spanish word for *pollen*, and *polinización* means *pollination*.

- Students may benefit from a review of the academic term *characteristics*, explained in Lesson 2. Encourage a discussion of the characteristics of genres (or types) of movies, games, or music. Offer a sentence starter, such as, *Some characteristics of classical music are . . .*

↻ Comprehensible Input

Vocabulary in Context: Picture It!

1. **Say the Term** Say each term slowly, artificially stressing each syllable. Have students repeat. Then say the term more naturally and have students repeat.

2. **Introduce Word Meaning** Connect each term to the visual that illustrates it.

3. **Demonstrate** Use gestures and visuals to demonstrate each term.

4. **Apply** After all of the terms have been discussed, have students demonstrate understanding with Talk About It.

Talk About It

Guide Discussion Before students start their independent discussion, check for understanding with the following sentence starters.

1. *Plants that have flowers are called . . .* (angiosperms.)

2. *A plant that forms seeds in cones is a . . .* (gymnosperm.)

3. *The movement of pollen from the male part of a flower to the female part is called . . .* (pollination.)

4. *Plants make food inside structures called . . .* (chloroplasts.)

5. *Chloroplasts are green because they contain . . .* (chlorophyll.)

6. *Vascular tissue that transports food through a plant is . . .* (phloem.)

R T I Response to Intervention

If students have difficulty pronouncing the words *xylem* and *phloem* . . .

Then tell them that *xylem* sounds like it starts with *z* and *phloem* sounds like it starts with *f*. Give examples of other words with similar spelling and pronunciation, such as *xylophone*.

Your Turn

Guide Discussion Draw or display pictures on the board for students to use in their descriptions. Be sure to include both angiosperms and gymnosperms.

Plants

 # Language Production

Do You Understand?

Comprehension Support Remind students that both these illustrations appear in Picture It.

Model Model the process of answering the questions by partially completing the questions about the pine cone. For example, say: *I know that this picture shows a cone because the same picture is in Picture It.*

Talk About It

Guide Discussion Have students work in pairs to complete the sentences. If students have difficulty distinguishing between gymnosperms and angiosperms, refer them to Picture It.

Your Turn

Guide Discussion Listen to student discussions as they compare cones and flowers. Help them correct any mistakes or misunderstandings as needed.

A Closer Look

On Their Own Have students work in pairs to complete this word study activity. Have students give a definition for *germination* in their own words.

Do You Understand?

Look at the pictures. Then answer the questions.

What is this? <u>cone</u>	What is this? <u>flower</u>
What does it do? <u>produce seeds</u>	What does it do? <u>produce seeds in fruits</u>
What kind of plant is it found on? <u>gymnosperm</u>	What kind of plant is it found on? <u>angiosperm</u>

Talk About It
Complete the sentences.

1. A plant that produces flowers is called a(n) . . . angiosperm.
2. In plants, male reproductive cells are carried to female cells in . . . pollen.
3. The plant structure that will grow into a new plant is the . . . seed.
4. A plant that has seeds but not flowers is called a(n) . . . gymnosperm.

Your Turn
Talk to a partner about cones and flowers. How are they similar? How are they different?

> **A Closer Look**
>
> **Related Words** *Pollen, pollination,* and *pollinator* are all related words. *Pollen* is a powdery material that carries male sex cells in plants. *Pollination* is the act of moving pollen from the male part of a flower to the female part of a flower. A *pollinator* is the thing that moves the pollen. Look at the related words below. What do you think *germination* means? Fill in your definition.
>
> germinate: to begin to grow
> germination: <u>the act of beginning to grow</u>

Leveled Language Proficiency

Students at each proficiency level should be able to perform the following tasks.

Listening/Speaking

Early Beginner/Beginner Point to the correct term or plant structure in response to questions. Say aloud key terms about plant characteristics, using appropriate pronunciation, with assistance.

Early Intermediate Follow oral instructions to identify different terms or plant parts represented on the diagram. Use simple spoken sentences to describe the cone and flower parts of plants.

Intermediate Summarize oral descriptions of the relationship between plant parts or processes in their own words. Use complete spoken sentences to compare terms such as *xylem* and *phloem, angiosperms* and *gymnosperms.*

Advanced/Transitioning Restate or paraphrase complex oral explanations to show understanding. Give a clear oral description of the similarities and differences between an angiosperm and a gymnosperm.

Your Turn

Draw a line to connect each picture with the term that it *best* matches.

seed

chloroplast

angiosperm

gymnosperm

Talk and Write About It

Complete the statements about plants.

1. The main difference between angiosperms and gymnosperms is <u>angiosperms have flowers but gymnosperms do not</u>.
2. The main difference between xylem and phloem is <u>water flows through the xylem, while food is conducted through the phloem</u>.
3. Chlorophyll is found in <u>chloroplasts in plant cells</u>.
4. Pollination occurs when <u>pollen is carried from a male flower part to a female flower part</u>.

Produce Language

Write about some characteristics of plants.

_____

_____

_____

_____

_____

Leveled Language Proficiency

Students at each proficiency level should be able to perform the following tasks.

Reading/Writing

Early Beginner/Beginner Choose the correct term for the corresponding images. Answer questions about plants by writing the correct term.

Early Intermediate Read through the lesson to find references to a particular term. Write short phrases about plant structures or types of plants.

Intermediate Summarize to demonstrate comprehension of simple text about different types of plants and their structures. Write a brief definition of each term.

Advanced/Transitioning Understand grade-level textbook descriptions of the functions of plant structures and the similarities and differences between angiosperms and gymnosperms. Write complete sentences using two or more vocabulary terms.

Assess Understanding

Your Turn

Model As you review this activity, encourage student volunteers to use a complete sentence to describe each word-picture pair. Sentences may be simple or complex, depending on the language level of the particular volunteer.

Talk and Write About It

On Their Own Encourage students to use the pictures from Your Turn to help them answer the questions. Ask, *What does the picture show? Why is it an example of . . . ?*

Produce Language

On Their Own Have a student volunteer re-read the Big Question. Give students time to write, and then have them share their work with a partner. Then have volunteers read their responses to the class.

Wrap Up

Table Talk Have students reflect on what they learned. Encourage students to build fluency by reading their writing in groups or to the class.

✔ **Learned** and applied vocabulary related to plants

✔ **Heard** statements about the functions of different plant structures

✔ **Written** statements about angiosperms and gymnosperms

Animals

Vocabulary radial symmetry, bilateral symmetry, exoskeleton, endoskeleton, ectotherm, endotherm, external fertilization, internal fertilization, amniotic egg, complete metamorphosis, incomplete metamorphosis, mammary gland

Materials photos of various animals

Science Background

- Animals can be radially symmetrical, like a sea star. Most animals are bilaterally symmetrical, meaning that two mirror images can be created by dividing the body in half.

- External fertilization occurs outside the female's body, and internal fertilization occurs inside the female's body.

- Some animals undergo metamorphosis, which involves significant changes in form during the life cycle.

Frontload the Lesson

 What are the characteristics of animals?

Talk About It

Build Background Give students time to think about the characteristics of each animal. Then have them share with a partner and compare the animals. Ask students: *If the bird or fish caught a worm or insect, is what they caught an animal?* (yes) Be sure students understand that worms and insects are examples of animals.

Content and Language

Predict

Model Read the Big Question and the objectives aloud. Encourage students to explain the objectives in their own words.

Guide Discussion Ask students to discuss how animals are different from other life forms, such as plants.

Animals

Big Question What are the characteristics of animals?

You will . . .
- Compare and contrast different types of animals.
- Identify characteristics of animals.
- Use terms that describe animals.

Talk About It

Look at the pictures of animals below. Then answer the questions.

1. What do you know about each animal?
2. How would you describe the size and shape of each animal?
3. In what ways are two or more of the animals alike? In what ways are two or more of the animals different?

Predict

Look at the Big Question and the "You will . . ." statements at the top of the page. Describe what you think you are going to learn in this lesson.

I think I am going to learn about . . .

Leveled Instruction

Early Beginner/Beginner Help students connect to the material by asking them to draw two different animals in their notebooks. As you describe characteristics of animals, point to individual student drawings and say *yes* if the animal drawn exhibits that characteristic and *no* if it does not.

Early Intermediate/Intermediate Remind students that humans are animals, too. Have them work in pairs to discuss which characteristics apply to humans. Offer them questions to guide their discussion, such as *Do humans have a hard skeleton on the outside (exoskeleton)?*

Advanced/Transitioning Have students create animal profile posters, choosing a variety of both invertebrates and vertebrates. The posters should depict the animals' types of symmetry and skeleton. Encourage students to identify additional characteristics to include in their work. Hang their posters in the classroom for the duration of the lesson.

Academic Vocabulary

- Write the following list of prefixes and their meanings. Then have students discuss how they can use the prefix meanings to help them understand some of the vocabulary terms.

  bi- means "two"
  ex-, exo-, and *ecto-* mean "outside"
  endo- means "inside"
  in- can mean "inside" or "not"
  a- means "not"

- Write the terms *mammary gland* and *mammal* on the board. Point out the similarity between the terms. Explain that only mammals have mammary glands. Have students list some examples of mammals and nonmammals.

- Write the terms *ectotherm* and *endotherm* on the board. Point out that ectotherms are sometimes called "cold-blooded" and endotherms are sometimes called "warm-blooded." Emphasize that the terms *cold-blooded* and *warm-blooded* are misleading, because the temperature of an ectotherm's blood is warm if the external environment is warm.

- Students may have difficulty pronouncing *symmetry*. Point out the correct pronunciation, in each syllable, of the letter *y*. Explain that neither *sym-* nor *-try* are pronounced with a long *i* sound, like *try* or *I*. Instead, *y* makes the short *i* sound, as in *syllable* or *crystal,* and the long *e* sound as in *pretty*.

Comprehensible Input

Vocabulary in Context: Picture It!

1. **Say the Term** Say each term slowly, artificially stressing each syllable. Have students repeat. Then say the term more naturally and have students repeat.

2. **Introduce Word Meaning** Connect each term to the visual that illustrates it.

3. **Demonstrate** Use gestures and visuals to demonstrate each term.

4. **Apply** After each term has been discussed, have students demonstrate understanding with Talk About It.

Talk About It

Guide Discussion Before students start their independent discussion, check for understanding with the following sentence starters:

1. *An egg is fertilized inside the body during . . .* (internal fertilization.)

2. *An egg is fertilized outside the body during . . .* (external fertilization.)

3. *A skeleton on the outside of a body is a(n) . . .* (exoskeleton.)

4. *A skeleton inside a body is a(n) . . .* (endoskeleton.)

5. *An egg with a shell and membranes is called a(n) . . .* (amniotic egg.)

6. *Mother animals that feed their young with milk have . . .* (mammary glands.)

RTI Response to Intervention

If students have difficulty with the term *metamorphosis* . . .

Then break the word into its syllables, pronounce each syllable separately, and combine the syllables. Also, point out that the letters *ph* make the /f/ sound, as in *phone* and *photo*.

Your Turn

Guide Discussion Provide students with photos of animals or animal magazines so they can find examples of animals that illustrate the characteristics shown in the Picture It box.

Animals

↻ Language Production

Do You Understand?

Comprehension Support Before students start the activity, remind them that *exo-* means "outside" and *endo-* means "inside."

Model Demonstrate how students can ask themselves questions to help them do the activity. Say, *Does this animal have bones inside its body or does it have a hard outer skeleton?*

Talk About It

Guide Discussion Read the sentence starters aloud with students. Have students describe the animals from Do You Understand? with a partner before writing their responses.

Your Turn

Guide Discussion Listen to and encourage student discussions. Clarify misunderstandings as they arise. Ask student volunteers to share their responses, and use them to create a class list. Sample animals with exoskeletons: spiders, insects, and ticks. All vertebrates have endoskeletons.

In Other Words

Model Read the example sentence aloud for students and have them repeat it. Then ask, *What is another way to say this? What is another word, or words, for the verb* to regulate? Have students take turns reading the sentence aloud, choosing one of the yellow-highlighted words to fill in the space each time. Then have students suggest their own sentences that use forms of the verbs *to regulate, to control,* and *to adjust.*

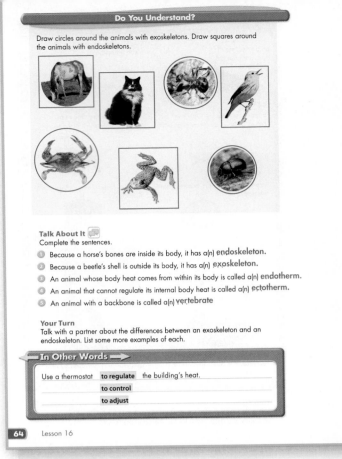

Do You Understand?

Draw circles around the animals with exoskeletons. Draw squares around the animals with endoskeletons.

Talk About It 💬
Complete the sentences.
① Because a horse's bones are inside its body, it has a(n) endoskeleton.
② Because a beetle's shell is outside its body, it has a(n) exoskeleton.
③ An animal whose body heat comes from within its body is called a(n) endotherm.
④ An animal that cannot regulate its internal body heat is called a(n) ectotherm.
⑤ An animal with a backbone is called a(n) vertebrate

Your Turn
Talk with a partner about the differences between an exoskeleton and an endoskeleton. List some more examples of each.

In Other Words ➡

Use a thermostat	to regulate	the building's heat.
	to control	
	to adjust	

64 | Lesson 16

Leveled Language Proficiency

Students at each proficiency level should be able to perform the following tasks.

Listening/Speaking

Early Beginner/Beginner Follow simple oral directions, such as *draw a circle* or *draw a square*. Request clarification of key concepts with words and short phrases.

Early Intermediate Demonstrate comprehension of oral questions about animals by giving simple responses. Orally list animals with an exoskeleton or endoskeleton.

Intermediate Identify the main points of an oral discussion about characteristics of animals. Orally describe the difference between complete and incomplete metamorphosis.

Advanced/Transitioning Follow multiple-step oral directions. Orally rephrase ideas and thoughts to explain the characteristics of different types of animals.

Your Turn
Draw a line to connect each term to the animal that has that characteristic.

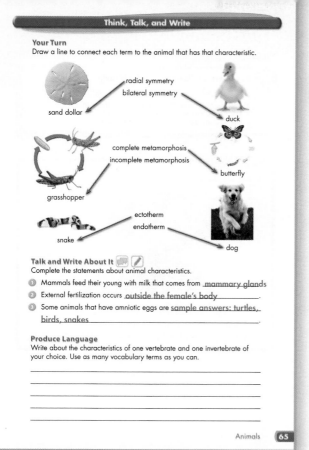

Talk and Write About It

Complete the statements about animal characteristics.

1. Mammals feed their young with milk that comes from <u>mammary glands</u>
2. External fertilization occurs <u>outside the female's body</u>.
3. Some animals that have amniotic eggs are <u>sample answers: turtles,</u>
   <u>birds, snakes</u>.

Produce Language
Write about the characteristics of one vertebrate and one invertebrate of your choice. Use as many vocabulary terms as you can.

_____
_____
_____
_____
_____

Leveled Language Proficiency

Students at each proficiency level should be able to perform the following tasks.

Reading/Writing

Early Beginner/Beginner Use reading strategies, such as rereading or asking questions, to comprehend printed sentences about an animal. Create an illustrated book describing characteristics of an animal.

Early Intermediate Follow simple print directions to complete an activity. Write complete sentences to restate key concepts.

Intermediate Independently read and comprehend questions about radial and bilateral symmetry. Respond in writing to such questions.

Advanced/Transitioning Use knowledge of word parts to determine the meaning of unfamiliar words encountered in reading. Summarize in writing the key points of a classroom discussion about several examples of animal characteristics.

↻ Assess Understanding

Your Turn

Model Read directions and terms with students. Help struggling students by asking questions, such as *Does a duck have radial symmetry or bilateral symmetry?* or *Is a dog's body temperature determined by the temperature outside its body?*

Talk and Write About It

On Their Own Before students begin writing, review the key terms in Picture It. Define the terms and give examples orally or with pictures.

Produce Language

On Their Own As a class, choose a vertebrate and an invertebrate, and model writing a description of those animals on the board. Then ask students to choose other animals (not the models) to describe. Leave your models up for students' reference as they write.

Wrap Up

Table Talk Have students reflect on the Big Question and what they learned. Encourage students to build fluency by reading their writing in groups or to the class.

✔ **Learned** and applied vocabulary related to animal characteristics

✔ **Spoken** statements about differences between animals

✔ **Written** statements describing the characteristics of an animal

Lesson 17

The Human Body

Vocabulary homeostasis, gland, stimulus, response, muscle tissue, nervous tissue, connective tissue, epithelial tissue

Science Background

- The levels of organization in the human body consist of cells, tissues, organs, and organ systems.

- All of the body systems work together to maintain homeostasis and keep the body in balance.

- Muscles are made of muscle tissue. Nervous tissue makes up the brain and other related body structures. Connective tissue makes up bones, fat, and other body parts. Epithelial tissue makes up skin as well as the internal surfaces of the digestive system.

- Glands are part of the endocrine system, which uses chemical signals called *hormones* to help control body functions.

Frontload the Lesson

How does your body work?

Talk About It

Build Background Call on volunteers to talk about the last time they did any sort of exercise and how their body reacted. Have them relate the experience to the picture.

Content and Language

Predict

Model Read the Big Question and the objectives aloud. Have students repeat after you. Encourage students to ask questions about the objectives.

Guide Discussion Have students use the lesson title and the Big Question as they make their predictions.

Big Question How does your body work?

You will . . .
- Describe how the conditions in your body stay stable.
- Learn about four types of tissue found in the body.
- Use new vocabulary terms to describe how your body works.

Talk About It

Look at the picture below.

1. What is this person doing?
2. Why do you think the person is doing these things?
3. What do you think will be the effects of the person's actions?

Predict

Look at the Big Question and the "You will . . ." statements at the top of the page. Describe what you think you are going to learn in this lesson.

I think I am going to learn about . . .

66   Lesson 17

Leveled Instruction

Early Beginner/Beginner Provide extra visual support to help students identify the body's different organ systems. On a piece of chart paper, draw each system and write words related to that system's functions. Leave these visuals up throughout the lesson.

Early Intermediate/Intermediate Ask students to connect the lesson to their own experiences. Have them work in groups to list different stimuli and responses that they have noticed taking place in their bodies. Have them share their responses with the class.

Advanced/Transitioning Encourage students to find out more about what happens when the body's systems are *not* in balance. Have students research a specific body system and explain what can happen when an organ within that system does not function properly. Ask them to share their research findings with the class.

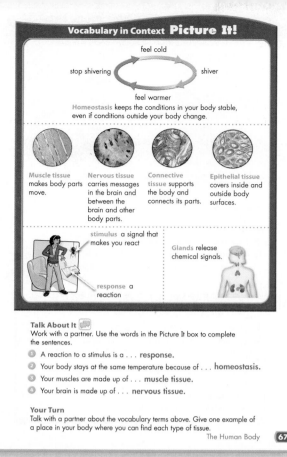

Vocabulary in Context **Picture It!**

feel cold

stop shivering ← → shiver

feel warmer

Homeostasis keeps the conditions in your body stable, even if conditions outside your body change.

Muscle tissue makes body parts move.

Nervous tissue carries messages in the brain and between the brain and other body parts.

Connective tissue supports the body and connects its parts.

Epithelial tissue covers inside and outside body surfaces.

stimulus a signal that makes you react

Glands release chemical signals.

response a reaction

Talk About It

Work with a partner. Use the words in the Picture It box to complete the sentences.

1. A reaction to a stimulus is a . . . **response.**
2. Your body stays at the same temperature because of . . . **homeostasis.**
3. Your muscles are made up of . . . **muscle tissue.**
4. Your brain is made up of . . . **nervous tissue.**

Your Turn

Talk with a partner about the vocabulary terms above. Give one example of a place in your body where you can find each type of tissue.

The Human Body **67**

Academic Vocabulary

- Cognates are words that have the same or similar roots and meanings in two languages. Have students share any vocabulary terms they recognize as cognates to words in their first language. Most of the terms in this lesson have cognates in Spanish. For example *stimulus* is *estímulo* and *gland* is *glándula*.

- Students may be familiar with the word *response* as a synonym of *answer*. Explain that a question is a kind of stimulus, and an answer is a response to that stimulus.

- Note that *response* has a Spanish cognate, *respuesta*. The word *respuesta* also means "answer."

↻ Comprehensible Input

Vocabulary in Context: Picture It!

1. **Say the Term** Say each term slowly, artificially stressing each syllable. Have students repeat. Then say the term more naturally and have students repeat.

2. **Introduce Word Meaning** Connect each term to the visual that illustrates it.

3. **Demonstrate** Use gestures and visuals to demonstrate each term. For example:

   - When students do not expect it, drop a book on the floor. Have them notice their *response* and point out that the dropping of the book was the *stimulus*.

   - Point to your muscles, your head, and your skin. Say, *My muscles are made up of* muscle tissue. *My brain contains* nervous tissue. *My skin is made up of* epithelial tissue. Draw a bone and say, *Bones and fat are made up of* connective tissue.

4. **Apply** After all of the terms have been discussed, have students demonstrate understanding with Talk About It.

Talk About It

Guide Discussion Ask students to look back at the terms in the Picture It box. Tell them to use one of these terms to finish each sentence.

RTI Response to Intervention

If students have difficulty with the spelling or pronunciation of the word *nervous* . . .

Then point out that the *-ous* word ending is usually pronounced like *-us*.

Your Turn

Guide Discussion Encourage students to use complete sentences. Offer sentence frames, such as, *Epithelial tissue can be found in* . . .

↻ Language Production

Do You Understand?

Comprehension Support Start by asking students to describe what they see in the diagram. Say, *What does the blue color of the arrow represent? (cold, cooling) What does the red color represent? (warmth, heating)* Make sure that students understand the term "maintain homeostasis." If necessary, review Lesson 2, where the term is introduced.

Model Prompt students to name and write each step of the cycle. Say, *First the mouse feels cold. What happens next?* Continue for the remaining steps.

Talk About It

Guide Discussion Read the statements aloud with students as they work together to complete each one. Remind students to use the Picture It box for help if they need it.

Your Turn

Guide Discussion Review the meanings of the words with students by having them find and read the terms and related sentences in the Picture It box. You may want to provide sentence starters, such as, *When the mouse gets frightened, the nervous tissue in its brain . . .*, before students begin their discussions.

A Closer Look

On Their Own Have students work in pairs to complete this word-study activity. Have them choose one of the two words and provide an additional example, scientific or not. Their partner can listen to the example and determine which meaning the students are using.

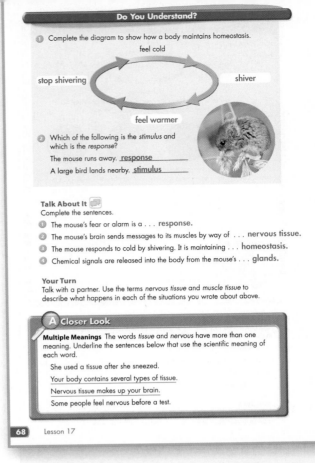

Do You Understand?

1. Complete the diagram to show how a body maintains homeostasis.

feel cold

stop shivering

shiver

feel warmer

2. Which of the following is the *stimulus* and which is the *response*?
The mouse runs away. __response__
A large bird lands nearby. __stimulus__

Talk About It
Complete the sentences.

1. The mouse's fear or alarm is a . . . **response**.
2. The mouse's brain sends messages to its muscles by way of . . . **nervous tissue**.
3. The mouse responds to cold by shivering. It is maintaining . . . **homeostasis**.
4. Chemical signals are released into the body from the mouse's . . . **glands**.

Your Turn
Talk with a partner. Use the terms *nervous tissue* and *muscle tissue* to describe what happens in each of the situations you wrote about above.

A Closer Look

Multiple Meanings The words *tissue* and *nervous* have more than one meaning. Underline the sentences below that use the scientific meaning of each word.

She used a tissue after she sneezed.
Your body contains several types of tissue.
Nervous tissue makes up your brain.
Some people feel nervous before a test.

68   Lesson 17

Leveled Language Proficiency

Students at each proficiency level should be able to perform the following tasks.

Listening/Speaking

Early Beginner/Beginner Point to corresponding images after hearing key terms spoken aloud. Describe *homeostasis* with gestures and short phrases.

Early Intermediate Follow oral instructions with some repetition. Respond to questions about how the body works with simple sentences.

Intermediate Follow oral directions with little to no help. Use complete sentences to describe how the body works.

Advanced/Transitioning Follow oral directions independently. Explain, using complete and complex sentences, what types of tissue are found in the human body, and what the functions of each type are.

Your Turn

Look at the different types of tissue found in the body. Then fill in the chart.

Type of tissue	One place it is found in the body	What it does to help the body
muscle tissue	muscles	move
nervous tissue	sample: brain	direct and control body processes
connective tissue	sample: bones	gives your body support
epithelial tissue	sample: skin	protects your body

Talk and Write About It

Complete the statements about how the body works.

1. Muscle tissue helps _your body move_ .
2. Bones and fat are examples of _connective tissue_ .
3. Nervous tissue carries messages from the brain to _____
   other parts of the body .

Produce Language

Write three sentences describing how your body works. Use as many vocabulary terms as you can.

_____
_____
_____
_____

The Human Body **69**

Leveled Language Proficiency

Students at each proficiency level should be able to perform the following tasks.

Reading/Writing

Early Beginner/Beginner Choose the correct term from a list of different types of body tissue. Correctly label illustrations of key terms.

Early Intermediate Match short phrases about the body with the correct vocabulary term. Write short phrases to describe body processes and functions.

Intermediate Compare written responses to questions about how the body works. Write about homeostasis using concrete examples from experience.

Advanced/Transitioning Read paragraphs that describe body systems and how they function together. Write a summary of how different systems help the body work.

↻ Assess Understanding

Your Turn

Model Review how each type of tissue helps the body work before students begin. You may wish to write out the correct responses in random order on the board and have students use them to complete the chart in the appropriate order.

Talk and Write About It

On Their Own Have students read the statements with a partner and then work individually to complete them. Have pairs compare their work when finished and discuss differences in their responses to arrive at a correct answer.

Produce Language

On Their Own After students write their answers, have them compare their descriptions in pairs. Then, lead a discussion to address the Big Question, *How does your body work?*

Wrap Up

Table Talk Have students reflect on what they learned. Encourage students to build fluency by reading their writing in groups or to the class.

✔ **Learned** about how the body and how it functions

✔ **Read** questions and sentences about the human body

✔ **Heard** explanations of homeostasis, stimuli and responses, and body tissues

Bones, Muscles, and Skin

Vocabulary skeleton, vertebrae, joint, ligament, tendon, skeletal muscle, smooth muscle, cardiac muscle, striated muscle, epidermis, dermis, pore, hair follicle

Science Background

- The skeleton has five major functions. It provides shape and support, enables movement, and protects internal organs. It also produces blood cells and stores minerals and other materials.

- The body contains three types of muscle: skeletal, smooth, and cardiac.

- Skeletal muscles work in pairs to move bones.

- The skin has two main layers, the epidermis and the dermis.

 Frontload the Lesson

 What are the structures and functions of bones, muscles, and skin?

Talk About It

Build Background After students complete the activity, have students share the words they came up with. Record their words on the board in columns under the headings: *Bones, Muscles, Skin*.

 Content and Language

Predict

Model Read the objectives and the Big Question aloud. As students repeat after you, correct any mispronunciations that students are making.

Guide Discussion Help students use the Big Question to infer what they will learn.

Bones, Muscles, and Skin

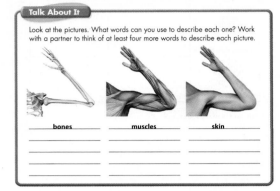

Big Question What are the structures and functions of bones, muscles, and skin?

You will . . .
- Locate where bones, muscles, and skin are in the body.
- Identify the three types of muscle tissue.
- Use new vocabulary words related to bones, muscles, and skin.

Talk About It

Look at the pictures. What words can you use to describe each one? Work with a partner to think of at least four more words to describe each picture.

bones _____

muscles _____

skin _____

Predict

Look at the Big Question and the "You will . . ." statements at the top of the page. Describe what you think you are going to learn in this lesson.

I think I am going to learn about . . .

Leveled Instruction

Early Beginner/Beginner Ask students to point to an image that shows bones. Then have them point to images that represent muscles and skin. As they point, have students repeat each word: *bones, muscles, skin.*

Early Intermediate Have students read aloud words that describe pictures of bones, muscle, or skin.

Intermediate Ask simple questions about the bones, muscles, and skin. Expect students to provide answers in phrases or complete sentences.

Advanced/Transitioning Partner these students with beginning students. Have them share simple descriptions of bone, muscles, and skin, explaining any words that are unfamiliar to beginning students.

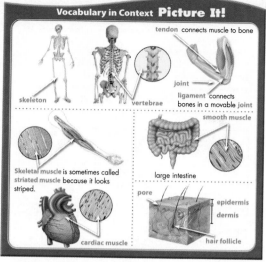

Vocabulary in Context **Picture It!**

tendon connects muscle to bone

joint

ligament connects bones in a movable joint

skeleton

vertebrae

smooth muscle

large intestine

Skeletal muscle is sometimes called striated muscle because it looks striped.

pore

epidermis

dermis

cardiac muscle

hair follicle

Talk About It

Work with a partner. Use the words in the Picture It box to finish the sentences.

1 Your heart is made of a type of muscle called . . . cardiac muscle.
2 The insides of your stomach and intestines have a type of muscle called . . . smooth muscle.
3 The outer layer of your skin is the . . . epidermis.
4 The bones in your joints are held together by . . . ligaments.
5 Your backbone is made up of small bones called . . . vertebrae.
6 All the bones in your body are part of your . . . skeleton.

Your Turn

With a partner, talk about some of the things bones, muscles, or skin do for your body each day. Use the vocabulary words from the Picture It box.

Bones, Muscles, and Skin **71**

Academic Vocabulary

- Write *pore* and *pour* on the board, explaining that they are homophones: words that sound the same but have different spellings and meanings. Pronounce the words and ask students to repeat. Have students identify the word that refers to an opening in the skin. Ask students if they can define the other word. They might also list rhyming words, such as *store, your,* and *floor.*

- Write the term *vertebrae* on the board and have a volunteer draw a backbone showing individual vertebrae. Then cover up or erase the *e* and pronounce *vertebra.* Ask a new volunteer to circle one vertebra. Review the terms *vertebrate* and *invertebrate* from the Animals lesson, having students underline *vertebra* in each term.

- Write *skeletal muscle* on the board, circling the *sk* and *sc* letter combinations. Say the term slowly, pointing out the silent *c.* Check for pronunciation as students point to the term in the Picture It box and read it aloud.

- Most of the terms in this lesson have cognates in Spanish. Have students share any vocabulary terms they recognize as cognates to words in their first languages.

Comprehensible Input

Vocabulary in Context: Picture It!

1. **Say the Term** Say each term slowly, artificially stressing each syllable. Have students repeat. Then say the term more naturally and have students repeat.

2. **Introduce Word Meaning** Connect each term to the visual that illustrates it.

3. **Demonstrate** Use gestures and visuals to demonstrate. For example:

   - Hold out your arm. Ask students which type of muscle you are using. Repeat the term: *skeletal muscle.*

   - Use your palm to pat a heartbeat on your chest. Ask students which type of muscle the heart is made of. Repeat the term: *cardiac muscle.*

   - Have students repeat after you, as you say the three types of muscles: *skeletal muscle, cardiac muscle,* and *smooth muscle.*

4. **Apply** After all of the terms have been discussed, have students demonstrate understanding with Talk About It.

Talk About It

Guide Discussion First challenge students to complete as many sentences as they can without looking back at other images or activities. Then allow them to consult other pages to complete the remaining sentences.

RTI Response to Intervention

If students have difficulty putting emphasis on the correct syllable of each word . . .

Then point out that almost all of the terms in this lesson are pronounced with emphasis on the first syllable. The only exception is *epidermis.* As you say the words, have students repeat them chorally. Challenge them to find the exception.

Your Turn

Guide Discussion Encourage students to quiz each other, asking, *Where in your body is _____ found?*

Bones, Muscles, and Skin

↻ Language Production

Do You Understand?

Comprehension Support Before students start the activity, have them review the vocabulary terms for this lesson. Explain that each clue is a phrase that describes bones, muscles, or skin. Read through the clues with students. Ask them if they understand each clue. If not, answer any questions to make sure that all students understand the clues. Pick a number to do as an example with the class. Then have pairs continue on their own, guiding them as needed.

Model Demonstrate how students can make sentences out of each clue to help them do the activity. For example, the clue *"has pores and hair follicles"* can be turned into the sentence *"Skin has pores and hair follicles."*

Talk About It

Guide Discussion Read the sentences aloud with students as they work together to complete the items.

Your Turn

Guide Discussion Listen to student discussions as they compare their answers. Help them correct any mistakes or misunderstandings as needed.

A Closer Look

On Their Own Have students work in pairs to complete this word study activity. Ask if they can think of any other words that form uncommon plurals. List these in singular and plural form on the board.

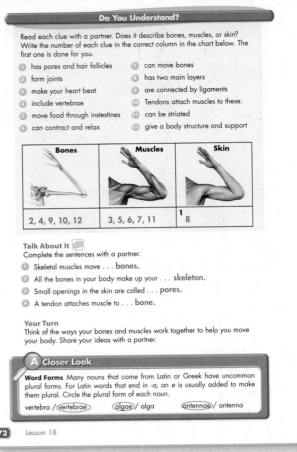

Do You Understand?

Read each clue with a partner. Does it describe bones, muscles, or skin? Write the number of each clue in the correct column in the chart below. The first one is done for you.

1. has pores and hair follicles
2. form joints
3. make your heart beat
4. include vertebrae
5. move food through instestines
6. can contract and relax
7. can move bones
8. has two main layers
9. are connected by ligaments
10. Tendons attach muscles to these.
11. can be striated
12. give a body structure and support

Bones	Muscles	Skin
2, 4, 9, 10, 12	3, 5, 6, 7, 11	1, 8

Talk About It 💬
Complete the sentences with a partner.
1. Skeletal muscles move . . . bones.
2. All the bones in your body make up your . . . skeleton.
3. Small openings in the skin are called . . . pores.
4. A tendon attaches muscle to . . . bone.

Your Turn
Think of the ways your bones and muscles work together to help you move your body. Share your ideas with a partner.

🔍 A Closer Look

Word Forms Many nouns that come from Latin or Greek have uncommon plural forms. For Latin words that end in -a, an e is usually added to make them plural. Circle the plural form of each noun.

vertebra / (vertebrae)   (algae) / alga   (antennae) / antenna

72 | Lesson 18

Leveled Language Proficiency

Students at each proficiency level should be able to perform the following tasks.

Listening/Speaking

Early Beginner/Beginner Demonstrate, by pointing or gestures, concepts heard in speech. Respond aloud to discussion questions about bones, muscles, and skin.

Early Intermediate Follow oral instructions to identify different parts of body diagrams. Use lesson vocabulary terms in short spoken phrases or simple sentences.

Intermediate Respond to simple spoken questions about body structures. Use complete spoken sentences to describe the different structures of bones, muscles, and skin.

Advanced/Transitioning Participate in a discussion about body structures. Use compound and complex sentences to orally describe and explain the functions of bones, muscles, and skin.

Your Turn

Do each action by pointing to the place on the boy's body. Say aloud what you are doing.

1. Point to one of the joints in his body.
2. Point to the epidermis.
3. Point to a place on his body where there are ligaments.
4. Point to a place on his body where you would find cardiac muscle.
5. Point to a place on his body where you would find smooth muscle.
6. Point to a place on his body where you would find skeletal muscle.

Talk and Write About It

Complete the statements about bones, muscles, and skin.

1. The skeleton is made up of <u>bones</u>
2. The backbone is made up of small bones called <u>vertebrae</u>
3. Ligaments are found in a place where <u>two bones meet</u>.
4. Two examples of joints in the human skeleton are <u>sample answer: the knee and the elbow</u>
5. The two main layers of skin are called <u>the dermis and the epidermis</u>.

Produce Language

Describe some of the reasons you need bones, muscles, and skin, to help you survive. Write your description. Use as many vocabulary terms as you can.

_____
_____
_____
_____
_____

Bones, Muscles, and Skin **73**

Leveled Language Proficiency

Students at each proficiency level should be able to perform the following tasks.

Reading/Writing

Early Beginner/Beginner Find the correct term on a labeled drawing. Label a sketch with the correct names of the different structures of bones, muscles, and skin.

Early Intermediate Match short phrases with the correct vocabulary term. Write short phrases to describe the different structures of bones, muscles, and skin.

Intermediate Compare responses to questions about bones, muscles, and skin. Write a description of the different structures of bones, muscles, and skin.

Advanced/Transitioning Read aloud sentences that describe different body structures. Write a summary of the different structures of bones, muscles, and skin.

Assess Understanding

Your Turn

Model Encourage students to restate each action using first-person construction, rather than simply repeating the written words verbatim. For example, students could say, *I am pointing to the boy's epidermis.* Point out and encourage practice of different verb forms and language functions, such as the functions of asking, commanding, and describing.

Talk and Write About It

On Their Own Encourage student groups to talk about the structures and functions of bones, muscles, and skin.

Produce Language

On Their Own Have student pairs both write and talk about the three types of muscles. Then, lead a discussion to address the Big Question, *What are the structures and functions of bones, muscles, and skin?* If necessary, remind students of the meaning of the words *structures* (forms; shapes) and *functions* (jobs; tasks; purposes).

Wrap Up

Table Talk Have students reflect on what they learned. Encourage students to build fluency by reading their writing in groups or to the class.

✔ **Learned** and applied vocabulary related to bones, muscles, and skin

✔ **Read** statements about the structures and functions of bones, muscles, and skin

✔ **Heard** statements about the structures of bones, muscles, and skin

Digestion and Nutrition

Vocabulary epiglottis, esophagus, stomach, small intestine, liver, gallbladder, pancreas, large intestine, rectum, anus, digestion, absorption, villi, nutrient, enzyme

Materials poster diagram of the digestive system; pictures of foods from each food group; cutout sheets *Some Organs of the Digestive System* (Student Book, Resources section)

Science Background

- Food provides your body with materials to grow and repair tissues. It also provides energy for everything you do. People need six types of nutrients: carbohydrates, fats, proteins, vitamins, minerals, and water.

- The digestive system has three main functions: digestion, absorption, and elimination.

- Digestion is the physical breakdown of food into smaller chemical compounds that can be absorbed by the body.

↻ Frontload the Lesson

How is food broken down into materials your body can use?

Talk About It

Build Background Help students brainstorm some of the healthier snacks by asking, *What snack might a doctor, dentist, or nutritionist reccommend?*

↻ Content and Language

Predict

Model Read the Big Question and the objectives aloud. Model rephrasing the question as a statement that begins with the sentence starter.

Guide Discussion Encourage students to scan the title, headings, and pictures to make their predictions.

Big Question How is food broken down into materials your body can use?

You will . . .
- Explain how the body uses nutrients in food for energy.
- Identify the parts of the digestive system.
- Identify nutrients and other substances needed by the body.
- Use terms related to nutrition and digestion.

Talk About It

Think about some snacks that you enjoy. Draw a picture of one healthful snack and one snack that should be eaten only once in a while.

more healthful	less healthful

Talk about healthful snacks you can eat frequently and less healthful snacks that should be eaten only occasionally.

1. A healthful snack I like is . . .
2. You can eat this snack frequently because . . .
3. A less healthful snack is . . .
4. You should eat this snack only occasionally because . . .

Predict

Look at the Big Question and the "You will . . ." statements at the top of the page. Describe what you think you are going to learn in this lesson.

I think I am going to learn about . . .

74 Lesson 19

Leveled Instruction

Early Beginner/Beginner Offer beginners the option to draw pictures of familiar foods. Beginners can consult with more advanced students to label the drawings with vocabulary terms and everyday words in both English and the students' native language(s).

Early Intermediate Provide examples and then ask students to classify familiar foods as "more healthful" and "less healthful." Students should be able to say and write the names of familiar snacks.

Intermediate Encourage students to form sentences that compare, such as, *An apple is healthier than chips.*

Advanced/Transitioning Have groups of students use the internet to read nutrition labels. Then encourage them to explain the features, such as sugar, fat, and salt content, that make a food less healthful.

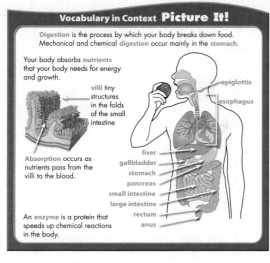

Vocabulary in Context **Picture It!**

Digestion is the process by which your body breaks down food. Mechanical and chemical **digestion** occur mainly in the **stomach**.

Your body absorbs **nutrients** that your body needs for energy and growth.

villi tiny structures in the folds of the small intestine

Absorption occurs as nutrients pass from the villi to the blood.

An **enzyme** is a protein that speeds up chemical reactions in the body.

epiglottis
esophagus
liver
gallbladder
stomach
pancreas
small intestine
large intestine
rectum
anus

Talk About It
Work with a partner. Use the words in the box above to complete the sentences.

1. Food is broken down during . . . **digestion.**
2. Nutrients move into your blood during . . . **absorption.**
3. The tube that joins your mouth and stomach is your . . . **esophagus.**
4. A protein that breaks down chemicals in food is called an . . . **enzyme.**
5. The flap of tissue that stops food from entering the lungs is the . . . **epiglottis.**
6. The pouch where mechanical and chemical digestion of food occurs is the . . . **stomach.**

Your Turn
Digestion and absorption help your body take in nutrients, such as carbohydrates, proteins, fats, vitamins, and minerals. With a partner, list some foods that contain each of these nutrients.

Digestion and Nutrition **75**

Academic Vocabulary

- Explain how the terms *nutrient* and *nutrition* are related. Tell students the words are both related to the energy and materials that food provide. List other related terms, such as *nutritious, malnutrition, nutritional information,* and *nutritionist,* and have students use their knowledge of word structure to determine the meanings of the words.

- List the terms *digest, digestive system,* and *digestion.* Explain how the terms are related, but point out that they have different parts of speech.

- List some Spanish cognates for terms in this lesson, such as *nutriente, digestión, absorción, enzima, esófago,* and *estómago.*

- Use the key term *villi* to discuss the formation of some irregular plural nouns. Write, *villus, villi; octopus, octopi;* and *cactus, cacti* on the board. Then challenge student pairs to write the plural forms of: *crocus, fungus,* and *esophagus.* (*croci, fungi, esophagi*)

↻ Comprehensible Input

Vocabulary in Context: Picture It!

1. **Say the Term** Say each term slowly, artificially stressing each syllable. Have students repeat. Then say the term more naturally and have students repeat.

2. **Introduce Word Meaning** Connect each term to the visual that illustrates it.

3. **Demonstrate** Use gestures and visuals to demonstrate each term. For example:

   - Point to and move your finger up and down the line that connects your throat to your stomach while talking about the *esophagus.*

   - For the terms *epiglottis, small intestine, large intestine, liver, gallbladder, pancreas, rectum,* and *anus,* point to each structure in a poster diagram of the digestive system.

   - For *absorption* and *villi,* use your fingers to emphasize that villi increase surface area and allow for more absorption. Have students trace their fingers totally spread out and then a second time with four fingers touching each other. Ask which provides a greater surface area.

4. **Apply** After each term has been discussed, have students demonstrate understanding with Talk About It.

Talk About It

Guide Discussion Display the digestive system on a poster diagram. Have students explain what they think the job of each part is.

RTI Response to Intervention

If students have difficulty pronouncing some of the multi-syllable terms . . .

Then write the words on the board with spaces between the syllables. Have students practice saying the words in chunks.

Your Turn

Guide Discussion Pass around images of different types of foods from each food group. Have students talk about the nutrients that the foods in the pictures provide.

Digestion and Nutrition

↻ Language Production

Do You Understand?

Comprehension Support Before students start
the activity, use a poster diagram of the digestive
system or the diagram in the Picture It box or
one in the students' science textbook, to trace
the path of food through the mouth, esophagus,
stomach, small intestine, and large intestine.
Use sequence words, such as *first, second, next,
then,* and *finally.* Then ask students to locate and
cut out the cards in the Resources section at the
back of the book. Have students look through the
cards and ask any questions.

Model Demonstrate how students can ask
themselves questions to help them do the activity.
Say, *How does food get into my body? How
does food get to my stomach?*

Talk About It

Guide Discussion Review the sequence of the
digestive system by going over the Do You
Understand activity. Invite students to explain
parts of the digestive system to the class. Provide
sentence frames as necessary: *This is the _____.
It helps the body digest food by _____.*

Your Turn

Guide Discussion Listen to and encourage
student discussions. Clarify discussion points as
they arise. Use a classroom poster diagram to
trace the processes of digestion, absorption, and
elimination through the organs of the digestive
system.

Do You Understand?

Cut out the cards for "Some Organs of the Digestive System," in the
Resources section of this book. Put them in sequence order. Then label and
number the pictures here.

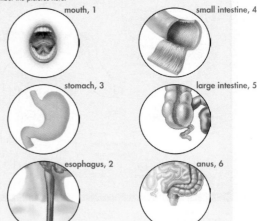

mouth, 1

small intestine, 4

stomach, 3

large intestine, 5

esophagus, 2

anus, 6

Talk About It
Work with a partner. Complete the sentences.
1. Your tongue and teeth are part of your . . . **mouth.**
2. After food leaves the stomach, it enters the . . . **small intestine.**
3. The last section of the digestive system is the . . . **large intestine.**
4. The pouch that connects the esophagus and small intestine is the . . . **stomach.**
5. As you swallow food, it enters your throat and then your . . . **esophagus.**

Your Turn
Work with a partner. Look at the pictures above. Talk about what happens
to food at each step.

Leveled Language Proficiency

Students at each proficiency level should be able to
perform the following tasks.

Listening/Speaking

Early Beginner/Beginner Use pictures or actions to respond
to oral questions about nutrition. Identify digestive system
vocabulary terms when prompted with a definition, picture,
or action.

Early Intermediate Use hand gestures or short phrases to
respond to oral questions about nutrition. Respond with
phrases and short sentences to questions about the parts of
the digestive system.

Intermediate Understand and participate in discussions
using appropriate words related to nutrients found in food.

Advanced/Transitioning Understand oral descriptions of
digestion and absorption. Orally summarize information
about nutrition.

Your Turn

The digestive system is shown below.
Label the parts.

esophagus

liver

stomach

gallbladder

pancreas

small intestinea

large intestine

rectum

anus

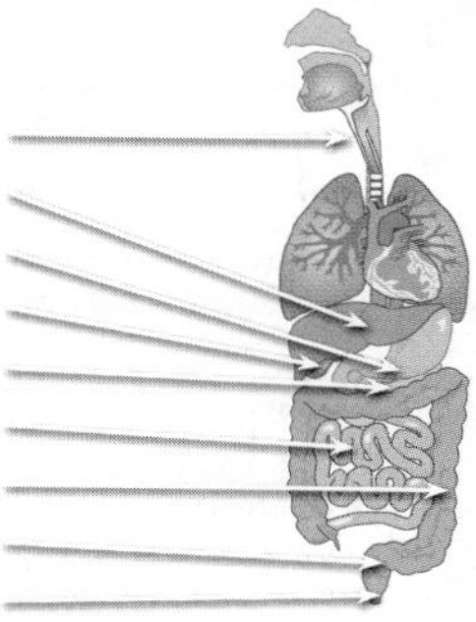

Talk and Write About It

Complete the statements about digestion and absorption.

1. A nutrient is _a source of energy or material found in food_.
2. Chemical digestion is achieved with the help of proteins called _enzymes_.
3. The rectum is a tube located _at the end of the large intestine_.
4. The job of villi is to _absorb nutrients in the small intestine_.

Produce Language

Write about the two processes that turn food into materials you can use.

_____

_____

_____

_____

_____

_____

Leveled Language Proficiency

Students at each proficiency level should be able to perform the following tasks.

Reading/Writing

Early Beginner/Beginner Read labels on illustrations of the digestive system. Write lists of words and short phrases to describe how food is broken down.

Early Intermediate Use context to understand meaning of new vocabulary. Organize ideas about the functions of parts of the digestive system in a graphic organizer.

Intermediate Apply knowledge of word analysis to better understand digestive system vocabulary. Write short sentences that describe the functions of some of the parts of the digestive system.

Advanced/Transitioning Make inferences while reading about nutrition. Write a paragraph explaining the difference between digestion and absorption.

Assess Understanding

Your Turn

Model Before students begin, list the terms needed to complete this activity on the board so they can use the list as a word bank. Point out the liver, gallbladder, pancreas, rectum, and anus on a classroom poster diagram or other visual aid, such as a video or the students' science textbook. Discuss the role of each organ in the digestive process. Introduce and explain the term *bile* as the substance the liver produces and the gallbladder stores to help the body break down fats.

Talk and Write About It

On Their Own Encourage students to look back at the Picture It box terms to help clarify meanings.

Produce Language

On Their Own Before writing, have students talk with a partner about the two processes that break down food into materials the body can use. Encourage students to discuss the difference between digestion and absorption.

Wrap Up

Table Talk Have students reread the Big Question as a way to reflect on what they learned. Encourage students to build fluency by reading their writing in groups or to the class.

✔ **Learned** and applied vocabulary related to digestion and nutrition

✔ **Heard** statements about nutrients that the body needs for energy and growth

✔ **Read** statements about the functions of the digestive system

Circulation

Vocabulary cardiovascular system, heart, atrium, ventricle, artery, vein, capillary, red blood cell, white blood cell, platelet, plasma, hemoglobin, blood pressure

Science Background

- The cardiovascular system delivers needed substances to cells, carries wastes away from cells, and regulates body temperature. In addition, blood contains cells that fight disease.

- The heart pumps blood to the body through blood vessels. Arteries carry blood away from the heart. Veins return blood to the heart. Capillaries connect arteries and veins, bringing oxygen and other substances to the tissues.

- Blood has four components: plasma, red blood cells, white blood cells, and platelets.

Frontload the Lesson

How does your body's transport system work?

Talk About It

Build Background Model for students how to find your pulse by feeling it on your inner wrist. **CAUTION:** Be sure to consider any health issues students may have before they do this activity. Adapt if needed. Paraphrase students' descriptions on a class list, emphasizing any key terms or concepts.

Content and Language

Predict

Model Read the Big Question and the objectives aloud. Use familiar language to further explain each objective.

Guide Discussion Ask students to connect any terms or ideas from their discussion with the ideas in their predictions.

Circulation

Big Question How does your body's transport system work?

You will . . .
- Explain how your heart pumps blood through your body.
- Describe the different parts of blood.
- Use terms related to the cardiovascular system.

Talk About It

Work with a partner. Take turns or choose roles for the exercise: timer/recorder and subject.

Step 1 Put two fingers on the thumb side of your wrist to feel your heartbeat. What do you notice?

Step 2 Now, have one or both partners do some exercise, such as jumping or running in place, for 60 seconds. When you are done, check your pulse again. How is it different?

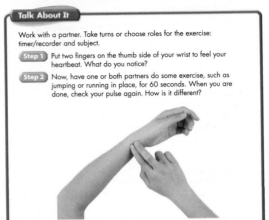

Predict
Look at the Big Question and the "You will . . ." statements at the top of the page. Describe what you think you are going to learn in this lesson.

I think I am going to learn about . . .

Leveled Instruction

Early Beginner/Beginner Ask students to reproduce the images of the cardiovascular system found in the Picture It box. (If possible, make photocopies of the images to distribute to students.) Have students use colors to differentiate between different terms. Encourage students to refer to this guide as they do the activities.

Early Intermediate/Intermediate Help students understand the vocabulary terms by pointing out opposites whenever possible. For example, say, *The arteries carry blood away from the heart, but the veins carry blood toward the heart.* Away *and* toward *are opposites.* Ask students to list other pairs of opposites that are used when describing the cardiovascular system.

Advanced/Transitioning Encourage students to research the functions of red and white blood cells. Have them work in small groups and present their findings to the other classmates.

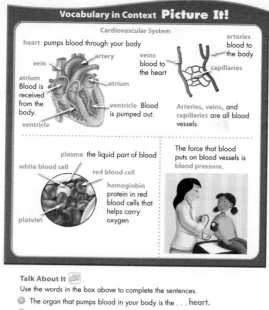

Academic Vocabulary

- Point out that *cardiovascular system* and *circulatory system* are different names for the same set of organs. Another name is *transport system*. Write these terms on the board, and discuss the meanings of the word parts to help students understand and remember both the structures and functions of this system.

- Point out that the word *atrium* is sometimes used to describe a large, central room in a house or building. Ask students how this relates to the scientific meaning of *atrium*. (Blood is received in the atrium of the heart, whereas people are received in the atrium of a building.)

- Write the term *blood pressure* on the board and underline *press*. Push against a wall and tell students that you are applying pressure. Explain that *blood pressure* is the term to describe how blood presses against the walls of the blood vessel.

- Use the key terms to discuss regular and irregular plural nouns. Write, *atrium, atria; artery, arteries;* and *ventricle, ventricles* on the board. Then challenge student pairs to write or say true statements containing each form of the noun.

Comprehensible Input

Vocabulary in Context: Picture It!

1. **Say the Term** Say each term slowly, artificially stressing each syllable. Have students repeat. Then say the term more naturally and have students repeat.

2. **Introduce Word Meaning** Connect each term to the visual that illustrates it.

3. **Demonstrate** Use gestures and visuals to demonstrate each term. For example:

   - Have students trace with a finger the flow of blood through the heart. Have students repeat each term as you say it.

   - Draw a simplified version of the illustration for veins and arteries. Say, *Arteries carry blood away from the heart. Veins carry blood back into the heart.*

   - Write the term *cardiovascular system* on the board. Point out that *cardio-* relates to the heart and *-vascular* relates to vessels.

4. **Apply** After each term has been discussed, have students demonstrate understanding with Talk About It.

Talk About It

Guide Discussion Read the sentence starters aloud for students. Remind them to look at the images in the Picture It box to help them visualize how blood flows through the cardiovascular system.

R T I Response to Intervention

If students have difficulty with the /sh/ sound in *blood pressure . . .*

Then underline the *ss* in the word. Point out that these letters sometimes make the /sh/ sound in the middle of the word. Give students other examples such as *tissue* and *impression*.

Your Turn

Guide Discussion Summarize the function of each italicized term for the students, and have them identify which one you are describing. Then have them talk to a partner about how blood flows through the body.

Circulation

⟳ Language Production

Do You Understand?

Comprehension Support Point out that the word *chamber*, which can also refer to a room, is used to describe each of the four areas of the heart. Review *right* and *left* with students, and explain that in the diagram, we see the right side of the heart on the left and the left side of the heart on the right.

Model Demonstrate how students can ask themselves questions to help them do the activity. Say, *Which chambers of the heart are found in the upper portion? Which are found in the lower portion?*

Talk About It

Guide Discussion Have students look back at the Do You Understand diagram and the illustrations in the Picture It box to help them complete the activity.

Your Turn

Guide Discussion After students finish their discussion, have volunteers describe the movement of the blood to the class, using the illustration in the Do You Understand activity as a visual aid.

A Closer Look

On Their Own Have students work in pairs to complete this word-study activity. Point out other homophone pairs related to the lesson— *right, write;* and *heart, hart.* Discuss common homophones, such as *hear, here; there, their, they're.* Emphasize that these homophones show up as common errors in spelling and writing. Then have students give examples of other homophones. If time allows, students can practice writing pairs of context sentences with a homophone pair of their choice.

Do You Understand?

Your heart has four chambers: the right atrium, the left atrium, the right ventricle, and the left ventricle. Label each chamber on the diagram.

Note: In the diagram, you see the right side of the heart on your left.

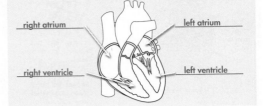

right atrium   left atrium

right ventricle   left ventricle

Talk About It
Talk with a partner. Complete the sentences.

1. Blood moves in and out of the cells and travels through the body in the . . . cardiovascular system.
2. The organ that pumps blood through the body is the . . . heart.
3. Each upper chamber of the heart is an . . . atrium.
4. Each lower chamber of the heart is a . . . ventricle.
5. The force that blood puts on blood vessels is . . . blood pressure.

Your Turn
Work with a partner. Talk about what happens when blood passes through each of the chambers of the heart.

> 🔍 **A Closer Look**
>
> **Homophones** The word *vein* sounds like the words *vain* and *vane,* but each word has a different meaning.
>
>   A *vein* is a blood vessel that carries blood to the heart.
>
>   A weather *vane* shows which way the wind is blowing.
>
>   A person who is *vain* is overly proud.
>
> Draw a picture to show the meaning of each word.

80 Lesson 20

Leveled Language Proficiency

Students at each proficiency level should be able to perform the following tasks.

Listening/Speaking

Early Beginner/Beginner Point to images that correspond to terms in response to hearing about the parts of the cardiovascular system. Use diagrams and pictures to say each of the components of the heart and blood.

Early Intermediate Respond with a word or phrase to spoken questions about the cardiovascular system. Use visual aids to orally describe how blood moves through the chambers of the heart.

Intermediate Briefly summarize how the cardiovascular system works after hearing a description of its processes. Ask questions to clarify understanding of how blood moves in the body.

Advanced/Transitioning Follow multiple-step oral directions independently. Without support, orally summarize key ideas about how blood moves through the heart and vessels of the cardiovascular system.

Your Turn

Write the name of each pictured item. Use the terms in the box.

| red blood cell | platelet | white blood cell | capillaries |

1. white blood cell
2. platelet
3. capillaries
4. red blood cell

Talk and Write About It

Complete the statements about the cardiovascular system.

1. Your heart's function in the body is to _pump blood through your body_
2. Arteries work to _carry blood away from the heart_.
3. Veins work to _carry blood into the heart_.
4. Arteries and veins are connected by _capillaries_.
5. The liquid portion of blood is the _plasma_.

Produce Language

Why is the cardiovascular system also called the body's transport system? Explain, using as many vocabulary terms as you can.

_____
_____
_____
_____

Assess Understanding

Your Turn

Model Read the terms in the box aloud with students. Remind them that they can look at the Picture It box for help.

Talk and Write About It

On Their Own Read the sentence starters aloud for students. Have them discuss their responses with a partner before writing them down.

Produce Language

On Their Own Point out to students that they should not only talk about how blood moves in and out of the heart, but also how the different components in blood function in the cardiovascular system.

Wrap Up

Table Talk Have students reread the Big Question as a way to reflect on what they learned. Encourage students to build fluency by reading their writing in groups or to the class.

✔ **Learned** and applied vocabulary related to the cardiovascular system

✔ **Heard** statements about how blood moves in the body

✔ **Spoken** statements about the important components found in blood

Leveled Language Proficiency

Students at each proficiency level should be able to perform the following tasks.

Reading/Writing

Early Beginner/Beginner Match key vocabulary terms to images or actions. Label diagrams of the cardiovascular system.

Early Intermediate Highlight key ideas in text that answer questions. Write lists to classify words related to the cardiovascular system.

Intermediate Identify the functions of parts of the cardiovascular system with little support from visual aids. Write complete sentences about the structures of the cardiovascular system.

Advanced/Transitioning Draw conclusions and make inferences from text about the cause of high and low blood pressure. Write a detailed paragraph explaining how blood moves through the body.

Respiration and Excretion

Vocabulary cellular respiration, pharynx, trachea, bronchi, lungs, diaphragm, alveoli, excretion, urine, kidneys, nephrons, ureters, urinary bladder, urethra

Materials chart paper

Science Background

- The respiratory system moves air into and out of the lungs. After air enters an alveolus within the lung, oxygen passes from the alveolus into the blood.

- The body needs oxygen because all of its cells use it in the process of cellular respiration, which releases energy from food molecules.

- The excretory system removes the wastes that cells produce. Excretion helps maintain homeostasis by keeping the body's internal environment stable and free of harmful chemicals.

↻ Frontload the Lesson

 What are the structures and functions of the respiratory and excretory systems?

Talk About It

Build Background Ask students to share the number of breaths they counted in a minute. Have students share their thoughts about how the body moves during respiration.

↻ Content and Language

Predict

Model Read the Big Question and the objectives aloud to model pronunciation for students.

Guide Discussion Encourage students to think about the Big Question and the Talk About It activity to help them make their predictions.

Respiration and Excretion

 Big Question What are the structures and functions of the respiratory and excretory systems?

You will . . .
- Name the structures of the respiratory and excretory systems.
- Explain the functions of the respiratory and excretory systems.
- Use vocabulary terms to describe body systems.

 Talk About It

How many times do you breathe in a minute? Take turns with a partner to count how many breaths you take while your partner watches the time. Then discuss the questions below.

1. Which parts of your body do you use when you breathe?
2. How does your body move when you breathe?
3. Where do you think the air goes after you breathe it in?

Predict
Look at Big Question and the "You will . . ." statements at the top of the page. Describe what you think you are going to learn in this lesson.

I think I am going to learn about . . .

Leveled Instruction

Early Beginner Ask students to point to specific terms related to the respiratory and excretory systems. If students point to pictures to help them answer questions, say each term aloud for them to hear.

Beginner Ask students to find particular terms related to the respiratory and excretory systems and to say each term aloud. Clarify any questions students have about pronunciation.

Early Intermediate/Intermediate Ask students questions about the general functions of the respiratory and excretory systems using complex sentences. Expect students to use more than one vocabulary term in phrases or complete sentences to summarize the functions of each system.

Advanced/Transitioning Partner these students with beginning students. Have them model how they structure more detailed answers. Their answers should accurately use multiple vocabulary terms and describe relationships between and among the terms.

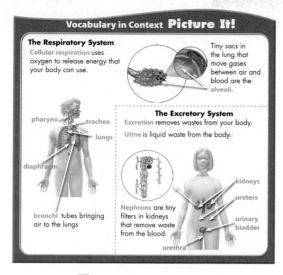

Vocabulary in Context **Picture It!**

The Respiratory System

Cellular respiration uses oxygen to release energy that your body can use.

Tiny sacs in the lung that move gases between air and blood are the **alveoli**.

pharynx
trachea
lungs
diaphragm

bronchi tubes bringing air to the lungs

The Excretory System

Excretion removes wastes from your body.

Urine is liquid waste from the body.

Nephrons are tiny filters in kidneys that remove waste from the blood.

kidneys
ureters
urinary bladder
urethra

Talk About It

Work with a partner. Use the terms in the box above to complete the sentences.

1. Nephrons are found inside the . . . kidneys.
2. Air passes from your nose through a structure inside your neck called the . . . pharynx.
3. Air moves into the lungs through tubes called . . . bronchi.
4. Gases move between air and blood in the lungs through . . . alveoli.
5. The process that uses oxygen to releases energy from food is called cellular respiration.
6. The watery fluid that contains waste is called . . . urine.

Your Turn

Talk with a partner about how air moves through the respiratory system and how urine moves through the excretory system.

Academic Vocabulary

- Explain to students that body systems, such as the *respiratory system* and the *excretory system,* are made up of organs that work together.

- Draw students' attention to how some words change from nouns to adjectives: *respiration, respiratory; excretion, excretory.*

- Ask students to think of other body systems that they have studied or heard about, and to identify the noun and adjective forms. (e.g., *circulation, circulatory*)

- As students learn the names for the different organs, you might explain that the function of the urinary bladder is to store urine as it collects for removal from the body. Students new to English may not know this meaning of *store.* Have them practice using *store* as a verb in other sentences. Then talk about the noun *store.* Ask, *What sorts of things might be stored at a store?*

↻ Comprehensible Input

Vocabulary in Context: Picture It!

1. **Say the Term** Say each term slowly, artificially stressing each syllable. Have students repeat. Then say the term more naturally and have students repeat.

2. **Introduce Word Meaning** Connect each term to the visual that illustrates it.

3. **Demonstrate** Use gestures and visuals to demonstrate each term. For example:

   - As you say the word *pharynx,* point to the top of your throat where the pharynx is located.

   - Then say the word *trachea* and move your hand down your throat to show the position of the trachea.

   - As you say the word *kidneys,* point to your back, just at the base of your rib cage, on either side of your spine.

4. **Apply** After all of the terms have been discussed, have students demonstrate understanding with Talk About It.

Talk About It

Guide Discussion Read the sentence starters chorally with students and have them work in pairs to complete the sentences.

RTI Response to Intervention

If students have difficulty pronouncing some of the names of organs within the two systems . . .

Then remind students that the *ch* in *bronchi* and *trachea* is pronounced like a *k.* Note that *ph* sounds like *f,* as in *pharynx* and *diaphragm,* and that the *g* in *diaphragm* is silent.

Your Turn

Guide Discussion Write the sequencing words *first, second, next,* and *last* on the board, and remind students to use them as they explain movement of air in the respiratory system and urine in the excretory system.

Respiration and Excretion

↻ Language Production

Do You Understand?

Comprehension Support Before students start the activity, encourage them to study the vocabulary terms in the Picture It box. Then challenge them to see how many terms they can fill in without looking back at the definitions.

Model Demonstrate how students can form sentences about the movement of air through the respiratory system. Encourage students to complete sentences such as: *First, air passes through . . . ; Then, air moves into . . . ; Next, the air enters . . .*

Talk About It

Guide Discussion Read the statements aloud with students as they work together to complete the sentences. Then have students work with partners to compare their completed sentences. Finally, have volunteers read the completed sentences aloud to review their work. In the places where several students have added the wrong word, go back to the presentation of that item to make sure that they understand it.

Your Turn

Guide Discussion Listen to student discussions as they compare their labels. Correct misinformation and pronunciation as needed. Encourage advanced students to add additional terms to the diagram, along with sketches, if necessary.

A Closer Look

On Their Own Have students work in pairs to complete this word study activity. Ask if they can come up with another example of a word that forms a plural with -*i*. (Examples: *cacti, fungi, alumni*)

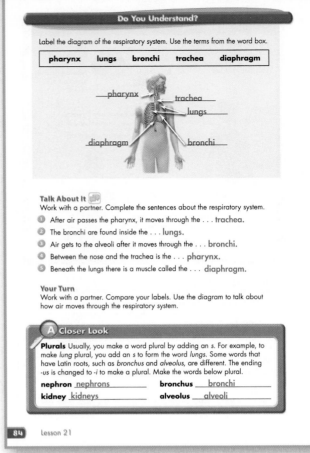

Do You Understand?

Label the diagram of the respiratory system. Use the terms from the word box.

pharynx	lungs	bronchi	trachea	diaphragm

pharynx   trachea
lungs
diaphragm   bronchi

Talk About It
Work with a partner. Complete the sentences about the respiratory system.
1. After air passes the pharynx, it moves through the . . . trachea.
2. The bronchi are found inside the . . . lungs.
3. Air gets to the alveoli after it moves through the . . . bronchi.
4. Between the nose and the trachea is the . . . pharynx.
5. Beneath the lungs there is a muscle called the . . . diaphragm.

Your Turn
Work with a partner. Compare your labels. Use the diagram to talk about how air moves through the respiratory system.

A Closer Look

Plurals Usually, you make a word plural by adding an *s*. For example, to make *lung* plural, you add an *s* to form the word *lungs*. Some words that have Latin roots, such as *bronchus* and *alveolus*, are different. The ending *-us* is changed to *-i* to make a plural. Make the words below plural.

nephron nephrons   bronchus   bronchi
kidney kidneys   alveolus   alveoli

84   Lesson 21

Leveled Language Proficiency

Students at each proficiency level should be able to perform the following tasks.

Listening/Speaking

Early Beginner/Beginner Gesture or point in response to oral questions about parts of the respiratory and excretory systems. Use a word or a short phrase in response to questions about these body systems.

Early Intermediate Use short phrases to respond to oral questions about parts of the respiratory and excretory systems. Use simple sentences to describe the functions of different structures within these body systems.

Intermediate Understand oral definitions of the terms related to the respiratory and excretory systems. Explain in complete sentences how air moves through the respiratory system and how urine moves through the excretory system.

Advanced/Transitioning Follow oral explanations of the relationship between different parts of each body system. Use complete and complex sentences to explain how air moves through the respiratory system and how urine moves through the excretory system.

Your Turn

Label the parts of the excretory system shown in the picture. Then discuss with a partner what occurs inside the kidneys.

kidneys

ureter

urethra

urinary bladder

Talk and Write About It 🗨️ ✏️

Complete the statements about the excretory system.

1. The function of the kidneys is to **remove wastes from the blood and produce urine** .
2. The function of the nephrons is to **filter blood** .
3. Ureters are tubes that connect the **kidneys with the urinary bladder** .
4. After urine moves through the urinary bladder, it moves _____ **out of the body through the urethra** .
5. The function of the urinary bladder is to **store urine** .

Produce Language

Write about the structures and functions of the respiratory and excretory systems. Use as many vocabulary terms as you can.

_____

_____

_____

_____

Leveled Language Proficiency

Students at each proficiency level should be able to perform the following tasks.

Reading/Writing

Early Beginner/Beginner Locate terms for each structure of the respiratory and excretory systems. Write the correct term to label the diagrams of these systems.

Early Intermediate Read to find references to the structures of the respiratory and excretory systems. Write short phrases to describe the function of each body system structure.

Intermediate Comprehend written instructions to identify different structures of the respiratory and excretory systems. Use basic but complete sentences in written descriptions of these systems.

Advanced/Transitioning Read aloud sentences that describe the structures and functions of the respiratory and excretory systems. Write complex sentences describing how these systems work to keep the body functioning.

↻ Assess Understanding

Your Turn

Model Remind students to consider the function of each structure as they determine the path of urine in the body. For example, say, *My kidneys have filters that allow urine to form. Urine flows away from the kidneys, so kidneys should be at the top of the system.*

Talk and Write About It

On Their Own Encourage students to talk in small groups about the functions of each structure in the excretory system before they begin to write.

Produce Language

On Their Own Have students write their responses and then discuss their answers in pairs. Finally, lead a discussion with the whole class to address the Big Question, *What are the structures and functions of the respiratory and excretory systems?*

Wrap Up

Table Talk Have students reflect on what they learned. Encourage students to build fluency by reading their writing in groups or to the class.

✔ **Heard** statements about the structures and functions of the respiratory and excretory systems

✔ **Spoken** statements about how the respiratory and excretory systems help to make the body work

✔ **Written** statements about how air moves through the respiratory system and how urine moves through the excretory system

Fighting Disease

Vocabulary infectious disease, noninfectious disease, phagocyte, pathogen, inflammatory response, toxin, immune response, T cell, B cell, antigen, antibody, immunity, vaccination

Materials index cards

 Science Background

- The four major types of pathogens are bacteria, viruses, fungi, and protists.

- In the inflammatory response, fluid and white blood cells fight pathogens near where the pathogens are located. In the immune response, cells in the blood target specific kinds of pathogens.

- You acquire active immunity when your own immune system produces antibodies. You acquire passive immunity when the antibodies come from an outside source.

Frontload the Lesson

 How does your body fight diseases?

Talk About It

Build Background Have students make cards as described. Model a few examples. Say, *I know the term* vaccination *well. I'm going to put that on the far right next to the label* Know Well.

Content and Language

Predict

Model Read the Big Question and the objectives aloud. Use more familiar language to describe some of the terms in the objectives. For example, use *illness* or *sickness* in place of *disease*.

Guide Discussion Ask students to repeat the objectives in their own words to a partner. Have them discuss the Big Question.

Fighting Disease

 Big Question How does your body fight diseases?

You will . . .
- Explain how the body fights diseases.
- Distinguish between infectious and noninfectious diseases.
- Use terms related to diseases.

Talk About It

Look at the vocabulary terms in the Picture It box on the next page. Write each term on a card. As your teacher reads each term, place the card on a line to show how well you know it.

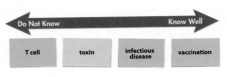

Do Not Know — Know Well

| T cell | toxin | infectious disease | vaccination |

What do you know about each term? Explain, using the sentence starters for support.
1. I do not know the term . . .
2. I have never heard or seen the term . . .
3. I'm not sure what it means, but I have heard the term . . .
4. I know the term . . .

Predict
Look at the Big Question and the "You will . . ." statements at the top of the page. Describe what you think you are going to learn in this lesson.

I think I am going to learn about . . .

Leveled Instruction

Early Beginner Pair beginners with more advanced learners. Have the advanced students hold up the cards for the beginners and ask, *Do you know the term . . . very well, a little, or not at all?* Answers can be given using hand gestures, such as a thumbs-up or thumbs-down.

Beginner Students may benefit from hearing each term more than once. After reading each term in the list aloud, go through each card as a group. Ask students questions to help them decide where to put the term on the line.

Early Intermediate/Intermediate Allow student pairs to work fairly independently. Students should be able to express the meanings of words they claim to know.

Advanced/Transitioning Students should be able to work independently and to assist beginner students. Encourage these students to model their thinking for beginners as they go through the lesson.

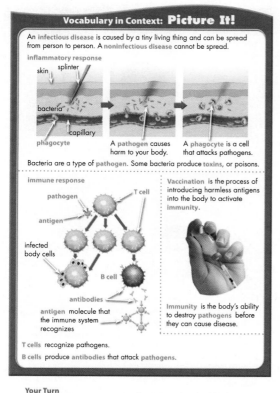

An **infectious disease** is caused by a tiny living thing and can be spread from person to person. A **noninfectious disease** cannot be spread.

inflammatory response

skin
splinter
bacteria
capillary
phagocyte

A **pathogen** causes harm to your body.

A **phagocyte** is a cell that attacks pathogens.

Bacteria are a type of **pathogen**. Some bacteria produce **toxins**, or poisons.

immune response

pathogen
T cell
antigen
infected body cells
B cell
antibodies

antigen molecule that the immune system recognizes

T cells recognize pathogens.

B cells produce **antibodies** that attack **pathogens**.

Vaccination is the process of introducing harmless antigens into the body to activate **immunity**.

Immunity is the body's ability to destroy **pathogens** before they can cause disease.

Your Turn
Talk with a partner about how infectious disease is spread. What kinds of pathogens are there?

Fighting Disease 87

Academic Vocabulary

- Write the term *phagocyte* on the board. Explain that the word part *-cyte* means "cell" and *phago-* comes from a Greek word that means "eating." Have students explain how this can help them understand the vocabulary term's meaning.

- Write the terms *infectious disease* and *noninfectious disease* on the board. Underline the word part *infect* in both words and explain that it means "to contaminate with a disease-causing substance." Then point out that the suffix *-ious* means "having the quality of" and the prefix *non-* means "not." Have students discuss how to determine meaning using these word parts.

- Write the term *pathogen* on the board. Explain that the word is a combination of the Greek word *pathos*, meaning "disease," and the Greek word *gignesthai*, meaning "to be born."

- For the sake of simplicity, *pathogen* has been defined as a living thing that causes disease. Viruses, which are one type of pathogen, are not really alive, because they do not carry out life processes such as growth, metabolism, or response to stimuli. Viruses do reproduce, but they require the cells of living things to do so.

↻ Comprehensible Input

Vocabulary in Context: Picture It!

1. **Say the Term** Say each term slowly, artificially stressing each syllable. Have students repeat. Then say the term more naturally and have students repeat.

2. **Introduce Word Meaning** Connect each term to the visual that illustrates it.

3. **Demonstrate** Use gestures and visuals to demonstrate each term.

4. **Apply** After each term has been discussed, have students demonstrate understanding with Talk About It.

Talk About It

Guide Discussion Before students start their independent discussion, check for understanding with the following sentences.

1. *A flu shot is a type of . . .* (vaccination.)

2. *You get some diseases only once because you develop an . . .* (immunity.)

3. *Bacteria and viruses are examples of . . .* (pathogens.)

4. *Some pathogens produce a poison, or . . .* (toxin.)

5. *White blood cells that engulf and destroy all pathogens are called . . .* (phagocytes.)

6. *White blood cells that recognize different types of pathogens are called . . .* (T cells.)

7. *White blood cells that produce antibodies to destroy pathogens are called . . .* (B cells.)

R T I Response to Intervention

If students have difficulty with the term *vaccination . . .*

Then explain that in the first syllable, the *c* makes a /k/ sound, but in the second syllable it makes an /s/ sound.

Your Turn

Guide Discussion If students have difficulty identifying pathogens other than bacteria, explain that viruses and some fungi and protists can also be pathogens.

Language Production

Do You Understand?

Comprehension Support Before students start the activity, model an example so students understand the activity.

Model Say, *I know that the common cold is caused by a virus and can be spread from person to person. It must be an infectious disease, so I will draw a line connecting the common cold to the term* infectious.

Talk About It

Guide Discussion As the class reviews each completed sentence, have students use examples that they are familiar with to further illustrate the meaning of each term.

Your Turn

Guide Discussion Listen to and encourage student discussions. Clarify misconceptions as necessary. Encourage volunteers to share their responses with the class.

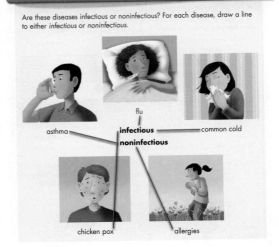

Do You Understand?

Are these diseases infectious or noninfectious? For each disease, draw a line to either *infectious* or *noninfectious*.

flu

asthma — **infectious** — common cold

noninfectious

chicken pox — — allergies

Talk About It
Complete the sentences.

1. An illness caused by a tiny living thing is an . . . **infectious disease.**
2. An illness you cannot catch from someone else is a . . . **noninfectious disease.**
3. The tiny living things that cause disease are called . . . **pathogens.**
4. When a harmless antigen is injected into your body to prevent disease, you have received a . . . **vaccination.**
5. Your body's ability to recognize and destroy pathogens before they can cause disease is called . . .**immunity.**

Your Turn
Work with a partner. Talk about an infectious disease and what you think the human body does to fight the disease.

88   Lesson 22

Leveled Language Proficiency

Students at each proficiency level should be able to perform the following tasks.

Listening/Speaking

Early Beginner/Beginner Point to pictures in response to oral questions about infectious and noninfectious diseases. Orally describe an illness using relevant words and phrases.

Early Intermediate Respond to simple questions about infectious diseases using simple sentences. Using key vocabulary, orally describe one of the ways the body fights disease.

Intermediate Summarize a partner's ideas about how the body fights disease after a brief discussion. Explain with simple sentences and phrases the difference between phagocytes, T cells, and B cells.

Advanced/Transitioning Follow multiple-step oral directions independently. Orally summarize the immune response.

Think, Talk, and Write

Your Turn

Look at the terms in the Word Bank. List terms in the correct box to show which type of response the term relates to. Some terms belong in both boxes.

inflammatory response

pathogen
phagocyte

Word Bank

T cell
phagocyte
B cell
antibody
pathogen

immune response

pathogen
T cell
B cell
antibody

Talk and Write About It

Complete the statements about how your body fights disease.

1. Phagocytes, T cells, and B cells are types of white blood cells that attack pathogens
2. B cells produce antibodies that destroy pathogens
3. In the inflammatory response, phagocytes engulf and destroy pathogens
4. In the immune response, T cells and B cells target specific pathogens and destroy them
5. Toxins are substances that are produced by some bacteria and can damage body cells

Produce Language

Look back at the Big Question. Describe three ways your body fights disease. Use as many vocabulary terms as you can.

_____

_____

_____

_____

_____

Fighting Disease **89**

Leveled Language Proficiency

Students at each proficiency level should be able to perform the following tasks.

Reading/Writing

Early Beginner/Beginner Point to the terms *immune response* and *inflammatory response* in text and use gestures or drawings to explain the difference between the two. Write labels for diagrams that show how the body fights disease.

Early Intermediate Read and follow simple written directions. Draw pictures with captions that show how the body fights disease.

Intermediate Summarize a text about how the body fights disease, using complete sentences and key terms. Write a short paragraph describing the three lines of defense that the body has against disease.

Advanced/Transitioning Read supplementary texts from the library or the Internet that expand on the lesson's topics. Using key vocabulary, write a detailed paragraph about the body's protection against disease.

Assess Understanding

Your Turn

Model Briefly discuss inflammatory and immune responses before students categorize the words.

Talk and Write About It

On Their Own Have student volunteers draw diagrams on the board to represent the cells and pathogens. Have them draw illustrations to show how the body defends itself.

Produce Language

On Their Own Before writing, make a three-column chart on the board with the headings *1, 2,* and *3.* Discuss with students the three ways the body protects itself from disease (first, barriers such as the skin and stomach acid that prevent pathogens from entering the bloodstream; second, the inflammatory response; third, the immune response). List key words and phrases associated with each line of defense as they come up.

Wrap Up

Table Talk Have students read the Big Question as a way to reflect on what they learned. Encourage students to build fluency by reading their writing in groups or to the class.

✔ **Learned** and applied vocabulary related to infectious and noninfectious diseases

✔ **Spoken** statements about how the body fights disease

✔ **Read** statements explaining the difference between infectious and noninfectious diseases

Lesson 23

The Nervous System

Vocabulary nerve, neuron, dendrite, axon, synapse, reflex, sensory neuron, motor neuron, interneuron, central nervous system, peripheral nervous system, retina, cochlea

Materials covered box (such as shoe box with lid), oranges

 Science Background

- The central nervous system (the brain and spinal cord) controls the body's functions. The peripheral nervous system connects the brain and spinal cord to the rest of the body.

- Nerve impulses are carried by neurons, or nerve cells. Impulses are picked up by the dendrites and travel through a neuron along the axon. At the axon tip, the impulse jumps across a gap called a synapse to another neuron, a muscle, or a gland.

 Frontload the Lesson

 How does your body sense and react to your surroundings?

Talk About It

Build Background Before class, place one orange in a covered box. Let students examine the box without opening it. Have students gently shake the box. Ask them what they hear. Open the box and allow students to handle the orange. Ask what they feel, see, and smell.

Content and Language

Predict

Model Read the Big Question and the objectives aloud. As students repeat after you, correct any mispronunciations they may make.

Guide Discussion Encourage students to use the Big Question and the lesson title as they make their predictions.

 Big Question How does your body sense and react to your surroundings?

You will . . .
- Understand how the nervous system sends information.
- Learn about the structure of nerves.
- Use terms related to the nervous system.

Talk About It

Use the chart below. With a partner, walk around the classroom. Write or draw what you see, hear, touch, and smell.

What I see	
What I hear	
What I touch	
What I smell	

Talk with your partner about the things on your chart. The nervous system helps you see, hear, touch, smell, and taste things.

Predict
Look at the Big Question and the "You will . . ." statements at the top of the page. Describe what you think you are going to learn in this lesson.

I think I am going to learn about . . .

Leveled Instruction

Early Beginner/Beginner Have students point to the vocabulary term *central nervous system* in the Picture It box. Then have them point to other terms as you say them aloud. Have them write the terms in their notebooks as they look at the pictures.

Early Intermediate/Intermediate Encourage students to write the new terms in their notebooks, using illustrations and writing definitions in their native language to help remember the meanings.

Advanced/Transitioning Have students write the terms in their notebooks, along with simple definitions in English using their own words. Encourage them to supplement these definitions with native-language definitions if this strategy is helpful. Have advanced students compose simple glossaries that can be used by beginning ELLs. The glossaries should include simple English definitions, definitions in the students' native language, and illustrations where possible.

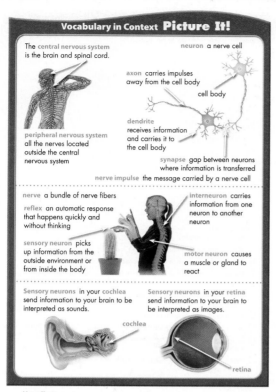

Vocabulary in Context Picture It!

The **central nervous system** is the brain and spinal cord.

neuron a nerve cell

axon carries impulses away from the cell body

cell body

dendrite receives information and carries it to the cell body

peripheral nervous system all the nerves located outside the central nervous system

synapse gap between neurons where information is transferred

nerve impulse the message carried by a nerve cell

nerve a bundle of nerve fibers

reflex an automatic response that happens quickly and without thinking

sensory neuron picks up information from the outside environment or from inside the body

interneuron carries information from one neuron to another neuron

motor neuron causes a muscle or gland to react

Sensory neurons in your **cochlea** send information to your brain to be interpreted as sounds.

Sensory neurons in your **retina** send information to your brain to be interpreted as images.

cochlea

retina

Your Turn
Talk with a partner about the central nervous system and the peripheral nervous system. What do the pictures show? Then, tell how nerve cells carry information throughout the body. Use as many vocabulary terms as you can.

The Nervous System **91**

Academic Vocabulary

The terms *impulse, nerve,* and *cord* are all multiple-meaning words that may confuse students depending on usage. Explain that students can use context clues to determine the correct meaning for each word.

Word	Meaning	Example
impulse	a sudden urge	She bought a song on *impulse*.
	a signal that moves along a nerve	A nerve *impulse* travels from dendrite to axon.
nerve	courage	It takes a lot of *nerve* to speak in front of people.
	a bundle of nerve fibers	A *nerve* carries information from the body to the brain.
cord	a thick string	Kim tied the sticks together with a *cord*.
	a part of the central nervous system	The spinal *cord* connects to the brain.

Comprehensible Input

Vocabulary in Context: Picture It!

1. **Say the Term** Say each term slowly, artificially stressing each syllable. Have students repeat. Then say the term more naturally and have students repeat.

2. **Introduce Word Meaning** Connect each term to the visual that illustrates it.

3. **Demonstrate** Use gestures and visuals to demonstrate each term.

4. **Apply** After all of the terms have been discussed, have students demonstrate understanding with Talk About It.

Talk About It

Guide Discussion Before students start their independent discussion, check for understanding with the following:

1. *A nerve cell is also called a . . .* (neuron.)

2. *The part of the neuron that receives information is the . . .* (dendrite.)

3. *A bundle of nerve fibers is a . . .* (nerve.)

4. *The type of nerve cell that tells your hand to move is a . . .* (motor neuron.)

5. *The space between two neurons is a . . .* (synapse.)

6. *The brain and spinal cord make up the . . .* (central nervous system.)

7. *The nerves outside the brain and spinal cord make up the . . .* (peripheral nervous system.)

8. *A fly lands on your nose, and you blink. This fast response is a . . .* (reflex.)

R T I Response to Intervention

If students have trouble understanding the term *peripheral . . .*

Then explain that *peri-* means "surrounding" or "around." Emphasize that the peripheral nervous system surrounds the central nervous system.

Your Turn

Guide Discussion Ask volunteers to describe the parts of a neuron (*dendrite, cell body, axon*).

The Nervous System

Language Production

Do You Understand?

Comprehension Support Remind students that nerve cells are called neurons. Have them refer to Picture It for help with remembering the different parts of a neuron.

Model Demonstrate how students can ask themselves questions to help complete the activity. Say, *Which part of a neuron is a long fiber?* (the axon)

To help students understand the process of nerve-impulse transmission, divide the class into small groups. Have students stand side by side with their arms outstretched and their fingers almost touching. Explain that right hands are dendrites and left hands are axons. You will be the stimulus. Brush the right hand (dendrite) of the first student. The student transmits the information through the axon (left hand) by brushing the right hand (dendrite) of the next student, who transmits the impulse to the next student, and so on. Have the last student signal when he or she receives the information.

Talk About It

Guide Discussion Read the sentences aloud with students while you point to the relevant parts of the drawing. Draw a simple neuron on the board. Point to relevant parts during the discussion.

Your Turn

Guide Discussion Listen to students discuss the process of nerve-impulse transmission. Point out the connection to the Big Question. Help correct mistakes or misunderstandings.

Do You Understand?

Label the structures shown on the diagram.

axon.

dendrite.

synapse.

Talk About It
Complete the sentences.

1 A nerve cell is called a(n) . . . neuron.
2 The part of the neuron in which impulses begin is called the . . . dendrite.
3 The part of a neuron that carries an impulse away from the cell body is called the . . . axon.
4 Information travels from one neuron to the next across a gap. This gap is called a(n) . . . synapse.
5 A bundle of nerve fibers is called a(n) . . . nerve.
6 The brain and spinal cord are the two parts of the . . . central nervous system.
7 In the eye, nerve impulses travel to the brain from the structure called the . . . retina.
8 When you hear a sound, nerve impulses have traveled to your brain from the . . . cochlea.

Your Turn
Work with a partner. Talk about how a nerve impulse begins and how it travels through a neuron. Then talk about how an impulse passes from one neuron to another. Use the vocabulary terms as you talk.

92 Lesson 23

Leveled Language Proficiency

Students at each proficiency level should be able to perform the following tasks.

Listening/Speaking

Early Beginner Gesture in response to simple oral directions. Answer simple questions about nerves with *yes/no* or single words.

Beginner Follow simple oral directions to take part in the modeling activity. Ask and answer questions with single words and short phrases.

Early Intermediate/Intermediate Follow oral directions expressed in full sentences. Answer questions about reflexes using full sentences.

Advanced/Transitioning Follow oral directions expressed in complex sentences. Answer questions and summarize information about the central and peripheral nervous systems using complex sentences.

Your Turn

Label the diagram to show which types of neurons are involved in what is happening. Use the terms in the box.

interneuron	motor neuron	sensory neuron

sensory neuron

interneuron

motor neuron

Talk and Write About It

Complete these statements about the diagram above.

1. The process shown in the diagram is called a(n) <u>reflex</u>.
2. Sensory neurons pick up information from <u>internal or external environment</u>.
3. Motor neurons send impulses to <u>muscles or glands</u>.
4. Interneurons carry impulses <u>from one neuron to another</u>.

Produce Language

Write a description of one example of your body sensing its surroundings and reacting to them. Tell what happens in the nervous system. Use as many vocabulary terms as you can.

_____

_____

_____

_____

The Nervous System **93**

Leveled Language Proficiency

Students at each proficiency level should be able to perform the following tasks.

Reading/Writing

Early Beginner/Beginner Identify written words associated with a reflex. Write words and phrases to explain the functions of sensory neurons and motor neurons.

Early Intermediate Read and understand simple sentences. Write and number simple sentences about the sequence of events in a reflex.

Intermediate Read and understand material written in full sentences. Use short paragraphs and full sentences to describe the central and peripheral nervous systems.

Advanced/Transitioning Read and understand material written in full sentences and arranged in multiple paragraphs. Describe in detail how the nervous system transfers information throughout the body.

Assess Understanding

Your Turn

Model Read the instructions aloud with students. As you read, point to the different parts of the diagram. Make sure students understand where and why the reflex begins (finger touches cactus needle) and ends (finger pulls away).

Talk and Write About It

On Their Own Have partners talk about the reflex shown in the diagram. Make sure that students understand that the arrows do not show neurons, but rather show the path that the nerve impulse takes. Ask why there are arrows going up to the brain. (At the same time an impulse is traveling through the reflex arc in the spinal cord, another impulse travels to the brain. When the impulse reaches the brain, the girl is conscious of what has happened and feels pain, but because of the reflex, she has already removed her hand from the source of the pain.)

Produce Language

On Their Own Have students think about a stimulus that might initiate a reflex response (for example, touching or tasting something hot or getting a particle of dust in the eye). Then have them write about the reflex that occurs in response to that stimulus. After the writing activity, invite students to read aloud what they have written.

Wrap Up

Table Talk Have students reread the Big Question as a way to reflect on what they have learned. Encourage students to build fluency by reading their writing in groups or to the class.

✔ **Learned** and applied vocabulary about nerve impulses and neurons

✔ **Spoken** statements about how information travels through the nervous system

✔ **Written** statements about the reflex arc and the three neuron types involved

Lesson 24

The Endocrine System and Reproduction

Vocabulary endocrine gland, hormone, hypothalamus, pituitary gland, negative feedback, ovulation, zygote, embryo, fetus, placenta

Science Background

- The endocrine system helps control the body's activities. Hormones—the chemicals released by endocrine glands—are slower-acting than nerve impulses but have longer-lasting effects.

- The endocrine system controls almost every aspect of reproduction and growth.

Frontload the Lesson

How do hormones regulate body processes?

Talk About It

Build Background Model placing a term in a column. Say, *I know that a zygote is a fertilized egg, so I will put the term in the* Know *column.* Tell students not to be discouraged if they do not know many of these terms. Emphasize that they will learn the meanings of the terms as they go through the lesson. As students learn the terms, have them write short definitions in the *Learned* column, using their first language if necessary.

Content and Language

Predict

Model Read the Big Question and the objectives aloud. As students repeat after you, help with pronunciation as necessary.

Guide Discussion Encourage students to use the Big Question and the lesson title as they make their predictions.

The Endocrine System and Reproduction

Big Question How do hormones regulate body processes?

You will . . .
- Describe the functions of the endocrine system.
- Explain the connection between hormones and human development.
- Use terms related to the endocrine system and reproduction.

Talk About It

Look at the terms in Picture It. Write terms you **know** and those you **want** to know more about in the chart. Later, you will write the terms you **learn** in class.

Know	Want	Learned

Predict

Look at the Big Question and the "You will . . ." statements at the top of the page. Describe what you think you are going to learn in this lesson.

I think I am going to learn about . . .

Leveled Instruction

Early Beginner As you say a vocabulary term aloud, have students point to the term in the lesson. Have students respond to questions by pointing to pictures or words.

Beginner Give students simple oral directions. They can respond to simple questions about hormones and the endocrine system using single words and short phrases.

Early Intermediate/Intermediate Have students work with partners to help each other understand oral directions. Students should answer questions about hormones and the endocrine system using short sentences (early intermediate) or full sentences with some detail (intermediate).

Advanced/Transitioning Students should be able to follow directions independently. Ask questions about hormones and the endocrine system using complex sentences. Students should answer questions using complex sentences that include some detail.

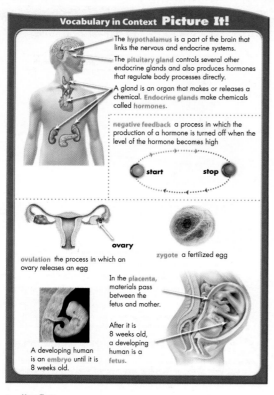

Vocabulary in Context **Picture It!**

The **hypothalamus** is a part of the brain that links the nervous and endocrine systems.

The **pituitary gland** controls several other endocrine glands and also produces hormones that regulate body processes directly.

A **gland** is an organ that makes or releases a chemical. **Endocrine glands** make chemicals called **hormones**.

negative feedback a process in which the production of a hormone is turned off when the level of the hormone becomes high

start stop

ovary

ovulation the process in which an ovary releases an egg

zygote a fertilized egg

In the **placenta**, materials pass between the fetus and mother.

A developing human is an **embryo** until it is 8 weeks old.

After it is 8 weeks old, a developing human is a **fetus**.

Your Turn
Talk with a partner about hormones and the endocrine system. Use as many vocabulary terms as you can.

The Endocrine System and Reproduction **95**

Academic Vocabulary

- Point out that in the word *ovary*, the *o* has a long sound, but in *ovulation*, the *o* has a short sound.

- A gland is an organ or tissue that produces a substance that the body needs. You might want to explain that biologists recognize two kinds of glands—endocrine and exocrine. Endocrine glands release substances directly into the blood. In contrast, exocrine glands release substances through tubes called ducts. Sweat glands and tear glands are exocrine glands, as are glands that release enzymes used in digestion.

- Cognates are words that have the same or similar roots and meanings in two languages. Have students share any vocabulary terms they recognize as cognates to words in their first languages. For example, the Spanish word for ovary is *ovario*.

↻ Comprehensible Input

Vocabulary in Context: Picture It!

1. **Say the Term** Say each term slowly, artificially stressing each syllable. Have students repeat. Then say the term more naturally and have students repeat.

2. **Introduce Word Meaning** Connect each term to the visual that illustrates it.

3. **Demonstrate** Use gestures and visuals to demonstrate each term.

4. **Apply** After all of the terms have been discussed, have students demonstrate understanding with Talk About It.

Talk About It

Guide Discussion Before students start their independent discussion, check for understanding with the following sentence starters.

1. *A fertilized egg is called a . . .* (zygote.)

2. *A woman's ovaries release one egg each month. This event is called . . .* (ovulation.)

3. *A chemical made by an endocrine gland is a . . .* (hormone.)

4. *The nervous and endocrine systems are linked by a part of the brain called the . . .* (hypothalamus.)

5. *Several of the body's endocrine glands are controlled by the . . .* (pituitary gland.)

6. *A membrane that connects a fetus with its mother is called the . . .* (placenta.)

RTI Response to Intervention

If students have trouble saying *pituitary* and *hypothalamus* . . .

Then write the words on the board and break them down syllable by syllable. Have students repeat after you.

Your Turn

Guide Discussion Before students discuss the endocrine system, make sure they understand what hormones are and the function they perform in the body.

The Endocrine System and Reproduction

↻ Language Production

Do You Understand?

Comprehension Support Read the directions and the terms in the box aloud with students. Consider providing a detailed illustration of the endocrine system, or referring students to a diagram in their textbook, as a way of introducing the names and locations of glands in the endocrine system, such as the thyroid gland, the adrenal glands, and so forth.

Model Demonstrate how students can ask themselves questions to help them complete the activity. For example, say, *Which parts of the endocrine system are in your skull?*

Talk About It

Guide Discussion Read the sentence starters aloud with students as they work to complete the sentences. To clarify the concept of negative feedback, use the example of a thermostat. When the air temperature in a room becomes low enough, the thermostat responds by turning the heat on. Later, when the air becomes warm enough, the thermostat turns the heat off. This cycle continues over and over, maintaining a relatively stable temperature in the room.

Your Turn

Guide Discussion Remind students that the hypothalamus is part of the brain, so it is located in the skull along with the rest of the brain. The hypothalamus and the pituitary gland work closely together; therefore, their location next to each other enables efficient "communication."

A Closer Look

On Their Own Have students work in pairs to complete this word study activity. Draw an oval on the board as a clue if needed.

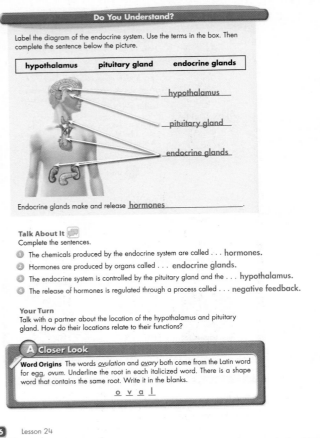

Do You Understand?

Label the diagram of the endocrine system. Use the terms in the box. Then complete the sentence below the picture.

| hypothalamus | pituitary gland | endocrine glands |

hypothalamus

pituitary gland

endocrine glands

Endocrine glands make and release _hormones_.

Talk About It 💬
Complete the sentences.
1. The chemicals produced by the endocrine system are called . . . hormones.
2. Hormones are produced by organs called . . . endocrine glands.
3. The endocrine system is controlled by the pituitary gland and the . . . hypothalamus.
4. The release of hormones is regulated through a process called . . . negative feedback.

Your Turn
Talk with a partner about the location of the hypothalamus and pituitary gland. How do their locations relate to their functions?

🔍 A Closer Look

Word Origins The words *ovulation* and *ovary* both come from the Latin word for egg, *ovum*. Underline the root in each italicized word. There is a shape word that contains the same root. Write it in the blanks.

o v a l

96   Lesson 24

Leveled Language Proficiency

Students at each proficiency level should be able to perform the following tasks.

Listening/Speaking

Early Beginner Point to diagrams and images to show comprehension of endocrine and reproductive terms. Repeat key terms and concepts after they have been presented.

Beginner Point to images to respond to statements about the endocrine and reproductive systems. Ask and answer questions with single words and short phrases.

Early Intermediate/Intermediate Orally explain the functions of various parts of the endocrine system after hearing their names. Answer questions and participate in discussions using full sentences.

Advanced/Transitioning Follow oral directions expressed in complex sentences. Answer questions and use complex sentences to explain basic information about the endocrine and reproductive systems.

Your Turn

Match each term with a picture. Write numbers to put the pictures in order.

embryo   2

ovulation   3

zygote   4

fetus   1

Talk and Write About It

Complete these statements about reproduction.

1. When ovulation occurs, an egg <u>is released from an ovary</u>.
2. A developing human from eight weeks to birth is called a <u>fetus</u>.
3. The three stages of development between fertilization and birth are <u>zygote, embryo, fetus</u>
4. The placenta is important to the fetus because <u>it enables the exchange of materials between the fetus and its mother</u>.

Produce Language

Look at the Big Question. Write about what you learned in this lesson. Then complete the Know/Want/Learned chart. Add terms you learned.

_____

_____

_____

_____

Assess Understanding

Your Turn

Model Read the instructions aloud with students. As you read, point to the terms, the pictures, and the lines for the numbers. Then read the terms aloud with students.

Talk and Write About It

On Their Own Have partners take turns reading and completing each sentence aloud. Then have each student write his or her responses.

Produce Language

On Their Own After students review the Big Question, have them write and talk about reproduction and the endocrine system. After the writing activity, invite students to read what they have written aloud to the class.

Be sure that students finish up the lesson by writing terms they learned in their K/W/L charts.

Wrap Up

Table Talk Have students reflect on the Big Question and what they learned. Encourage students to build fluency by reading their writing in groups or to the class.

✔ **Learned** and applied vocabulary related to the endocrine system and reproduction

✔ **Spoken** statements about glands, hormones, negative feedback, and human development

✔ **Written** statements about reproduction, particularly about the stages of human development

Leveled Language Proficiency

Students at each proficiency level should be able to perform the following tasks.

Reading/Writing

Early Beginner/Beginner Identify written words associated with reproduction. Write lists of words and phrases to describe hormones, reproduction, and human development.

Early Intermediate Read and understand simple sentences about how hormones regulate the body's processes. Write simple sentences about the endocrine system and reproduction.

Intermediate Read and understand descriptions of the reproductive and endocrine systems written in full sentences. Describe hormones, reproduction, and the stages of human development in short paragraphs using full sentences.

Advanced/Transitioning Read and understand full sentences and paragraphs on the endocrine system and its role in reproduction. Write coherent descriptions of reproduction, as well as the connection between the nervous system and endocrine system.

LIFE SCIENCE STUDENT BOOK RESOURCES

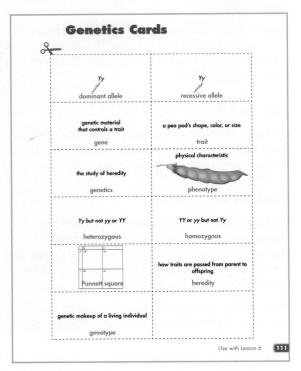

page 111

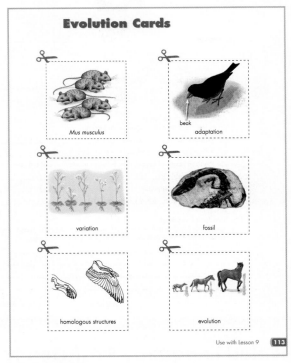

page 113

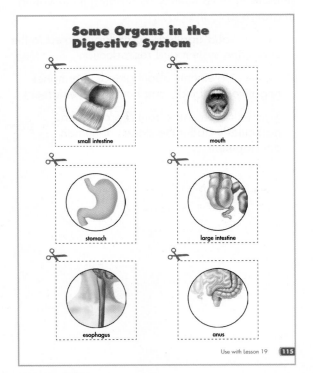

page 115

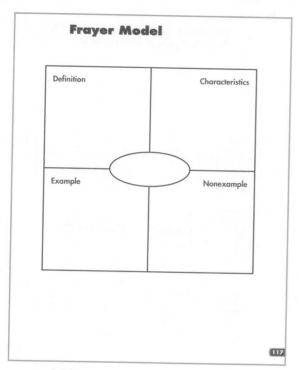

page 117

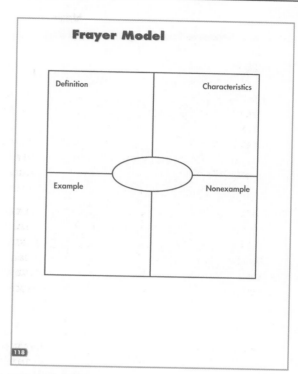

page 118

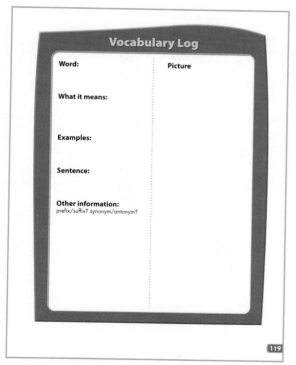

page 119

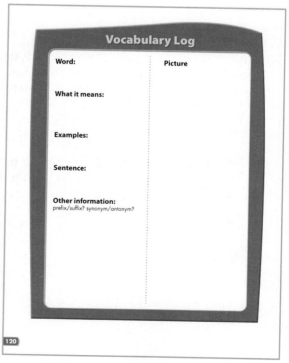

page 120

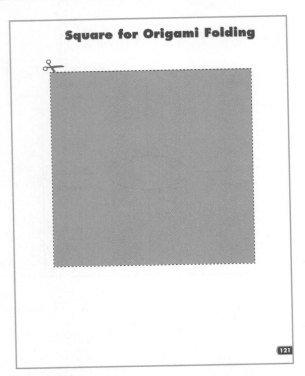

page 121

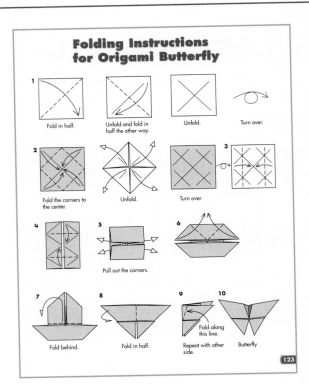

page 123

CREDITS

Illustrations

2, 3, 4, 19, 45, 47, 48, 51, 52, 113 Greg Harris; **3, 6, 36, 51, 60, 98, 99, 100, 103, 105** Kenneth Batelman; **5, 10, 30, 51, 60, 63, 79, 88** Nathan Jarvis; **6, 14, 15, 16, 19, 29, 52, 54, 98, 102, 104** Rob Schuster; **7, 66** Dave Cockburn; **7, 9, 18, 38, 39, 41, 43, 46, 62, 63** Laurie O'Keefe; **7, 51, 52, 55, 57, 58, 59, 60, 61, 63, 65, 71, 75, 77, 80, 98, 102, 104** Precision Graphics; **7, 8** Theresa Sakno; **14** Jonathan Massie; **15, 35, 42, 57, 113** Steve McEntee; **31, 34, 35, 63, 71, 79, 81, 95, 97, 113** John Edwards; **35** J. B. Woolsey; **39** Robert Hynes; **43, 44** Kevin Jones; **43, 51, 55, 61, 65, 67, 69, 71, 95, 97, 104, 105** Peter Bull; **51** Karen Minot; **63** Big Sesh Studios; **71** Leonello Calvetti; **76, 83, 84, 85, 113** Martha Spellman; **83, 84** Fran Milner; **83, 85** John Foerster; **104** Robin Boyer; **123** Reproduced with permission by Dover Publications from Easy Origami by John Montroll, October 1992./©Dover Publications.

Photographs

Every effort has been made to secure permission and provide appropriate credit for photographic material. The publisher deeply regrets any omission and pledges to correct errors called to its attention in subsequent editions.

Unless otherwise acknowledged, all photographs are the property of Pearson Education, Inc.

Photo locators denoted as follows: Top (T), Center (C), Bottom (B), Left (L), Right (R), Background (Bkgd)

Cover

Origami "Grasshopper" designed and folded by Brian Chan, in handmade Origamido® paper by Richard L. Alexander and Michael G. LaFosse.

6 Fedor Sidoro/Fotolia, Creatas/Thinkstock, Gina Rothfels/Fotolia, Mite/Fotolia, ste72/Fotolia, Tony Campbell/Fotolia; **7** CDC, Creatas/Thinkstock, DLILLC/Corbis/SuperStock, Grey rabbit/SuperStock, Thinkstock, Tom Brakefield/Thinkstock; **8** CDC, Garry DeLong/Fotolia; **9** Thinkstock, Tom Brakefield/Thinkstock; **10** Martin Kreutz/SuperStock; **18** michal81/Fotolia; **23** Ferenc Szelepcsenyi/Fotolia; **27** Jupiterimages/Getty images/Thinkstock; **31** Johnny Lye/Fotolia; **35** Michael Gray/Fotolia; **37** Chungking/Fotolia; **43** Getty Images/Thinkstock; **46** Creatas/Thinkstock; **47** Fedor Sidoro/Fotolia, ©DK Images, Alan Dyck/Fotolia, alle/Fotolia, DK Images, Eric Isselee/Fotolia, GlobalP/iStockphoto, Gudellaphoto/Fotolia, Ignacio Barragan/Fotolia, Jupiterimages/gettyimages/Thinkstock, photocreo/Fotolia, Ronnie Howard/Fotolia, RSaraiva/Fotolia, SuperStock; **49** Comstock/Fotolia, Fotolia; **51** Jupiterimages/Thinkstock, Nigel Monckton/Fotolia; **52** Burtsc/Fotolia, Tom Mc Nemar/Fotolia; **61** ©Royalty-Free/Corbis, Comstock/Thinkstock; **62** Hemera Technologies/Thinkstock; **63** Fabrice Beauchehe/Fotolia, Kirill Zdorov/Fotolia, Rick Carlson/Fotolia; **64** Feng Yu/Fotolia, Getty Images/Jupiterimages/Thinkstock, Mite/Fotolia, Roger de Montfort /Fotolia, Steve Byland/Fotolia, Thinkstock; **65** Anatolii/Fotolia, Brand X Pictures/Thinkstock, Ignacio Barragan/Fotolia, Photosani/Fotolia; **67** Catalin Petolea/Fotolia; **68** RSaraiva/Fotolia; **70** ©Linda Bucklin/Shutterstock; **71** (TC) Steve Gorton/©DK Images; **73** Creatas/Thinkstock; **78** Tim Ridley/©DK Images; **87** Scott Van Blarcom/Fotolia; **91** (TL) ©/DK Images, Image Source/Corbis; **93** Image Source/Corbis; **98** EuToch/Fotolia; **100** Zedcor Wholly Owned/Getty Images/Thinkstock; **103** Terex/Dreamstime LLC, Britvich/Dreamstime LLC, Chiyacat/Dreamstime LLC; **113** Michael Gray/Fotolia.

CONTENTS

Lesson 2

Matter

Vocabulary matter, physical property, chemical property, element, atom, molecule, compound, mixture, mass, volume, density, physical change, chemical change, law of conservation of mass

Materials clear container, water, rock and wooden block (approximately the same size), piece of paper

Science Background

- Every form of matter has two kinds of properties—physical and chemical.

- An atom is the basic unit from which elements are made. An element cannot be broken down into other substances. Two or more atoms held together by a chemical bond form a molecule.

- A compound is formed by two or more elements that are chemically combined.

- A substance that undergoes a physical change is still the same substance after the change. Chemical changes produce new substances with new and different chemical and physical properties.

Frontload the Lesson

What is matter?

Talk About It

Build Background Choose any object in the room and talk about its physical properties, such as color, texture, and shape.

Content and Language

Predict

Model Read the Big Question and the objectives aloud. Explain that matter makes up any substance, material, or thing, even the invisible air.

Guide Discussion Use the Big Question to ask students what the lesson is about. *(matter)*

Matter

Big Question What is matter?

You will . . .
- Understand that matter is made of atoms, which may combine to form molecules.
- Differentiate physical properties from chemical properties.
- Use new terms to describe matter.

Talk About It

Look at the picture. Work with a partner to answer the questions below.

1. What parts of the sandwich do you see?
2. What words can you use to describe each part of the sandwich?
3. How can you change the sandwich?

Predict
Look at the Big Question and the "You will . . ." statements at the top of the page. Describe what you think you are going to learn in this lesson.

I think I am going to learn about . . .

6   Lesson 2

Leveled Instruction

Early Beginner Ask students to find pictures in the lesson that illustrate the concepts of *physical change* and *chemical change*. Have them draw another example of each type of change.

Beginner Ask students questions about how they can change matter. Ask them to name ways they can change a piece of paper.

Early Intermediate/Intermediate Encourage students to work independently. Have them illustrate the difference between an *atom*, a *molecule*, and a *compound*.

Advanced/Transitioning As students work through course material in their science textbook, or do further online research, have them create an illustration that describes the law of conservation of mass. Encourage volunteers to explain their illustrations to the class.

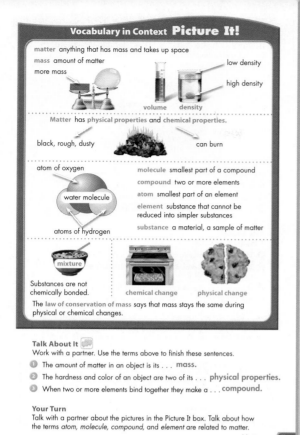

Vocabulary in Context Picture It!

matter anything that has mass and takes up space
mass amount of matter
more mass

low density

high density

volume   density

Matter has physical properties and chemical properties.

black, rough, dusty   can burn

atom of oxygen

water molecule

atoms of hydrogen

molecule smallest part of a compound
compound two or more elements
atom smallest part of an element
element substance that cannot be reduced into simpler substances
substance a material, a sample of matter

mixture

Substances are not chemically bonded.   chemical change   physical change

The law of conservation of mass says that mass stays the same during physical or chemical changes.

Talk About It
Work with a partner. Use the terms above to finish these sentences.
1 The amount of matter in an object is its . . . **mass.**
2 The hardness and color of an object are two of its . . . **physical properties.**
3 When two or more elements bind together they make a . . . **compound.**

Your Turn
Talk with a partner about the pictures in the Picture It box. Talk about how the terms *atom, molecule, compound,* and *element* are related to matter.

Matter **7**

Academic Vocabulary

- Point out to students that several terms in the lesson are multiple-meaning words. *Matter* can refer to the physical substances around us, which is its scientific meaning. *Matter* is also used in an idiom—*what's the matter*—which means "Is something wrong?"

- Tell students that *property* has a scientific meaning and a common meaning. The scientific meaning of the word is "a characteristic" or "a way to describe something." The common meaning is "something that someone owns."

- Students may be familiar with *volume* as it relates to sound. Explain that the volume of matter is the amount of space it takes up.

- Cognates are words that have the same or similar roots and meanings in two languages. Have students share any vocabulary terms that they recognize as cognates to words in their first languages. For example, in Spanish, the word *masa* is a cognate for *mass* and *volumen* is a cognate for *volume.*

↻ Comprehensible Input

Vocabulary in Context: Picture It!

1. **Say the Term** Say each term slowly, artificially stressing each syllable. Have students repeat. Then say the term more naturally and have students repeat.

2. **Introduce Word Meaning** Connect each term to the visual that illustrates it.

3. **Demonstrate** Use gestures and visuals to demonstrate each term. For example:

   - Place a rock and a block of wood into a container of water. Point out how the rock sinks, while the block floats. Say, *The rock has greater density. That means it has more mass within a given amount of space, or volume.*

   - Tear a piece of paper in two. Say, *Tearing the paper is a physical change. The substances in the paper remain the same. If I use fire to burn the paper, that would be a chemical change. The smoke and ash are different substances than those in paper.*

4. **Apply** After all of the terms have been discussed, have students demonstrate understanding with Talk About It.

Talk About It

Guide Discussion Read the sentences aloud. Remind students to use the terms in the Picture It box to complete the sentences. As students give their answers, have them point to the corresponding image.

RTI Response to Intervention

If students have difficulty pronouncing the word *physical* . . .

Then remind them that *ph* makes an *f* sound in English. Write and say the word *fizz* for students. Slowly say the word *physical*, pointing to *fizz* as you say the first syllable.

Your Turn

Guide Discussion Remind students to refer to the images that correspond to these terms. Encourage students to re-create these images and label them accordingly to help them relate the terms to *matter.*

Matter

Language Production

Do You Understand?

Comprehension Support Remind students of the beginning of the lesson. Have students brainstorm the words they used to describe the sandwich. Say, *Now you can use words like* matter *and* mixture *to describe what you see.*

Model Read the statements aloud with students. Demonstrate how students can ask themselves questions to help them do the activity. Say, *Is a sandwich a mixture? If you answer* yes, *write* true *on the line. If you answer* no, *write* false *on the line.*

Talk About It

Guide Discussion Read the statements aloud with students as they work together to complete the sentences.

Your Turn

Guide Discussion Remind students that the Big Question is *What is matter?* Have them refer to the list of vocabulary terms as they describe classroom objects.

In Other Words

Model Read the example sentence aloud for students and have them repeat it. Then ask, *What is another way to say this? What is another word, or words, for* properties? Have students take turns reading the sentence aloud, choosing one of the yellow-highlighted words to fill in the space each time. Then have students suggest their own sentences that use the word *properties.* They might read one of the lesson objectives or other sentences in the lesson for practice. Then have them discuss properties of a good story or properties of a good teacher, to give them practice using the term in other contexts.

Do You Understand?

Here is the sandwich you talked about in the beginning of this lesson. Decide if each statement below the picture is **true** or **false**.

1. __true__ The sandwich is a mixture.
2. __false__ Cutting the sandwich is a chemical change.
3. __false__ Bread is an element.
4. __true__ Everything in the sandwich is matter.
5. __false__ The sandwich does not have volume or mass.

Talk About It
Complete the sentences.

1. Toasting bread causes a change that is a . . . **chemical change.**
2. The molecules in the bread, the meat, the plate, and the air are made of . . . **atoms.**
3. When you describe a tomato as red and smooth, you tell about its . . . **physical properties.**
4. The amount of space the sandwich takes up is its . . . **volume.**

Your Turn
Talk with a partner about another object you see in the classroom. Describe its physical properties. Then give examples of possible physical changes of the object.

In Other Words

Some physical	properties	of matter are color and texture.
	characteristics	
	qualities	

8   Lesson 2

Leveled Language Proficiency

Students at each proficiency level should be able to perform the following tasks.

Listening/Speaking

Early Beginner/Beginner Gesture or point to respond to oral directions. Repeat vocabulary terms in response to questions.

Early Intermediate Use single words or short spoken phrases to respond to questions. Tell what a physical property is. Tell three physical properties of a common object without support.

Intermediate Follow oral directions with little to no help. Use complete spoken sentences to describe properties of matter.

Advanced/Transitioning Follow oral directions independently. Use complete sentences to orally explain the differences among *mass, volume,* and *density.*

Your Turn

Label the diagram and complete the sentences. Use the terms from the box.

compound	atom	element	molecule

<u>atom</u> of nitrogen

ammonia <u>molecule</u>

Hydrogen is an <u>element</u> .

Ammonia is a <u>compound</u> .

<u>atom</u> of hydrogen

Talk and Write About It

Complete the statements about how matter can be described.

1. Some examples of elements are <u>oxygen, hydrogen, nitrogen</u>
2. An atom is the smallest unit <u>of an element</u>
3. When two atoms bind together they form <u>a molecule</u> .
4. Two or more elements that chemically combine form <u>a compound</u> .
5. The amount of matter stays the same during physical or chemical changes according to <u>the law of conservation of mass</u> .

Produce Language

Write about how some physical and chemical properties of all matter. Use as many vocabulary terms as you can.

_____

_____

_____

_____

Leveled Language Proficiency

Students at each proficiency level should be able to perform the following tasks.

Reading/Writing

Early Beginner/Beginner Identify words in context that describe matter. Write the names of processes that are involved in changes of matter.

Early Intermediate Read to find out about atoms, molecules, and compounds. Write short phrases that explain how matter is made of different elements.

Intermediate Read aloud and summarize sentences that describe properties of matter. Use complete sentences to paraphrase the meaning of key vocabulary terms.

Advanced/Transitioning Read aloud sentences that describe physical and chemical changes. Write complete and original sentences that describe physical and chemical change.

Assess Understanding

Your Turn

Model Read the terms and labels with students. Tell students that this diagram is similar to the one for water in the Picture It box, but it is of a different substance, ammonia. Ammonia is sometimes used for cleaning. Have students refer to the diagram and sentences in the Picture It box if needed to help them complete the activity.

Talk and Write About It

On Their Own Have students work in pairs to read the statements aloud. Have them write their responses individually before returning to their partners to review their answers. Point out to students that they might not have the exact same wording in their responses, but that does not necessarily mean that one is incorrect.

Produce Language

On Their Own Reread the Big Question to students before they begin. Remind students to write about the different properties of matter, how matter is measured, and how it changes.

Wrap Up

Table Talk Have students reflect on what they learned. Encourage students to build fluency by reading their writing in groups or to the class.

✔ **Learned** and applied vocabulary related to matter

✔ **Spoken** statements about the properties of matter

✔ **Written** statements about how matter changes

Lesson 3

States of Matter

Vocabulary solid, liquid, surface tension, viscosity, gas, pressure, melting point, vaporization, boiling point, Charles's Law, directly proportional, Boyle's Law, inversely proportional

Materials ice cubes, plastic cup or zipper seal bag, desk lamp, container with water

Science Background

- At a solid's melting point, its particles vibrate so fast that they break free from their fixed positions.

- Vaporization occurs when the particles in a liquid gain enough thermal energy to move independently.

- The volume of a gas changes in relation to changes in pressure and temperature.

States of Matter

Big Question When and how can a substance change form?

You will . . .
- Describe how shape and volume are used to identify states of matter.
- Identify the points at which substances change states.
- Use key terms to describe different states of matter.

Talk About It

Look at the pictures below. Talk about what is happening to the water in each picture.

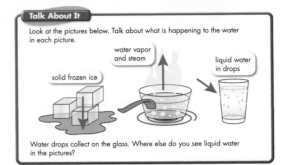

water vapor and steam

solid frozen ice

liquid water in drops

Water drops collect on the glass. Where else do you see liquid water in the pictures?

Predict
Look at the Big Question and the "You will . . ." statements at the top of the page. Describe what you think you are going to learn in this lesson.

I think I am going to learn about . . .

↻ Frontload the Lesson

When and how can a substance change form?

Talk About It

Build Background Put an ice cube in a clear plastic drinking glass—or in a zipper-seal plastic bag—and have students observe it. If possible, place it under the heat of a desk lamp. Ask, *What is happening to the ice cube as time passes?* (It's melting.) Point out that the ice cube's *state of matter* is changing from a solid to a liquid.

↻ Content and Language

Predict

Model Read the Big Question and the objectives aloud. Review the meanings of the words *matter* and *volume* with students.

Guide Discussion Encourage students to use the visuals to help them make their prediction.

Leveled Instruction

Early Beginner/Beginner Ask students to find pictures in the lesson that illustrate the concepts of *melting point* and *boiling point*. Offer them examples from everyday life to help them connect to the concept.

Early Intermediate/Intermediate Encourage students to visualize the foods in their freezer at home. Have them name a frozen food item and identify whether temperature changes can affect the state of the food.

Advanced/Transitioning After students complete the lesson, have them create a visual that describes Charles's Law and Boyle's Law. They can use the Picture It box or other sources as a reference. Have them present their work to their classmates and display it for reference.

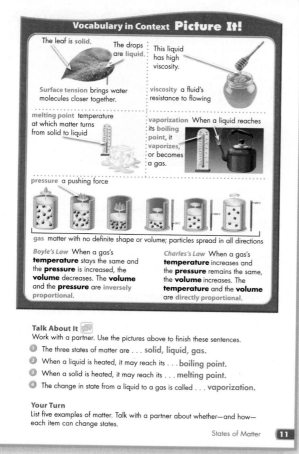

Vocabulary in Context Picture It!

The leaf is solid.

The drops are liquid.

This liquid has high viscosity.

Surface tension brings water molecules closer together.

viscosity a fluid's resistance to flowing

melting point temperature at which matter turns from solid to liquid

vaporization When a liquid reaches its **boiling point**, it vaporizes, or becomes a gas.

pressure a pushing force

gas matter with no definite shape or volume; particles spread in all directions

Boyle's Law When a gas's **temperature** stays the same and the **pressure** is increased, the **volume** decreases. The **volume** and the **pressure** are inversely proportional.

Charles's Law When a gas's **temperature** increases and the **pressure** remains the same, the **volume** increases. The **temperature** and the **volume** are directly proportional.

Talk About It

Work with a partner. Use the pictures above to finish these sentences.

1. The three states of matter are . . . solid, liquid, gas.
2. When a liquid is heated, it may reach its . . . boiling point.
3. When a solid is heated, it may reach its . . . melting point.
4. The change in state from a liquid to a gas is called . . . vaporization.

Your Turn

List five examples of matter. Talk with a partner about whether—and how—each item can change states.

States of Matter **11**

Academic Vocabulary

- Point out that *Boyle* in Boyle's Law is the name of a scientist who experimented with the pressure and volume of gas. It is just a coincidence that the name sounds like *boil* in boiling point.

- You might also use the terms *Charles's Law* and *Boyle's Law* to teach the proper formation of possessives: Add an apostrophe + "s" to names that end in "s." Add only an apostrophe to plurals that end in "s." Add an apostrophe + "s" to irregular plurals (such as *people* and *children*) which do not end in "s."

- Cognates are words that have the same or similar roots and meanings in two languages. Have students share any vocabulary terms they recognize as cognates to words in their first languages. For example, in Spanish, the word *sólido* is a cognate for *solid*, and *líquido* is a cognate for *liquid*.

- Point out that *directly proportional* means that variables go in the same *direction*. Explain that the term *inverse* means "opposite," and that *inversely proportional* means variables go in the opposite direction.

↻ Comprehensible Input

Vocabulary in Context: Picture It!

1. **Say the Term** Say each term slowly, artificially stressing each syllable. Have students repeat. Then say the term more naturally and have students repeat.

2. **Introduce Word Meaning** Connect each term to the visual that illustrates it.

3. **Demonstrate** Use gestures and visuals to demonstrate each term. For example:

   - Show an ice cube and a glass of water. Say, *The ice cube is solid. The water is liquid. They are the same substance.*

   - Pour a little bit of water on the table and have students watch it flow. Explain that water flows fast because of low viscosity. Ask students to consider what would happen if you instead spilled honey on the table.

4. **Apply** After all of the terms have been discussed, have students demonstrate understanding with Talk About It.

Talk About It

Guide Discussion Read the statements aloud with students. Have them work with partners to complete the sentences.

RTI Response to Intervention

If students have difficulty pronouncing the double-*s* in *pressure* . . .

Then model correct pronunciation having students repeat. Then write the word on the board covering up the first sylllable, so that only the word *sure* is showing. Have students read and pronounce *sure* and *pressure* several times in sequence.

Your Turn

Guide Discussion Brainstorm common items with students and write them on the board. Mark each item with an *s*, an *l*, or a *g* to show its state of matter. After students talk to a partner, have a class discussion on what could cause each item's state of matter to change.

States of Matter

↻ Language Production

Do You Understand?

Comprehension Support As students look at the picture of the pot boiling on the stove, ask them to describe what they see. Ask them what the flame is doing to the soup. Ask them what will happen if the flame continues to burn for a long time.

Model Demonstrate how students can ask themselves questions to help them label the parts of the picture. Say, *I see there are terms for three states of matter in the word box. Which part of the picture might be a solid? Which part is a liquid?*

Talk About It

Guide Discussion Read the statements aloud with students as they work together to complete them. If students have difficulty understanding the concepts of *definite volume* and *definite shape,* then have them picture three balloons balloon filled with water, air, and cement. Have them picture what happens when the balloon is peeled away on each type of matter. You can also review the meanings of *definite* and *indefinite.* Explain that *definite* things are well defined, and *indefinite* things are vague, or undefined.

Your Turn

Guide Discussion Listen to students talk about when they have seen matter change states. Remind them that the Big Question is *When and how can a substance change form?*

In Other Words

Model Read the example sentence aloud. Then ask, *What is another way to say this? What is another word, or words, for* therefore? Have students take turns reading the sentence aloud, choosing one of the yellow-highlighted words to fill in the space each time. Then have students suggest their own sentences for *therefore.* Point out that *therefore* is a formal, academic word, used mostly in lectures, speeches, papers, and debates. Such words can sound dry, if repeated. To vary use of *therefore* and *thus,* students can use *hence, so, consequently* and the phrases "for this reason," and "because of this."

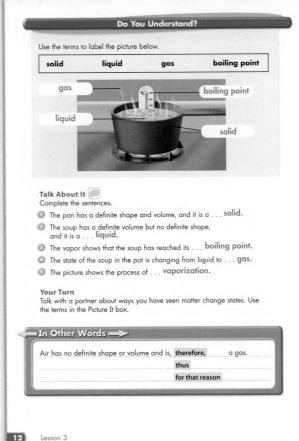

Do You Understand?

Use the terms to label the picture below.

| solid | liquid | gas | boiling point |

- gas
- boiling point
- liquid
- solid

Talk About It 📖
Complete the sentences.

1. The pan has a definite shape and volume, and it is a . . . **solid.**
2. The soup has a definite volume but no definite shape, and it is a . . . **liquid.**
3. The vapor shows that the soup has reached its . . . **boiling point.**
4. The state of the soup in the pot is changing from liquid to . . . **gas.**
5. The picture shows the process of . . . **vaporization.**

Your Turn
Talk with a partner about ways you have seen matter change states. Use the terms in the Picture It box.

⟵ In Other Words ⟹

Air has no definite shape or volume and is, | **therefore,** | a gas.
| **thus** |
| **for that reason** |

12   Lesson 3

Leveled Language Proficiency

Students at each proficiency level should be able to perform the following tasks.

Listening/Speaking

Early Beginner/Beginner Point to images to respond to spoken questions about the key terms. Say the terms that describe the three states of matter.

Early Intermediate Use short phrases to respond to questions. Tell what pressure is and how it affects the volume of a gas.

Intermediate Follow oral directions with little to no help. Tell how surface tension and viscosity are related to liquids. Speak in complete sentences.

Advanced/Transitioning Follow oral directions independently. Explain, in spoken sentences, the difference between an object's melting point and its boiling point.

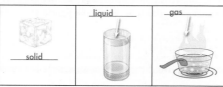

Think, Talk, and Write

Your Turn

Identify the state of matter for each picture. Then circle the word that describes the shape and volume of each state.

	liquid	gas
solid		

Shape: (definite)	**Shape:** definite	**Shape:** definite
indefinite	(indefinite)	(indefinite)
Volume: (definite)	**Volume:** (definite)	**Volume:** definite
indefinite	indefinite	(indefinite)

Talk and Write About It

Complete the statements about the states of matter.

1. When matter reaches its melting point, <u>a solid becomes a liquid</u>.
2. When matter reaches its boiling point, <u>a liquid becomes a gas</u>.
3. When pressure rises and the temperature stays the same, gas volume <u>decreases</u>.
4. When temperature rises and pressure remains the same, gas volume <u>increases</u>.
5. Surface tension brings molecules of liquid <u>closer together</u>.

Produce Language

Write what you learned in this lesson about changes in matter. Use as many vocabulary terms as you can.

_____

_____

_____

_____

_____

States of Matter **13**

Leveled Language Proficiency

Students at each proficiency level should be able to perform the following tasks.

Reading/Writing

Early Beginner/Beginner Locate words that describe matter. Write the names of processes that are involved in changes of matter.

Early Intermediate Read to find out what a *state of matter* is. Write short phrases that explain what happens to the particles in matter to make a liquid reach its boiling point.

Intermediate Comprehend phrases that describe Charles's Law and Boyle's Law. Write complete sentences to paraphrase the meaning of both laws.

Advanced/Transitioning Read aloud sentences that describe Charles's Law and Boyle's Law. Write complete and original sentences that relate both laws to how matter changes states.

↻ Assess Understanding

Your Turn

Model Remind students to review visuals and activities from this lesson. Review the terms *definite* and *indefinite*. Say, Definite *means that the shape or volume is defined or clear.* Make sure that students also understand that *indefinite* means the opposite of *definite,* that is, not definite and clear. If time is available, extend the language lesson by also introducing related words, such as *finite, infinite, define, defined,* and *undefined.*

Talk and Write About It

On Their Own Read the statements aloud to students. Have students discuss their ideas with a partner before writing their responses.

Produce Language

On Their Own Reread the Big Question with students before they write. Give them time to discuss their writing with a partner. Ask student volunteers to share their sentences with the class.

Wrap Up

Table Talk Have students reflect on what they learned. Encourage students to build fluency by reading their writing in groups or to the class.

✔ **Learned** and applied vocabulary related to changes in matter

✔ **Spoken** statements about how matter changes

✔ **Written** statements about what causes matter to change from one state to another

Lesson 4

Elements and the Periodic Table

Vocabulary atom, electron, nucleus, proton, neutron, atomic number, isotope, mass number, atomic mass, periodic table, chemical symbol, period, group

Materials index cards, poster of the periodic table, modeling clay

 Science Background

- At the center of an atom is a tiny, dense nucleus containing protons and neutrons. Surrounding the nucleus is a cloudlike region of moving electrons.

- The periodic table includes each element's atomic number, chemical symbol, name, and atomic mass.

- The properties of an element can be predicted from its location in the periodic table.

Frontload the Lesson

How is the periodic table organized?

Talk About It

Build Background Read the directions aloud. Then read the terms aloud as students sort them into piles. To help students decide which pile to sort each term into, model by saying, *I have never heard the word* isotope. *I will put the card in Pile 3. I've heard* atomic mass, *but I don't know what it means. I will put the card in Pile 2.*

Content and Language

Predict

Model Read the Big Question and the objectives aloud. Check student understanding.

Guide Discussion Ask students to read the objectives with a partner. Have them say a few elements that they are familiar with.

Elements and the Periodic Table

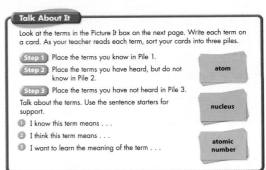

Big Question How is the periodic table organized?

You will . . .
- Identify the parts of an atom.
- Use the periodic table.
- Use terms related to atoms and the periodic table.

Talk About It

Look at the terms in the Picture It box on the next page. Write each term on a card. As your teacher reads each term, sort your cards into three piles.

Step 1 Place the terms you know in Pile 1.

Step 2 Place the terms you have heard, but do not know in Pile 2.

Step 3 Place the terms you have not heard in Pile 3.

Talk about the terms. Use the sentence starters for support.

1. I know this term means . . .
2. I think this term means . . .
3. I want to learn the meaning of the term . . .

Predict

Look at the Big Question and the "You will . . ." statements at the top of the page. Describe what you think you are going to learn in this lesson.

I think I am going to learn about . . .

14 Lesson 4

Leveled Instruction

Early Beginner Have students point to pictures and use gestures to answer questions. When students point to a picture, say the term aloud and write the term on the board.

Beginner Keep a list of key terms on the board for students to refer to when answering questions about atoms and the periodic table.

Early Intermediate/Intermediate These students should respond to questions about the properties of atoms with complete sentences and examples. For additional practice, extend the Produce Language activity on page 17 by having students repeat the exercise for multiple elements, or present their element data in the form of "What Am I?" riddles.

Advanced/Transitioning Have these students partner with beginner students. Encourage them to model how they think about, talk about, and write about atoms and the periodic table.

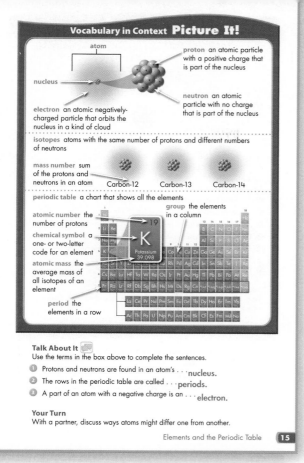

Vocabulary in Context Picture It!

atom

proton an atomic particle with a positive charge that is part of the nucleus

nucleus

neutron an atomic particle with no charge that is part of the nucleus

electron an atomic negatively-charged particle that orbits the nucleus in a kind of cloud

isotopes atoms with the same number of protons and different numbers of neutrons

mass number sum of the protons and neutrons in an atom

Carbon-12   Carbon-13   Carbon-14

periodic table a chart that shows all the elements

atomic number the number of protons

group the elements in a column

chemical symbol a one- or two-letter code for an element

atomic mass the average mass of all isotopes of an element

period the elements in a row

K
Potassium
39.098

Talk About It
Use the terms in the box above to complete the sentences.

1. Protons and neutrons are found in an atom's . . . nucleus.
2. The rows in the periodic table are called . . . periods.
3. A part of an atom with a negative charge is an . . . electron.

Your Turn
With a partner, discuss ways atoms might differ one from another.

Academic Vocabulary

- Students may think of the nucleus of a cell when they see and hear the term *nucleus*. Point out that the nucleus of an atom is different, but both are in the center.

- Point out that a *symbol* stands for something. Encourage students to think of common symbols they might see on road signs.

- Write the word *organize* on the board. Explain that when you organize something, you sort it into groups. Have students discuss objects that they sort, such as classroom materials or laundry at home. Ask, *What is the purpose of sorting?* (To make objects easier to use, understand, or find.)

- Cognates are words that have the same or similar roots and meanings in two languages. Have students share any vocabulary terms they recognize as cognates to words in their first languages. The words *atom, nucleus, proton, electron,* and *neutron* all have cognates in Spanish.

↻ Comprehensible Input

Vocabulary in Context: Picture It!

1. **Say the Term** Say each term slowly, artificially stressing each syllable. Have students repeat. Then say the term more naturally and have students repeat.

2. **Introduce Word Meaning** Connect each term to the visual that illustrates it.

3. **Demonstrate** Use gestures and visuals to demonstrate each term. For example:

   - For the term *proton*, draw a plus sign (+) on the board. Then draw a negative sign (−) for the term *electron*.

   - For the term *nucleus*, draw a medium-sized circle on the board with a smaller circle inside it at the center. Say the word *nucleus* as you point to the smaller circle.

   - Display a periodic table as you say *periodic table*. Point to the individual boxes as you say *element*. Move your finger up and down over one column as you say *group* and back and forth over a row as you say *period*.

4. **Apply** After each term has been discussed, have students demonstrate understanding with Talk About It.

Talk About It

Guide Discussion Call on volunteers to use the terms in Picture It in oral sentences. Use prompts, such as *Who can use the word* proton *in a sentence?*

RTI Response to Intervention

If students have difficulty saying the terms *periodic table* and *period* . . .

Then write the terms on the board and underline the letters *io* in each term. Explain that in both terms, the *i* makes the sound /ee/. In *periodic*, the *o* makes its usual short sound /o/, but in *period*, the *o* is pronounced as a schwa. Point to each term and say it aloud with students.

Your Turn

Guide Discussion Ask students guiding questions, such as *What parts make up an atom?* and *How can atoms be different from each other?*

Elements and the Periodic Table

⟳ Language Production

Do You Understand?

Comprehension Support Before students start the activity, talk about the properties of each of the atomic particles, including where they can be found.

Model Demonstrate how students can ask themselves questions to help them complete the activity. Say, *Which particle is found in the nucleus and has a positive charge? Which particle is found outside of the nucleus and has a negative charge?*

Talk About It

Guide Discussion Give students examples of isotopes, such as carbon-12 and carbon-13. Explain that the extra neutron changes the mass of the atom or the mass number. The mass helps scientists identify the isotope.

Your Turn

Guide Discussion If time permits, have students make a model of an atom using modeling clay. They can use three colors to represent the three types of atomic particles. Have students describe their models using key terms.

In Other Words

Model Read the example sentence aloud for students and have them repeat it. Then ask, *What is another way to say this? What is another word, or words, for the word* particle? Have students take turns reading the sentence aloud, choosing one of the yellow-highlighted terms to fill in the space each time. Then have students suggest their own sentences, about atoms or about matter, that use the word *particle*.

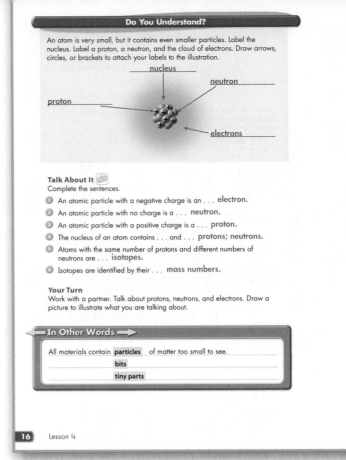

Do You Understand?

An atom is very small, but it contains even smaller particles. Label the nucleus. Label a proton, a neutron, and the cloud of electrons. Draw arrows, circles, or brackets to attach your labels to the illustration.

Talk About It
Complete the sentences.
1. An atomic particle with a negative charge is an . . . electron.
2. An atomic particle with no charge is a . . . neutron.
3. An atomic particle with a positive charge is a . . . proton.
4. The nucleus of an atom contains . . . and . . . protons; neutrons.
5. Atoms with the same number of protons and different numbers of neutrons are . . . isotopes.
6. Isotopes are identified by their . . . mass numbers.

Your Turn
Work with a partner. Talk about protons, neutrons, and electrons. Draw a picture to illustrate what you are talking about.

◄— In Other Words —►

All materials contain	**particles**	of matter too small to see.
	bits	
	tiny parts	

16   Lesson 4

Leveled Language Proficiency

Students at each proficiency level should be able to perform the following tasks.

Listening/Speaking

Early Beginner/Beginner Gesture or point in response to oral questions about atoms. Use single words or short spoken phrases to describe atoms.

Early Intermediate Follow oral directions with help. Tell about the properties of atoms using short spoken phrases or simple sentences.

Intermediate Follow oral directions with little to no help. Using complete sentences, ask and answer questions about atomic particles and isotopes.

Advanced/Transitioning Follow multiple-step oral directions. Orally describe various elements and their atomic properties to others.

Your Turn

The periodic table contains information about each element. Look at this part of the periodic table. Label the *chemical symbol, atomic mass,* and *atomic number.*

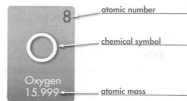

atomic number _____

chemical symbol _____

atomic mass _____

Talk and Write About It 💬 ✏️

Complete the statements about the periodic table.

1. The periodic table shows <u>all of the elements, information about them, and how the elements relate to each other</u>.

2. The atomic mass tells you <u>the average mass of all isotopes of an element</u>.

3. The atomic number is equal to <u>the number of protons an atom has</u>.

4. The chemical symbol for oxygen is <u>the letter O</u>.

5. The groups of the periodic table are shown in <u>columns</u>.

6. The periods of the periodic table are shown in <u>rows</u>.

Produce Language

Choose one element. Find it on the periodic table. Write about the element's properties using as many vocabulary terms as you can.

_____

_____

_____

_____

_____

_____

Elements and the Periodic Table **17**

Leveled Language Proficiency

Students at each proficiency level should be able to perform the following tasks.

Reading/Writing

Early Beginner/Beginner Match pictures to corresponding terms. Write a list of words and phrases that describe properties of an element.

Early Intermediate Read sentences about atoms. Write descriptions of atoms using multiple sentences in a logical order.

Intermediate Summarize a passage about the periodic table. Use details and examples to write about an element in the periodic table.

Advanced/Transitioning Make inferences about elements and their properties while reading. Revise writing to clarify key ideas about elements and the periodic table.

↻ Assess Understanding

Your Turn

Model Review with students what the different pieces of information in the periodic table tell us about an element. Use the illustration of the periodic table in the Picture It box, or use, if available, a large classroom poster of the periodic table for reference.

Talk and Write About It

On Their Own Read each sentence starter aloud with students. Have partners discuss answers before writing.

Produce Language

On Their Own Before students begin writing, use a sample element to discuss what they can find out about it from the periodic table. Model for students how to use the periodic table to identify atomic number, atomic mass, and chemical symbol. Write sentences that include key terms on the board.

Wrap Up

Table Talk Have students reflect on the Big Question and what they learned. Encourage students to build fluency by reading their writing in groups or to the class.

✔ **Learned** and applied vocabulary related to atoms and the periodic table

✔ **Spoken** statements about how the periodic table is organized

✔ **Written** statements about the properties of an element

Lesson 5

Metals, Nonmetals, and Radioactive Elements

Vocabulary metal, luster, malleable, ductile, conductivity, reactivity, nonmetal, diatomic molecule, metalloid, semiconductor, radioactive decay, nuclear reaction, radioactivity, half-life

Materials clear plastic cups, plastic spoons, metal spoons, very warm water

 Science Background

- Most metals are good conductors of heat and electricity. Most metals also have high luster, are malleable, and are ductile.

- Most nonmetals are poor conductors. They are usually dull and brittle.

- During radioactive decay, an unstable nucleus splits to form two or more nuclei with a release of energy. Because the number of protons in the nucleus changes, the identity of the atom changes.

Frontload the Lesson

What are the properties of metals, nonmetals, and radioactive elements?

Talk About It

Build Background Distribute materials and review safety guidelines. Have students work in small groups. Students should observe that heat is transferred to the metal spoon but not to the plastic spoon.

Content and Language

Predict

Model Read the Big Question and the objectives aloud with students.

Guide Discussion Have students rephrase the Big Question as a statement about what they will learn.

 Big Question What are the properties of metals, nonmetals, and radioactive elements?

You will . . .
- Identify physical properties of metals, nonmetals, and metalloids.
- Contrast the conductivity of metals and nonmetals.
- Use key terms to explain how radioactivity affects an element.

Talk About It

You can test how fast heat moves through an object by placing it in warm water.

Step 1 Pour very warm water into two cups.

Step 2 Place a metal spoon in one cup. Place a plastic spoon in the other cup.

Step 3 Wait a few minutes. Which spoon feels warmer?

Read the terms in the Picture It box while your teacher reads them aloud. Raise your hand if you hear a word that describes something about the spoons.

Predict

Look at the Big Question and the "You will . . ." statements at the top of the page. Describe what you think you are going to learn in this lesson.

I think I am going to learn about . . .

18 Lesson 5

Leveled Instruction

Early Beginner Introduce some of the vocabulary terms using examples in the classroom or by demonstrating the concept as you say the term. For example, act as if you are bending or flattening on a material as you say *malleable*. Point to a shiny object and say *luster*.

Beginner Students can answer simple questions using one of the vocabulary terms. Model how to answer the question using the term in a simple sentence, and have students repeat the answer after you. For example, an answer might be *The diatomic molecule is made of two atoms*.

Early Intermediate/Intermediate Guide students in using the vocabulary terms to write complete sentences about metals, nonmetals, and radioactive elements. Have students read their sentences aloud.

Advanced/Transitioning Ask students questions about metals, nonmetals, and radioactive elements that elicit complex answers, both oral and written, composed of several sentences.

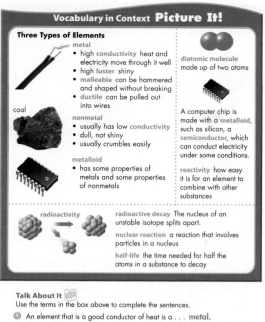

Vocabulary in Context Picture It!

Three Types of Elements

metal
- high **conductivity** heat and electricity move through it well
- high **luster** shiny
- **malleable** can be hammered and shaped without breaking
- **ductile** can be pulled out into wires

coal

nonmetal
- usually has low **conductivity**
- dull, not shiny
- usually crumbles easily

metalloid
- has some properties of metals and some properties of nonmetals

diatomic molecule made up of two atoms

A computer chip is made with a **metalloid**, such as silicon, a **semiconductor**, which can conduct electricity under some conditions.

reactivity how easy it is for an element to combine with other substances

radioactivity

radioactive decay The nucleus of an unstable isotope splits apart.

nuclear reaction a reaction that involves particles in a nucleus

half-life the time needed for half the atoms in a substance to decay

Talk About It
Use the terms in the box above to complete the sentences.
1. An element that is a good conductor of heat is a . . . metal.
2. The time it takes half the atoms of a substance to split apart is its . . . half-life.
3. The word *shiny* describes an element that has high . . . luster.
4. An element that can easily be bent and flattened is . . . malleable.
5. A molecule that is made up of two atoms is called a . . . diatomic molecule.
6. The nucleus of an atom splits apart during . . . radioactive decay.

Your Turn
Tell a partner how one blue term relates to one of the pictures.

Metals, Nonmetals, and Radioactive Elements   **19**

Academic Vocabulary

- Write the terms *identify* and *contrast* from the objectives on the board. Explain that *identify* means to point out something. *Contrast* means to tell how two or more things are different. Demonstrate how to use the terms in sentences, and then ask students to identify and contrast various items in the classroom.

- Caution students that the terms *radioactive decay* and *radioactivity* have nothing to do with a radio. The root word *radio-* in *radioactive* describes how energy and particles *radiate*, or move away from the reaction in all directions.

- Point out that the words *decay* and *reaction* have multiple meanings. In this lesson, *decay* means the breakdown of an atomic nucleus. In everyday usage, it means "rot." The word *reaction* refers to the chemical combining of atoms (for the word *reactivity*) or a change in an atomic nucleus (for a *nuclear reaction*). In everyday conversation, the word *reaction* means "any action or emotion that occurs in response to an event."

↻ Comprehensible Input

Vocabulary in Context: Picture It!

1. **Say the Term** Say each term slowly, artificially stressing each syllable. Have students repeat. Then say the term more naturally and have students repeat.

2. **Introduce Word Meaning** Connect each term to the visual that illustrates it.

3. **Demonstrate** Use gestures and visuals to demonstrate each term. For example:

   - As you say the word *reactivity*, point to a picture or an object with rust, or write the word rust on the board. Point out that iron combines with oxygen to form ferrous oxide, or rust. Explain that the metal has undergone a chemical reaction. This demonstrates the *reactivity* of the metal.

   - Emphasize to students that some elements have a higher reactivity than others. Sodium, for example, is highly reactive, whereas the noble gases are nonreactive under normal conditions.

4. **Apply** After all the terms have been discussed, have students demonstrate understanding with Talk About It.

Talk About It

Guide Discussion Have students look back at the pictures in the Picture It box and match words from the questions to the pictures. They can then use these pictures to complete these sentences.

R T I Response to Intervention

If students have difficulty with the word *semiconductor* . . .

Then explain that the prefix *semi-* means "partly" or "somewhat." Therefore, a *semiconductor* is sometimes a conductor.

Your Turn

Guide Discussion Read aloud the instructions. Then model the activity for students by explaining that the copper wire is a *metal*. It has high *luster* because it is shiny.

Metals, Nonmetals, and Radioactive Elements

Language Production

Do You Understand?

Comprehension Support Before students start the activity, briefly describe each picture and read the terms aloud with students. Explain that each picture represents one of the vocabulary terms listed next to it. Suggest that students look back at the Picture It box if they need help.

Model Demonstrate how students can ask themselves questions to help them complete the activity. Say, *What does the picture show? Which of the terms best tells about the picture?*

Talk About It

Guide Discussion Read the sentences aloud with students. Then have them work with a partner to choose the best vocabulary term to complete each sentence.

Your Turn

Guide Discussion Listen to students as they discuss the pictures and vocabulary terms. Help students describe the pictures and pronounce the words as needed.

A Closer Look

On Their Own Have students work in pairs to complete this word study activity. If necessary, demonstrate or review how to find words by alphabetical order in an index or glossary. Allow time for students to search and list words together. Then list on the board the examples of science words with these prefixes, such as *dichotomous key, dicot, diploid, divide, division, divergent, non-contact force,* and *nonrenewable resource.*

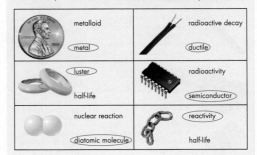

Do You Understand?

Look at each picture. Circle the word that *best* tells about the picture.

	metalloid		radioactive decay
	(metal)		(ductile)
	(luster)		radioactivity
	half-life		(semiconductor)
	nuclear reaction		(reactivity)
	(diatomic molecule)		half-life

Talk About It
Complete the sentences.

1. A material that can sometimes conduct electricity is a . . . semiconductor.
2. An element that is not a metal or a metalloid is a . . . nonmetal.
3. A reaction that involves particles in a nucleus is a . . . nuclear reaction.
4. The ease with which an element can combine with other elements is its . . . reactivity.
5. An element with properties of both a metal and a nonmetal is a . . . metalloid.
6. A substance that can easily be pulled out into a wire is . . . ductile.
7. The ability of a material to transfer heat is the material's . . . conductivity.

Your Turn
With a partner, talk about why you chose each word for the pictures above.

> **A Closer Look**
>
> **Word Parts** The prefix *di-* means "two." A *diatomic molecule* is a molecule made of two atoms. The prefix *non-* means "not." A *nonmetal* is a substance that is not a metal. What other science words begin with the prefixes *di-* or *non-*? (Hint: Check the index or glossary of several science books.)

20   Lesson 5

Leveled Language Proficiency

Students at each proficiency level should be able to perform the following tasks.

Listening/Speaking

Early Beginner/Beginner Respond to one- or two-step oral directions during activities. Use one or two spoken words to identify or describe metals, nonmetals, and radioactivity.

Early Intermediate Identify everyday examples of metals and nonmetals based on oral descriptions. Use vocabulary terms related to metals, nonmetals, and radioactivity to complete spoken sentences.

Intermediate Paraphrase oral descriptions related to metals, nonmetals, and radioactivity. Compare and contrast metals, nonmetals, and metalloids using complex spoken sentences.

Advanced/Transitioning Analyze qualities of metals, nonmetals, and metalloids based on oral descriptions. Discuss and describe examples of metals and nonmetals in conversation.

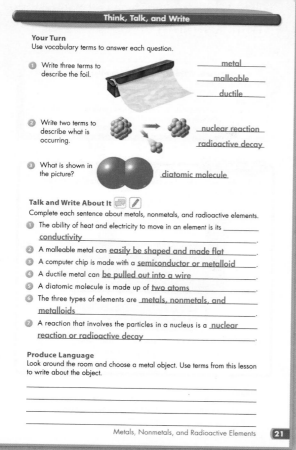

Think, Talk, and Write

Your Turn
Use vocabulary terms to answer each question.

1. Write three terms to describe the foil.
   - metal
   - malleable
   - ductile

2. Write two terms to describe what is occurring.
   - nuclear reaction
   - radioactive decay

3. What is shown in the picture?
   - diatomic molecule

Talk and Write About It
Complete each sentence about metals, nonmetals, and radioactive elements.

1. The ability of heat and electricity to move in an element is its _conductivity_.
2. A malleable metal can _easily be shaped and made flat_.
3. A computer chip is made with a _semiconductor or metalloid_.
4. A ductile metal can _be pulled out into a wire_.
5. A diatomic molecule is made up of _two atoms_.
6. The three types of elements are _metals, nonmetals, and metalloids_.
7. A reaction that involves the particles in a nucleus is a _nuclear reaction or radioactive decay_.

Produce Language
Look around the room and choose a metal object. Use terms from this lesson to write about the object.

_____
_____
_____
_____

Metals, Nonmetals, and Radioactive Elements   **21**

Leveled Language Proficiency

Students at each proficiency level should be able to perform the following tasks.

Reading/Writing

Early Beginner/Beginner Match pictures related to metals, nonmetals, and radioactivity with words. Complete written sentences with vocabulary related to lesson topics.

Early Intermediate Follow written directions for an activity about conductivity. Formulate *wh-* questions about metals in writing.

Intermediate Interpret written information about nuclear reactions. Write descriptions of metals using complex sentences.

Advanced/Transitioning Infer details about radioactivity from written descriptions. Write a paragraph that compares and contrasts metals, nonmetals, and metalloids.

↻ Assess Understanding

Your Turn

Model Suggest that students review the terms in the Picture It box before completing the activity. Then demonstrate how they can determine which word or words best answer each question. For example, say, *Which words tell about the foil in the picture?*

Talk and Write About It

On Their Own Read the instructions and sentence starters aloud with students. Point out that some sentences can be correctly completed in different ways.

Produce Language

On Their Own Emphasize to students that they should first choose an object and then think about terms they could use to describe it. Provide help as needed with spelling and sentence structure.

Wrap Up

Table Talk Have students reflect on the Big Question and what they learned. Encourage students to build fluency by reading their writing in groups or to the class.

✔ **Learned** differences among metals, nonmetals, and metalloids

✔ **Spoken** vocabulary related to metals, nonmetals, and radioactivity

✔ **Written** sentences to describe properties of metals

Lesson 6

Atoms and Ions

Vocabulary valence electron, ion, electron dot diagram, chemical bond, polyatomic ion, ionic bond, ionic compound, chemical formula, subscript, crystal

Materials photographs and micrographs of crystals; 3-D models of molecules of crystals

Science Background

- The energy of an electron is related to its distance from the nucleus; the farther it is from the nucleus, the greater its energy. The electrons in the energy level farthest from the nucleus are called *valence electrons*. The number of valence electrons helps determine the chemical properties of an element.

- When a neutral atom loses a valence electron, it loses a negative charge and becomes a positive ion. If it gains a valence electron, it becomes a negative ion. In ionic bonding, a positive ion transfers an electron to a negative ion.

Frontload the Lesson

What are some ways in which elements bond to one another?

Talk About It

Build Background Read the instructions with students, and draw their attention to the periodic table and the symbols on it.

Content and Language

Predict

Model Read the Big Question aloud as students listen. Model rephrasing the question as a statement to say what the lesson will be about.

Guide Discussion Have students read the objectives aloud with you. Then have them tell what they think they will learn in this lesson.

Big Question What are some ways in which elements bond to one another?

You will . . .
- Learn how to draw electron dot diagrams for various elements.
- Explain the meaning of chemical formulas.
- Use vocabulary terms to explain how ions form.

Talk About It

Look at the Periodic Table of the Elements. The periods are rows and the groups are columns.

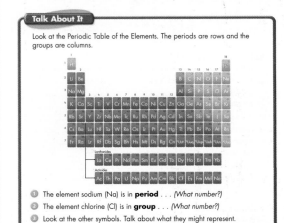

1. The element sodium (Na) is in **period** . . . *(What number?)*
2. The element chlorine (Cl) is in **group** . . . *(What number?)*
3. Look at the other symbols. Talk about what they might represent.

Predict
Look at the Big Question and the "You will . . ." statements at the top of the page. Describe what you think you are going to learn in this lesson.

    I think I am going to learn about . . .

22 Lesson 6

Leveled Instruction

Early Beginner Say one of the vocabulary terms, and ask students to point to a picture that represents it in the lesson. Have students repeat the name. Continue for all the other vocabulary terms.

Beginner To help students learn precise language, encourage them to use sentence frames to explain the concepts. Example: *A chemical bond is a type of _____ .* (force)

Early Intermediate/Intermediate Pair students together and encourage them to read the sentence starters with minimal help. Provide guidance with pronunciation of unfamiliar terms, such as *crystal*.

Advanced/Transitioning Emphasize academic vocabulary and insert academic language into conversational prompts. Have advanced students serve as teaching assistants, and call on them to introduce a topic. Ask them to demonstrate, draw, and/or explain on eor more topics in the lesson.

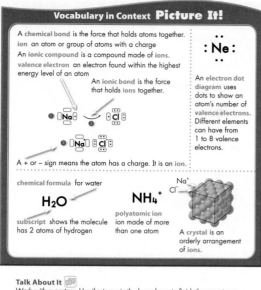

A **chemical bond** is the force that holds atoms together.
ion an atom or group of atoms with a charge
An **ionic compound** is a compound made of **ions**.
valence electron an electron found within the highest energy level of an atom

An **ionic bond** is the force that holds **ions** together.

An **electron dot diagram** uses dots to show an atom's number of **valence electrons**. Different elements can have from 1 to 8 valence electrons.

A + or − sign means the atom has a charge. It is an ion.

chemical formula for water

H_2O

subscript shows the molecule has 2 atoms of hydrogen

NH_4^+

polyatomic ion ion made of more than one atom

A **crystal** is an orderly arrangement of ions.

Talk About It

Work with a partner. Use the terms in the box above to finish these sentences.

1. An ion made of more than one atom is a . . . polyatomic ion.
2. In an atom, electrons with the highest energy are called . . . valence electrons.
3. Ions in an orderly arrangement form a . . . crystal.
4. The force that holds atoms together is a . . . chemical bond.
5. A diagram of 1 to 8 dots around an element's symbol is an . . . electron dot diagram.
6. A numeral in a chemical formula that tells the number of atoms in a compound is a . . . subscript.

Your Turn

Talk to a partner. Share one question or one statement about each of the blue vocabulary terms.

Atoms and Ions **23**

Academic Vocabulary

- The prefix *poly-* means "more than one." Thus the word *polyatomic* means "more than one atom." The prefix *sub-* means "under." Thus the word *subscript* refers to the small number placed slightly under the level of the letters in a formula. Ask students to talk about everyday words with the prefixes *poly-* and *sub-*.

- Explain the different meanings that the words *positive*, *negative*, and *charge* have in everyday life. In casual conversation, *positive* can mean "certain." *Negative* can mean "having a bad attitude." *Charge* can mean "buying something with a promise to pay in the future."

- Write the following academic terms on the board: *determine, become, transfer, diagram*. Explain the meaning of *determine*, and then use it in a sentence. For example, say, *Determine the number of students in the classroom*. Invite students to use the word in another sentence. Repeat this method for the other three academic terms.

- Have students share any vocabulary terms they recognize as cognates to words in their first languages. For example, the Spanish term *iones* is a cognate for *ion*. The Spanish term *cristal* is a cognate for *crystal*.

↻ Comprehensible Input

Vocabulary in Context: Picture It!

1. **Say the Term** Say each term slowly, artificially stressing each syllable. Have students repeat. Then say the term more naturally and have students repeat.

2. **Introduce Word Meaning** Connect each term to the visual that illustrates it.

3. **Demonstrate** Use gestures and visuals to demonstrate each term. For example:

   - As you say the term *crystal*, point to the sodium chloride crystal.

   - Point out the symbols for the sodium and chloride ions on the diagram. Indicate how these ions are arranged in a pattern.

   - Say, *The ions are arranged in a pattern to form the crystal*. Show students any photographs or micrographs you have available of crystals in their natural form.

4. **Apply** After all the terms have been discussed, have students demonstrate understanding with Talk About It.

Talk About It

Guide Discussion Have students work with a partner to complete the statements. Remind them to refer to the Picture It box above for help.

RTI Response to Intervention

If students have difficulty with pronouncing the word *crystal* . . .

Then remind students that the letter *y* can have the short *i* sound when it is in the middle of a word.

Your Turn

Guide Discussion Tell a partner about one of the blue terms, by making a statement "in your own words." Say, *H_2O is a chemical formula. This means that it shows what kind and how many atoms join together to form water.*

Atoms and Ions

Language Production

Do You Understand?

Comprehension Support Have students read aloud each of the vocabulary terms in the list. Correct their pronunciation as needed. Students should draw a line from each term to each of the pictures that represent the term. Explain that two, or even three, of the pictures may represent a term.

Model Demonstrate how ask questions to complete the activity. Say, *Which picture or pictures show a chemical formula?* Model drawing lines from the term *chemical formula* to: H_3O^+ and CO_2.

Talk About It

Guide Discussion Explain that each sentence can be completed with one of the vocabulary terms. Read each sentence starter aloud with students. Have students identify the correct vocabulary term. Repeat the sentence aloud with students, but this time include the vocabulary term at the end.

Your Turn

Guide Discussion As students discuss the pictures, make sure they understand that a chemical symbol can be used independently, but it is also used in the representation of an ion, an electron dot diagram, and a polyatomic ion.

In Other Words

Model Read the sentence aloud for students. Then ask, *What is another way to say this? What is another word, or words, for* transferred? Encourage students to read the sentence aloud in turn, each time choosing a new highlighted word for the term *transferred*.

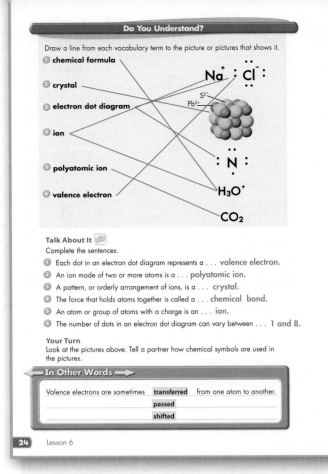

Do You Understand?

Draw a line from each vocabulary term to the picture or pictures that shows it.

1. chemical formula
2. crystal
3. electron dot diagram
4. ion
5. polyatomic ion
6. valence electron

Na^+ Cl^-
S^{2-}
Pb^{2+}
N
H_3O^+
CO_2

Talk About It

Complete the sentences.
1. Each dot in an electron dot diagram represents a . . . valence electron.
2. An ion made of two or more atoms is a . . . polyatomic ion.
3. A pattern, or orderly arrangement of ions, is a . . . crystal.
4. The force that holds atoms together is called a . . . chemical bond.
5. An atom or group of atoms with a charge is an . . . ion.
6. The number of dots in an electron dot diagram can vary between . . . 1 and 8.

Your Turn

Look at the pictures above. Tell a partner how chemical symbols are used in the pictures.

In Other Words

Valence electrons are sometimes	transferred	from one atom to another.
	passed	
	shifted	

24   Lesson 6

Leveled Language Proficiency

Students at each proficiency level should be able to perform the following tasks.

Listening/Speaking

Early Beginner/Beginner Point to corresponding pictures when simple terms related to atoms and ions are spoken. State the correct term related to atoms and ions in response to a picture of the term.

Early Intermediate Respond with short phrases to spoken questions about valence electrons, ions, and ionic bonds. Use simple sentences to orally describe terms related to atoms and ions.

Intermediate Distinguish between related terms, such as *ion* and *polyatomic ion*, based on oral descriptions. Use complex spoken sentences to describe electron dot diagrams, chemical formulas, and ionic compounds.

Advanced/Transitioning Make inferences about ionic compounds and crystals based on oral descriptions. Effectively communicate in conversation abstract ideas about valence electrons, chemical bonds, and ions.

Think, Talk, and Write

Your Turn

Choose a vocabulary term or terms from the word box to describe each item. Some items can have more than one term.

| ion | electron dot diagram | subscript |
| crystal | chemical formula | |

ion _____

electron dot diagram _____

crystal _____

HCO_3^-

ion, subscript, chemical formula

$: \ddot{Cl} :$

electron dot diagram

N_2O_3

chemical formula subscript

Talk and Write About It

Complete the statements about atoms and ions.

1. The bond that holds two ions together is an __ionic bond__.
2. The bond that holds two atoms together is a __chemical bond__.
3. A subscript tells __how many atoms of an element are present in a compound__.
4. An electron with the greatest energy in an atom is a __valence electron__.
5. One or more atoms with a positive or negative charge is an __ion__.
6. A compound made of ions is an __ionic compound__.

Produce Language

Look at the pictures above. Write three or four sentences telling what the pictures show about how elements bond to one another.

_____
_____
_____
_____

Atoms and Ions **25**

Leveled Language Proficiency

Students at each proficiency level should be able to perform the following tasks.

Reading/Writing

Early Beginner/Beginner Match written vocabulary terms with pictures related to ionic bonds. Label pictures related to chemical formulas, electron dot diagrams, and ionic bonds.

Early Intermediate Identify pictures related to atoms and ions from written descriptions. Formulate *wh-* questions about ionic bonding.

Intermediate Answer questions about ionic bonds in response to written descriptions. Use details to write short descriptions of chemical formulas and ionic bonds.

Advanced/Transitioning Infer details about ionic bonds from written descriptions. Produce paragraphs describing ionic bonds.

↻ Assess Understanding

Your Turn

Model Demonstrate how students can determine the correct term for each picture. For example, point to the picture showing the ionic bonding of sodium chloride. Say, *What does this picture show? Which vocabulary term tells about something in this picture?*

Talk and Write About It

On Their Own Read each sentence starter aloud with students. Have them choose the correct term to complete each sentence. Then have them read the sentence again, inserting the correct term at the end.

Produce Language

On Their Own Lead students in discussing how the pictures are related to elements bonding to one another. After students write their sentences, have them read the sentences aloud to a partner.

Wrap Up

Table Talk Have students reread the Big Question as a way to reflect on what they learned. Encourage them to build fluency by reading their writing in groups or to the entire class.

✔ **Learned** to draw electron dot diagrams

✔ **Heard** statements about ions and ionic bonds

✔ **Written** descriptions of how elements bond to one another

Covalent Bonds and Metallic Bonds

Vocabulary covalent bond, molecule, double bond, triple bond, molecular compound, nonpolar bond, polar bond, metallic bond, alloy

Materials index cards, red markers

 Science Background

- A bond is a force that holds particles together. A covalent bond forms when atoms share electrons.

- The term *molecule* is sometimes colloquially used to refer to any group of atoms, but the actual scientific meaning of the term refers to atoms that are joined by covalent bonds. Atoms joined by an ionic bond, such as sodium chloride (NaCl), do not form a molecule.

 Frontload the Lesson

 What are covalent bonds and metallic bonds?

Talk About It

Build Background Help students by discussing the various bonds between people, such as those between friends or family members. Explain that this is an everyday meaning of the word *bond*, separate from its science meaning.

Content and Language

Predict

Model Read the Big Question and the objectives aloud as students listen. Explain any terms that might be confusing, such as *share* and *form*.

Guide Discussion Have students explain to one another the clues they use to make their predictions. Point out the variety of text and picture clues.

Covalent Bonds and Metallic Bonds

 Big Question What are covalent bonds and metallic bonds?

You will . . .
- Explain how atoms can share electrons to form a covalent bond.
- Describe what polar bonds and nonpolar bonds are.
- Use vocabulary terms to describe covalent and metallic bonds.

Talk About It

Copy each term from the Picture It box on a piece of paper. As your teacher reads each term, <u>underline</u> it with colored pencils or crayons.

- Want to Know
- Have Heard
- Know

Step 1 Underline the terms you know in <u>green</u>.
Step 2 Underline the terms you have heard but are not sure of in <u>yellow</u>.
Step 3 Underline the terms that you want to know in <u>red</u>.

What do you know about each term? Explain, using the sentence starters.
- I want to know what . . . means.
- I think . . . means . . .
- I know . . . means . . .

Predict
Look at the Big Question and the "You will ..." statements at the top of the page. Describe what you think you are going to learn in this lesson.

I think I am going to learn about . . .

26 Lesson 7

Leveled Instruction

Early Beginner Ask simple questions that allow students to answer by acting out formations of different types of bonds.

Beginner Have students chorally read sentence starters about different types of bonds. Help them answer by choosing one of the vocabulary terms.

Early Intermediate/Intermediate Describe a simple type of bonding. Have students draw a picture that explains that type of bonding.

Advanced/Transitioning Encourage any students who are able to produce detailed explanations of covalent and metallic bonding to act as classroom experts and to be available to answer student questions on a topic of their choice. Provide extension opportunities by asking questions that require students to relate concepts or make inferences.

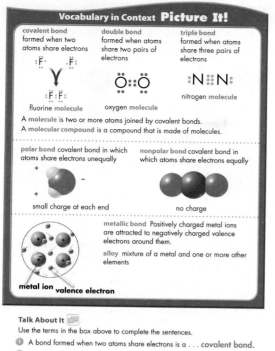

Vocabulary in Context Picture It!

covalent bond formed when two atoms share electrons

double bond formed when atoms share two pairs of electrons

triple bond formed when atoms share three pairs of electrons

fluorine molecule   oxygen molecule   nitrogen molecule

A **molecule** is two or more atoms joined by covalent bonds.
A **molecular compound** is a compound that is made of molecules.

polar bond covalent bond in which atoms share electrons unequally

small charge at each end

nonpolar bond covalent bond in which atoms share electrons equally

no charge

metallic bond Positively charged metal ions are attracted to negatively charged valence electrons around them.

alloy mixture of a metal and one or more other elements

metal ion valence electron

Talk About It

Use the terms in the box above to complete the sentences.

1. A bond formed when two atoms share electrons is a . . . covalent bond.
2. A covalent bond in which atoms share electrons equally is a . . . nonpolar bond.
3. A mixture of a metal and other elements is an . . . alloy.
4. A bond formed when atoms share two pairs of electrons is a . . . double bond.

Your Turn

With a partner, take turns telling about each of the terms in the Picture It box.

Academic Vocabulary

- Explain the meanings of *double* and *triple*. Ask students to use the terms in sentences and to draw pictures to represent the meanings.

- Explain the meanings of *sharing equally* and *sharing unequally*. Point out that a greater pull on an electron causes it to spend more time closer to one side of the molecule, resulting in unequal sharing. This causes the side that has a strong pull to have a slightly negative charge. Ask students to use the everyday meaning of these expressions in sentences.

- Cognates are words that have the same or similar roots and meanings in two languages. Have students share any vocabulary terms they recognize as cognates to words in their first languages. You may want to direct them to use a dictionary or multi-language science glossary to hunt for sample cognates.

↻ Comprehensible Input

Vocabulary in Context: Picture It!

1. **Say the Term** Say each term slowly, artificially stressing each syllable. Have students repeat. Then say the term more naturally and have students repeat.

2. **Introduce Word Meaning** Connect each term to the visual that illustrates it.

3. **Demonstrate** Use gestures and visuals to demonstrate each term. For example:

   - Help students understand the concept of double and triple bonds. Give each student three blank index cards. Have students draw a red dot on each card. Tell students the red dots represent electrons. Ask students to stand near a partner and pretend they are an atom. Ask them to place between themselves cards to show single (1 card each), double (2 cards), and triple (3 cards) covalent bonds.

   - For *metallic bond*, point to the metal ions in the picture. Say, *These are metal ions. They have a positive charge because the valence electrons move freely between the atoms.*

   - Point to the valence electrons. Say, *These are valence electrons. The force holding these electrons to the ions creates a metallic bond.*

4. **Apply** After all the terms have been discussed, have students demonstrate understanding with Talk About It.

Talk About It

Guide Discussion Have students look back at the pictures in the Picture It box. Ask them to use the terms to answer the questions.

R T I Response to Intervention

If students have difficulty with *covalent* . . .

Then write the term on the board and circle the word parts *co* and *valent*. Explain that *co* means "together," and *valent* refers to valence electrons. *Covalent* refers to atoms that share valence electrons.

Your Turn

Guide Discussion Listen as students discuss the vocabulary terms. Correct any pronunciation errors or misconceptions about the science concepts.

Covalent Bonds and Metallic Bonds

↻ Language Production

Do You Understand?

Comprehension Support Instruct students to discuss each picture with a partner. Have them talk about which of the two vocabulary terms best describes the picture, and then draw a line from that term to the picture. If students have difficulty, suggest that they review the Picture It box.

Model Read aloud the vocabulary terms near the first picture: *double bond, triple bond.* Ask, *Does the picture show a double bond or a triple bond?*

Talk About It

Guide Discussion Listen as students read the completed sentences and provide corrections as needed. Then ask students to say one additional sentence about each term. Model doing so for item 1: *Water is a molecular compound because it is two molecules of hydrogen and one of oxygen joined by covalent bonds.*

Your Turn

Guide Discussion Students should use this discussion as an opportunity to explain their choices. Listen to be sure students understand the terms and can use them correctly.

In Other Words

Model Read the sentence aloud for students. Then ask, *What is another way to say this? What is another word, or words, for* join? Encourage students to read the sentence aloud in turn, each time choosing a new highlighted term for the verb *to join.*

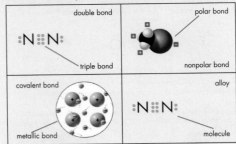

Do You Understand?

Draw a line from each picture to the vocabulary term that names it.

double bond | polar bond
triple bond | nonpolar bond
covalent bond | alloy
metallic bond | molecule

Talk About It
Complete the sentences.
1. A compound made of molecules is a . . . molecular compound.
2. A bond in which atoms share electrons unequally is a . . . polar bond.
3. A bond formed when atoms share three pairs of electrons is a . . . triple bond.
4. Two or more atoms joined by covalent bonds form a . . . molecule.
5. A bond between a metal ion and electrons around it is a . . .metallic bond.

Your Turn
Look at the pictures and words in the Do You Understand activity. Tell a partner why you chose the vocabulary term for each picture.

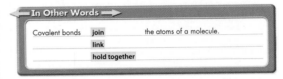

In Other Words →

Covalent bonds	join	the atoms of a molecule.
	link	
	hold together	

28   Lesson 7

Leveled Language Proficiency

Students at each proficiency level should be able to perform the following tasks.

Listening/Speaking

Early Beginner/Beginner Find a picture in the lesson that relates to a vocabulary term about covalent or metallic bonds that is spoken by the teacher. Say key terms aloud after identifying corresponding pictures or diagrams.

Early Intermediate Follow multi-step oral directions for identifying or drawing different types of bonds. Ask simple questions about covalent bonds and metallic bonds.

Intermediate Distinguish between related terms, such as *double bond* and *triple bond,* based on oral descriptions. Use complete spoken sentences to describe molecular compounds, metallic bonds, and alloys.

Advanced/Transitioning Understand spoken descriptions contrasting covalent bonds and metallic bonds. Effectively communicate in conversation abstract ideas about topics such as polar bonding and alloys.

28   Physical Science | Lesson 7

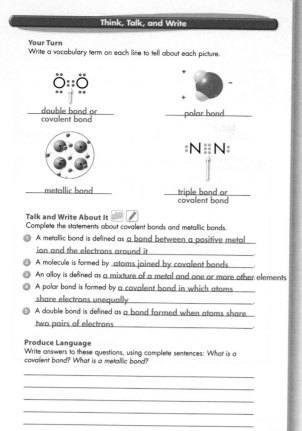

Think, Talk, and Write

Your Turn

Write a vocabulary term on each line to tell about each picture.

double bond or covalent bond

polar bond

metallic bond

triple bond or covalent bond

Talk and Write About It

Complete the statements about covalent bonds and metallic bonds.

1. A metallic bond is defined as <u>a bond between a positive metal ion and the electrons around it</u>

2. A molecule is formed by <u>atoms joined by covalent bonds</u>.

3. An alloy is defined as <u>a mixture of a metal and one or more other</u> elements

4. A polar bond is formed by <u>a covalent bond in which atoms share electrons unequally</u>

5. A double bond is defined as <u>a bond formed when atoms share two pairs of electrons</u>

Produce Language

Write answers to these questions, using complete sentences: *What is a covalent bond? What is a metallic bond?*

_____

_____

_____

_____

Covalent Bonds and Metallic Bonds **29**

Assess Understanding

Your Turn

Model Encourage students to talk to a partner about each picture before writing their answers. Demonstrate by pointing to the picture of the double-bonded oxygen atoms. Say, *What type of bond holds the oxygen atoms together?*

Talk and Write About It

On Their Own Tell students that they will write vocabulary terms in each blank to complete the sentences. If they have difficulty with the concepts or the spelling, encourage them to look back at the Picture It box for help.

Produce Language

On Their Own Students should use this activity as an opportunity to write sentences using the vocabulary terms they have learned. Suggest that they first talk with a partner about each question and how they should answer it. Then have them write two or three sentences to answer each question.

Wrap Up

Table Talk Have students reread the Big Question as a way to reflect on what they learned. Encourage students to build fluency by reading their writing in groups or to the entire class.

✔ **Learned** about polar and nonpolar bonds

✔ **Heard** statements about double and triple bonds

✔ **Read** descriptions of covalent bonds and metallic bonds

Leveled Language Proficiency

Students at each proficiency level should be able to perform the following tasks.

Reading/Writing

Early Beginner/Beginner Correctly read and understand simple labels related to covalent and metallic bonds. Accurately write one- or two-word labels onto diagrams.

Early Intermediate Follow written directions for activities about covalent bonds. Write simple sentences to describe different types of bonds.

Intermediate Answer questions about covalent and metallic bonds in response to written descriptions. Use details to write short descriptions of alloys and molecular compounds.

Advanced/Transitioning Infer meanings of words and concepts, such as *covalent bond, molecular compound,* and *polar bond,* based on recognition of word forms and word parts. Use complex sentences to produce detailed written descriptions of covalent and metallic bonding.

Lesson 8

Chemical Reactions

Vocabulary reactant, product, precipitate, exothermic reaction, endothermic reaction, open system, closed system, chemical equation, coefficient, synthesis, decomposition, replacement

Materials lemon juice and milk, baking soda and vinegar, a balloon, a candle and match

Science Background

- Chemical reactions involve observable changes in properties or in energy.

- Chemical reactions either release energy as new products form or absorb energy.

- In a chemical reaction, all of the atoms present at the start of the reaction are present at the end of the reaction.

Frontload the Lesson

What is a chemical reaction?

Talk About It

Build Background Read the instructions aloud. Tell students that a physical change alters the form or appearance of a substance but doesn't turn it into another substance. Example: tearing a piece of paper. In a chemical change, the atoms of a substance rearrange to make a new substance. Example: burning a piece of paper. Here, the rusting fork and decaying apple are chemical changes. The freshly sliced apple and crushed can are physical changes.

Content and Language

Predict

Model Read the Big Question and the objectives aloud with students.

Guide Discussion To help students make their prediction, encourage them to scan the pictures in the lesson first.

Big Question What is a chemical reaction?

You will . . .
- Understand what happens in a chemical reaction.
- Identify the different types of chemical reactions.
- Use key terms to describe chemical reactions.

Talk About It

Which sets of objects show a physical change? Which sets show a chemical change? Circle any set that shows a chemical change. Draw an X on any set that shows a physical change.

Predict
Look at the Big Question and the "You will . . ." statements at the top of the page. Describe what you think you are going to learn in this lesson.

I think I am going to learn about . . .

30 Lesson 8

Leveled Instruction

Early Beginner/Beginner Have students practice several times reading and saying the terms *chemical*, *reaction*, *reactant*, and *product*. Help them point to the appropriate pictures to identify chemical changes, reactants, and products.

Early Intermediate/Intermediate Have students work with a partner to describe what they think is happening in each of the chemical reactions shown. Assign different pairs to discuss: *What happens as the apple decomposes?* and *What happens as the metal fork rusts?* Then have students switch partners and reassign the two discussion questions.

Advanced/Transitioning Encourage students to do some writing about chemical reactions independently and to give examples of other chemical changes they know of and the products and reactants in each.

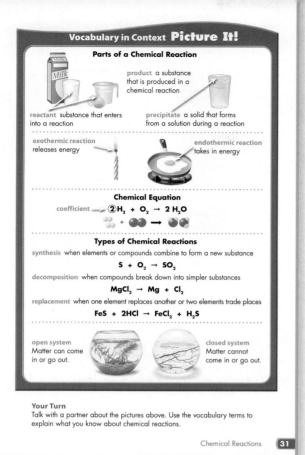

Vocabulary in Context **Picture It!**

Parts of a Chemical Reaction

product a substance that is produced in a chemical reaction

reactant substance that enters into a reaction

precipitate a solid that forms from a solution during a reaction

exothermic reaction releases energy

endothermic reaction takes in energy

Chemical Equation

coefficient

$$② H_2 + O_2 \rightarrow 2 H_2O$$

Types of Chemical Reactions

synthesis when elements or compounds combine to form a new substance

$$S + O_2 \rightarrow SO_2$$

decomposition when compounds break down into simpler substances

$$MgCl_2 \rightarrow Mg + Cl_2$$

replacement when one element replaces another or two elements trade places

$$FeS + 2HCl \rightarrow FeCl_2 + H_2S$$

open system Matter can come in or go out.

closed system Matter cannot come in or go out.

Your Turn
Talk with a partner about the pictures above. Use the vocabulary terms to explain what you know about chemical reactions.

Chemical Reactions **31**

Academic Vocabulary

- Explain that a chemical equation looks different than a mathematic equation, but that they are similar in some ways. The academic word *equation* refers to the act of making equal. A *chemical equation* is the symbolic representation of the reactants and products in a chemical reaction, in which both sides are equal.

- The academic word *system* refers to many parts which work together as a whole. Challenge students to find synonyms for the phrases *come in* and *go out*, used in defining the terms *open system* and *closed system*.

- The word *endothermic* combines the prefix *endo-*, which means "in" or "within," and the root word *therm*, which refers to heat, to mean "to take in heat." After explaining these word parts, ask students to infer the word parts in *exothermic* and to use their word analysis to help them remember the difference between *endothermic reactions* and *exothermic reactions*.

- The word *synthesis* refers to combining elements to make something more complex. The word *replacement* refers to one thing taking the place of another. Each word's common meaning relates closely to its use in the context of chemistry.

↻ Comprehensible Input

Vocabulary in Context: Picture It!

1. **Say the Term** Say each term slowly, artificially stressing each syllable. Have students repeat. Then say the term more naturally and have students repeat.

2. **Introduce Word Meaning** Connect each term to the visual that illustrates it.

3. **Demonstrate** Use gestures and visuals to demonstrate each term.

4. **Apply** After each term has been discussed, have students demonstrate understanding with Talk About It.

Talk About It

Guide Discussion Before students start their independent discussion, check for understanding with the following sentence starters:

1. *A solid that forms from a solution during a chemical reaction is a . . .* (precipitate.)

2. *A chemical reaction that releases energy is an . . .* (exothermic reaction.)

3. *A chemical reaction that takes in energy is an . . .* (endothermic reaction.)

4. *A type of chemical reaction where elements combine is . . .* (synthesis.)

5. *A type of chemical reaction where elements break down is . . .* (decomposition.)

6. *A system where matter cannot enter or leave is called a . . .* (closed system.)

7. *A number telling the amount of a substance in a chemical equation is a . . .* (coefficient.)

R T I Response to Intervention

If students have difficulty pronouncing the term *precipitate* . . .

Then point out the short vowel in the final syllable and distinguish this pronunciation from the verb form *to precipitate.*

Your Turn

Guide Discussion Ask students to use the terms in the Picture It box to discuss what they know about chemical reactions. Give examples to help guide discussion.

Chemical Reactions

↻ Language Production

Do You Understand?

Comprehension Support Read the directions aloud with students. Read the listed terms together. Describe what is happening in each picture.

Model Tell students to look at the first picture. Ask what it shows (a chemical reaction/ equation). Say, *The arrow is pointing to part of this reaction. Which term in the list describes this part of the reaction?*

Talk About It

Guide Discussion Read the sentences aloud with students as they work to complete the them. Refer to the pictures in the lesson as needed. Then have students work with partners to compare their completed sentences. Finally, have volunteers read the completed sentences aloud to correct them. In the places where several students have added the wrong word, go back to the presentation of that item to make sure that the students understand it.

Your Turn

Guide Discussion Listen to students discuss chemical reactions and help them correct any mistakes or misunderstandings. Encourage students to use all of the vocabulary terms in their discussions. As you circulate and listen to students talk, jot down any particularly apt example sentences that use key vocabulary. Write these sentences on the board. Correct them as needed, and ask students to read them aloud with you.

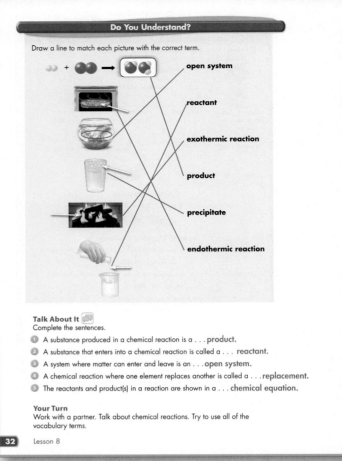

Do You Understand?

Draw a line to match each picture with the correct term.

- open system
- reactant
- exothermic reaction
- product
- precipitate
- endothermic reaction

Talk About It 💬
Complete the sentences.

1. A substance produced in a chemical reaction is a . . . product.
2. A substance that enters into a chemical reaction is called a . . . reactant.
3. A system where matter can enter and leave is an . . . open system.
4. A chemical reaction where one element replaces another is called a . . . replacement.
5. The reactants and product(s) in a reaction are shown in a . . . chemical equation.

Your Turn
Work with a partner. Talk about chemical reactions. Try to use all of the vocabulary terms.

32   Lesson 8

Leveled Language Proficiency

Students at each proficiency level should be able to perform the following tasks.

Listening/Speaking

Early Beginner/Beginner Repeat new vocabulary terms as a response to oral directions.

Early Intermediate Identify pictures relating to chemical reactions in response to spoken key terms. Explain key vocabulary terms using gestures and short spoken phrases.

Intermediate Comprehend and paraphrase oral descriptions of chemical reactions. Use simple spoken sentences to explain open and closed systems.

Advanced/Transitioning Participate in discussions about open and closed systems. Use complete and complex spoken sentences to explain different kinds of chemical reactions.

Your Turn
Label each chemical equation. Circle any coefficients.

synthesis	decomposition	replacement

1. $2H_2O_2 \rightarrow 2H_2O + O_2$ decomposition
2. $2Cu_2O + C \rightarrow 4Cu + CO_2$ replacement
3. $P_4 + 3O_2 \rightarrow P_4O_6$ synthesis
4. $Zn + 2HCl \rightarrow H_2 + ZnCl_2$ replacement
5. $CaCO_3 \rightarrow CaO + CO_2$ decomposition
6. $2Na + Cl_2 \rightarrow 2NaCl$ synthesis

Talk and Write About It
Complete the sentences.

1. Combining elements or compounds to form a new substance is _____ synthesis
2. In a replacement reaction, one element replaces or trades places with another element
3. In an endothermic reaction, heat is taken in
4. In an open system, matter can come in and go out
5. In a decomposition reaction, a compound breaks down into simpler substances

Produce Language
Write about one chemical reaction. Describe what takes place as the reaction occurs. Use as many vocabulary terms as you can.

_____
_____
_____
_____
_____
_____
_____
_____
_____

Chemical Reactions 33

Assess Understanding

Your Turn

Model Read the instructions and the terms in the box. Review the terms with students, encouraging them to look back at the Picture It box. Have students complete the activity, giving assistance as needed.

Talk and Write About It

On Their Own Provide help in reading each of the sentence stems as needed. Encourage partners to discuss their responses before writing.

Produce Language

On Their Own Have student groups both write and talk about what they've learned about chemical reactions. Encourage them to use as many vocabulary terms as possible.

Wrap Up

Table Talk Have students reflect on the Big Question and what they learned. Encourage students to build fluency by reading their writing in groups or to the class.

✔ **Learned** and applied vocabulary related to chemical reactions

✔ **Spoken** statements about types of chemical reactions

✔ **Written** sentences about chemical reactions

Leveled Language Proficiency

Students at each proficiency level should be able to perform the following tasks.

Reading/Writing

Early Beginner/Beginner Match each vocabulary term with the identifying picture. Write terms related to chemical reactions.

Early Intermediate Read and recall vocabulary terms and descriptions. Write short phrases to describe terms related to chemical reactions.

Intermediate Read and categorize a variety of chemical equations. Using key vocabulary terms, write complete sentences about what happens in a chemical reaction.

Advanced/Transitioning Read aloud sentences describing chemical reactions and open and closed systems. Use vocabulary terms to write complete, complex sentences with examples about what happens in different kinds of chemical equations.

Lesson 9

Acids, Bases, and Solutions

Vocabulary solution, solvent, solute, colloid, suspension, dilute solution, concentrated solution, solubility, saturated solution, acid, base, pH scale

Materials glasses or plastic cups, water, spoons, powdered lemonade mix; (optional) photos or real examples of the following: a bottle of vinegar, a banana, a bar of soap, and a bottle of drain cleaner

 Science Background

- A mixture can be a solution, a colloid, or a suspension, depending on the size of its larger particles. You can change the concentration of a solution by adding solute or by removing solvent.

- Acids are corrosive compounds that react with metals and carbonates. Bases don't react with metals, but they react with acids in a neutralization reaction.

↻ Frontload the Lesson

 What are the properties of acids, bases, and solutions?

Talk About It

Build Background Use the pictures to begin a class discussion about how matter can be combined. Discuss the idea that sugar cannot be spooned back out of the lemonade, but items in the trail mix can be separated.

↻ Content and Language

Predict

Model Read the Big Question and the objectives aloud. As students repeat after you, point out that the lesson is about solutions, but it is also about acids and bases.

Guide Discussion Ask students to choose one of the objectives and ask a question about it.

Acids, Bases, and Solutions

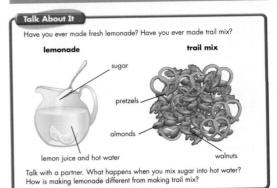

Big Question What are the properties of acids, bases, and solutions?

You will . . .
- Identify some different types of mixtures.
- Describe how to change the concentration of a solution.
- Differentiate between acids and bases.
- Use terms related to acids, bases, and solutions.

Talk About It

Have you ever made fresh lemonade? Have you ever made trail mix?

lemonade

trail mix

sugar

pretzels

almonds

lemon juice and hot water

walnuts

Talk with a partner. What happens when you mix sugar into hot water? How is making lemonade different from making trail mix?

Predict

Look at the Big Question and the "You will . . ." statements at the top of the page. Describe what you think you are going to learn in this lesson.

   I think I am going to learn about . . .

Leveled Instruction

Early Beginner Ask students to find a picture in the lesson that illustrates the concept of *solution*.

Beginner Direct students to discuss the pictures in the Picture It box. Then ask them to use the terms *solute* and *solvent* to describe two of the pictured objects.

Early Intermediate/Intermediate Encourage these students to work as leaders, readers, recorders, or reporters in the groups they work in to do the group activity with drink mix and water.

Advanced/Transitioning Have these students peer-review and peer-edit one another's writing to be sure that they use complete and complex sentences to describe acids, bases, and solutions, including the difference between a dilute solution and concentrated solution.

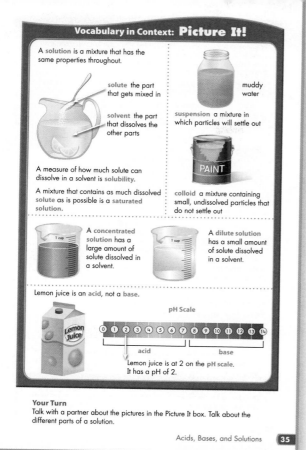

Academic Vocabulary

- Students may have heard the word *solution* in the context of an answer to a problem. You might tell students that when you solve a problem, the result is a solution; in science, when you dissolve a solute in a solvent, the result is also a solution.

- Students might be more familiar with scales that measure weight. Explain that other scales, similar to the pH scale, measure various things. Scale is also a multiple-meaning word. In biology, fish and some reptiles have scales, which are thin, flat structures covering their bodies.

- Point out that a *base* can also be the bottom of an object, on which the object stands or rests, or it can be one of four places on a baseball diamond.

- Cognates are words that have the same or similar roots and meanings in two languages. Have students share any vocabulary terms they recognize as cognates to words in their first languages. The words *solución*, *ácido*, and *base* (pronounced *bah-seh*) are Spanish cognates for *solution*, *acid*, and *base*.

↻ Comprehensible Input

Vocabulary in Context: Picture It!

1. **Say the Term** Say each term slowly, artificially stressing each syllable. Have students repeat. Then say the term more naturally and have students repeat.

2. **Introduce Word Meaning** Connect each term to the visual that illustrates it.

3. **Demonstrate** Use gestures and visuals to demonstrate each term.

4. **Apply** After all of the terms have been discussed, have students demonstrate understanding with Talk About It.

Talk About It

Guide Discussion Before students start their independent discussion, check for understanding with the following sentence starters:

1. *When you put sugar in water, the sugar is a . . .* (solute.)

2. *When you put sugar in water, the water is a . . .* (solvent.)

3. *A strong solution is more accurately called a . . .* (concentrated solution.)

4. *A small amount of solute in a lot of solvent is called a . . .* (dilute solution.)

5. *A substance that is low on the pH scale is an . . .* (acid.)

RTI Response to Intervention

If students have difficulty pronouncing the word *solubility* . . .

Then explain that the letter *u* is pronounced *u* in this word. Say each syllable slowly, emphasizing the *u*. Then say the word at a normal rate. Have students repeat the word at both the slow rate and the normal rate.

Your Turn

Guide Discussion Encourage students to discuss different parts of a solution and how they mix together. Encourage them to complete a sentence such as *A solution is made of . . .*

Acids, Bases, and Solutions

Language Production

Do You Understand?

Comprehension Support Before students do the activity, read through the directions, review the safety guidlines and procedures, and then hand out the materials: a glass or plastic cup of water, a spoon, and a premeasured amount of powdered lemonade mix. Have students reread the directions and follow each step of the activity in order, making sure they understand that the water is the solvent and the lemonade mix is the solute. **CAUTION:** Remind students not to eat or drink any materials or products in science activities.

Model Demonstrate how students can ask themselves questions to help them understand the process. Say, *What will happen when I add the solute to the solvent and stir it up well? What will happen when I add the lemonade mix to the water?*

Talk About It

Guide Discussion Read the sentences aloud with students as they work together to complete them.

Your Turn

Guide Discussion Listen to partners discuss the activity, providing prompts as needed.

A Closer Look

On Their Own Have students work in pairs to complete this word study activity. Discuss the variations in word meanings, and ask volunteers to use each word in a sentence.

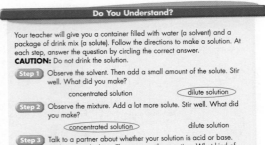

Do You Understand?

Your teacher will give you a container filled with water (a solvent) and a package of drink mix (a solute). Follow the directions to make a solution. At each step, answer the question by circling the correct answer.
CAUTION: Do not drink the solution.

Step 1 Observe the solvent. Then add a small amount of the solute. Stir well. What did you make?

concentrated solution   (dilute solution)

Step 2 Observe the mixture. Add a lot more solute. Stir well. What did you make?

(concentrated solution)   dilute solution

Step 3 Talk to a partner about whether your solution is acid or base. Explain your thinking. Then answer the question. What kind of solution do you think you just made?

(acid)   base

Talk About It
Complete the sentences.

① In a concentrated solution, there is a large amount of . . . solute
② A solution with a small amount of solute is . . . dilute
③ A solution with a pH of 3 is a(n) . . . acid
④ A solution with a pH of 11 is a(n) . . . base

Your Turn
Work with a partner. Take turns telling about the steps you followed and what happened.

A Closer Look

Word Forms Look at the words *concentrate*, *concentrated*, and *concentration*. Underline the parts of the second and third words that are the same as in the first word. How are the adjective and noun formed from the verb?

Leveled Language Proficiency

Students at each proficiency level should be able to perform the following tasks.

Listening/Speaking

Early Beginner/Beginner Gesture or point in response to oral directions to identify solutions, acids, and bases. Say the words that describe the terms *acid* and *base*.

Early Intermediate Follow spoken directions to make a solution. Use short spoken phrases to tell what happens when a solution becomes concentrated.

Intermediate Use pictures and oral descriptions to identify different kinds of solutions. Use complete spoken sentences to tell how the pH scale works.

Advanced/Transitioning Paraphrase oral descriptions of how solutions form. Differentiate between colloids and suspensions, and between acids and bases, using complete and complex spoken sentences.

Your Turn

Write **acid** or **base** next to each substance.

Substance	pH	Acid or Base?
hydrochloric acid	0	acid
lemon juice	2	acid
vinegar	3	acid
blood	7.5	base
soapy water	10	base
ammonia	11.5	base
drain cleaner	14	base

Talk and Write About It

Complete the statements about acids and bases.

1. Acids and bases are measured with a scale called <u>the pH scale</u>.
2. On the pH scale, acids are found between the numbers <u>0 and 7</u>.
3. On the pH scale, bases are found between the numbers <u>7 and 14</u>.
4. A solution can be either <u>an acid or a base</u>.

Produce Language

Write what you learned in this lesson about acids, bases, and solutions. Use as many vocabulary terms as you can.

_____
_____
_____
_____
_____
_____
_____
_____

Acids, Bases, and Solutions 37

Leveled Language Proficiency

Students at each proficiency level should be able to perform the following tasks.

Reading/Writing

Early Beginner/Beginner Locate words that describe solutes and solvents. Label different kinds of solutions.

Early Intermediate Read to find out what a pH scale is. Write short phrases that explain where some common substances fall on the pH scale.

Intermediate Summarize written phrases that describe solubility. List some substances that are more soluble than others.

Advanced/Transitioning Read aloud sentences that compare a diluted solution and a concentrated solution. Write a paragraph explaining the difference between diluted and concentrated solutions, giving examples.

Assess Understanding

Your Turn

Model You may want to have real examples or photos on hand of each substance listed, or draw sketches on the board. For *hydrochloric acid* a description should suffice. Remind students that the pH scale goes in order from greatest acidity to least, with greater numbers indicating that a substance is strongly base (or alkaline). The center of the scale is a neutral area, meaning these substances are neither acids nor bases. Read the names of the substances with students, providing visuals or explanations. Ask students to label each item on the chart according to its rating on the pH scale.

Talk and Write About It

On Their Own Encourage student groups to use the sample statements as a springboard to form their own sentences that explain acids and bases.

Produce Language

On Their Own Have student pairs both write and talk about what they learned about acids, bases, and solutions. Have them describe each of the topics of the lesson in their own words.

Wrap Up

Table Talk Have students reread the Big Question as a way to reflect on what they learned. Encourage students to build fluency by reading their writing in groups or to the class.

✔ **Learned** and applied vocabulary related to acids and bases

✔ **Heard** statements about how solutions are made

✔ **Read** about ways that acids, bases, and solutions are related to one another

Lesson 10

Motion

Vocabulary motion, reference point, International System of Units, distance, speed, velocity, slope, acceleration

Materials index cards, ball, metric ruler, pile of books

Science Background

- You can tell an object is in motion by its change in position relative to a reference point.

- To calculate speed, divide the distance an object travels by the time it takes to travel the distance. Velocity is speed in a given direction.

- Acceleration is the rate at which velocity changes. The acceleration of an object refers to the object's increasing speed, decreasing speed, or changing direction.

Frontload the Lesson

What are ways to describe the motion of an object?

Talk About It

Build Background As students look at the pictures, encourage them to be as verbal as possible about them. Have students use single words, phrases, or short sentences to describe what they see.

Content and Language

Predict

Model Ask students to read the Big Question and the objectives aloud. Correct any mispronunciations that they make as they read.

Guide Discussion Ask students to restate one of the objectives in their own words. Then ask students to predict what they might learn about that particular objective.

Motion

Big Question What are ways to describe the motion of an object?

You will . . .
- Identify and describe objects in motion.
- Calculate the speed and direction of a moving object.
- Use terms related to motion.

Talk About It

Talk about motion with a partner. How does the ball move? How does the seesaw move? How do you know when something is in motion?

Look at the terms in the Picture It! box. Write them on index cards. As your teacher reads the terms aloud, sort them into two piles.

| motion | reference point |

Step 1 Put words you used or heard during your discussion in Pile 1.
Step 2 Put words you did not use or hear in Pile 2.

Predict
Look at the Big Question and the "You will . . ." statements at the top of the page. Describe what you think you are going to learn in this lesson.

I think I am going to learn about . . .

38 Lesson 10

Leveled Instruction

Early Beginner Ask students to repeat the word *acceleration* after you and to find a picture in the lesson that demonstrates the concept.

Beginner Ask students to choose a picture from the lesson and ask a partner a question about it. Have the partners respond and then have students switch roles.

Early Intermediate/Intermediate Ask students to describe the movement of an airplane by using the words *speed, acceleration,* and *velocity.*

Advanced/Transitioning Partner these students with beginning students. Have the advanced students point out pictures in the lesson that illustrate the vocabulary terms. Ask them to explain key terms to the beginners.

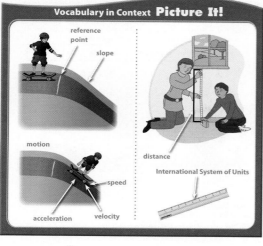

Vocabulary in Context **Picture It!**

reference point

slope

motion

distance

speed

acceleration

velocity

International System of Units

Talk About It
Work with a partner. Use the terms in the box above to complete the sentences.

1. When an object changes position, it is in . . . **motion.**
2. As the boy goes downhill, he increases his . . . and . . . **speed; velocity.**
3. You can see if something moves by comparing its location to a . . . **reference point.**
4. When you measure how far something moves, you are measuring . . . **distance.**
5. A moving object's speed in one direction is its . . . **velocity.**
6. To measure distances, people use the measurement system called the . . . **International System of Units.**
7. The steepness of a hill is its . . . **slope.**

Your Turn
Talk with a partner about the pictures in the Picture It box. Talk about ways that objects move.

Motion **39**

Academic Vocabulary

- Say the word *object* and use it in the context of the lesson. For example, say, *The object is in motion.* Explain that the word is used a noun. Then explain that the word *object* can also be used as a verb, meaning to disagree or to not like something. Point out that as a verb, the word is pronounced differently than the noun. Give a sample sentence, such as *I object to that idea.*

- Write the word *reference* on the board. Point out that the base word *reference* is *refer.*

Cultural Consideration

- Explain to students that the three main words in the term *International System of Units* should begin with capital letters because the term is a compound proper noun. The system of units is an agreed-upon system around the world, or among nations, for measuring matter. Units are abbreviated as SI units because of the French term *Système International.* Ask students to discuss some units they know about, such as liters, grams, kilograms, and so on.

↻ Comprehensible Input

Vocabulary in Context: Picture It!

1. **Say the Term** Say each term slowly, artificially stressing each syllable. Have students repeat. Then say the term more naturally and have students repeat.

2. **Introduce Word Meaning** Connect each term to the visual that illustrates it.

3. **Demonstrate** Use a ball, a ruler, and a pile of books to demonstrate the terms.

   - Move the ball from one point on a desk to another. Say, *This ball is in motion. It is changing position. The desk is not changing position. The desk is a good reference point.*

   - Take out the ruler and say, *We can measure the distance the ball moved using a ruler. This ruler shows the International System of Units, also called* the metric system.

   - Create a slope by leaning a board against the seat of a chair. Say, *This is a slope.* Release the ball at the top of the slope and say, *As the ball moves down the slope, its speed increases. The ball moves faster. Any changing speed is called* acceleration.

4. **Apply** After all of the terms have been discussed, have students demonstrate understanding with Talk About It.

Talk About It

Guide Discussion Ask students to choose a word related to each picture in the Picture It section and use it in a sentence.

RTI Response to Intervention

If students have difficulty pronouncing the word *acceleration* . . .

Then explain that *acceleration* is made up of the prefix *ac-*, the root *celer*, and the suffix *-ation*. Say each word part separately and then say them together.

Your Turn

Guide Discussion Encourage students to talk about different ways that objects move. They can talk about different speeds, directions, and a combination of both.

Motion

Language Production

Do You Understand?

Comprehension Support Partner students and give each student a book. Use a point on the wall, or put a small object, such as a plastic cup, on the floor to act as a reference point. Position students across from one another, and have one student push the book toward the other. Have students label the picture after they complete one push. The positions for students' labels will vary, so check understanding by having students explain their choices. A reference point, in particular, may be any fixed point you can see near the moving object. The three arrows all show *direction*. The three images of the book all show *position*. Discuss how a reference point can be used to determine whether motion has taken place. (If an object moves, its position will change relative to a reference point.).

Model As students do the activity, describe steps with vocabulary terms. Say, *The book accelerates. When it stops, you can see the distance it traveled.*

Talk About It

Guide Discussion Have students work in groups if they have trouble completing the sentences individually. Have them try different terms in the blanks if they are unsure about which one is correct.

Your Turn

Guide Discussion Listen to student discussions as they compare their answers. Help them correct any mistakes or misunderstandings they have about the difference between speed and velocity. Be sure they understand that speed is the distance traveled in a certain amount of time and velocity is the speed of an object in a given direction.

A Closer Look

On Their Own Review nouns, adjectives, and verbs with students. Ask students to identify which part of speech *reference* is when it is used in the term *reference point*. (adjective) Have students work in pairs to complete this word study activity. Ask volunteers to make up their own sentences using the word *reference*.

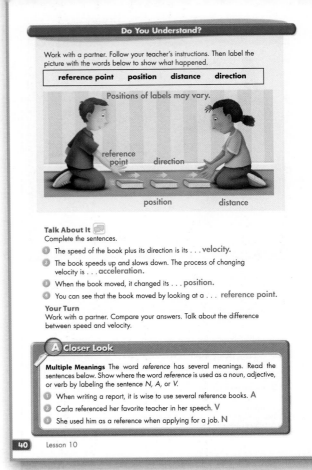

Do You Understand?

Work with a partner. Follow your teacher's instructions. Then label the picture with the words below to show what happened.

| reference point | position | distance | direction |

Positions of labels may vary.

Talk About It
Complete the sentences.
1. The speed of the book plus its direction is its . . . velocity.
2. The book speeds up and slows down. The process of changing velocity is . . . acceleration.
3. When the book moved, it changed its . . . position.
4. You can see that the book moved by looking at a . . . reference point.

Your Turn
Work with a partner. Compare your answers. Talk about the difference between speed and velocity.

A Closer Look

Multiple Meanings The word *reference* has several meanings. Read the sentences below. Show where the word *reference* is used as a noun, adjective, or verb by labeling the sentence N, A, or V.
1. When writing a report, it is wise to use several reference books. A
2. Carla referenced her favorite teacher in her speech. V
3. She used him as a reference when applying for a job. N

Leveled Language Proficiency

Students at each proficiency level should be able to perform the following tasks.

Listening/Speaking

Early Beginner/Beginner In response to a question, gesture or point to demonstrate the term *speed*. Use a word or a short phrase in response to questions about motion.

Early Intermediate Respond to an oral description of *distance* by finding pictures in the lesson that could illustrate an object that has gone a certain distance. Speak a short phrase to explain how the picture illustrates distance.

Intermediate Listen to a description of *acceleration*. Paraphrase what is being said using complete sentences.

Advanced/Transitioning Participate in a discussion about speed and velocity. Use complete and complex sentences to explain the difference between velocity and acceleration.

Your Turn

Look at the picture below. The girl on the trike moves. Circle a reference point that could show that she moves. Draw a line to show the distance between the bottom of the flag and the ground. Draw an "X" on a slope.

Students may circle any stationary point in the picture as a reference point.

The slide or the seesaw may be marked as a slope.

Talk and Write About It 💬 ✏️

Complete the statements about how objects move.

1. You can use the International System of Units to **measure distance**.
2. Velocity is the speed the girl is riding the trike in a certain **direction**.
3. As the girl goes down the slide, her speed changes. This is called **acceleration**.
4. When an object changes its position in relation to another object, it is in **motion**.
5. Some examples of a slope are **a hill and a slide**.

Produce Language

Write an example of one thing you have learned about motion. Use as many vocabulary terms as you can.

_____
_____
_____
_____
_____

Motion **41**

Leveled Language Proficiency

Students at each proficiency level should be able to perform the following tasks.

Reading/Writing

Early Beginner/Beginner Locate words that describe speed and motion. Draw and label pictures to show how to know that an object has moved.

Early Intermediate Read to find a reference to velocity. Write short phrases to describe the meaning of the term.

Intermediate Comprehend phrases that describe a reference point. Write a description of how a reference point can be used to determine the motion of an object.

Advanced/Transitioning Understand most of a grade-level textbook explanation of motion, velocity, and acceleration. Write and read aloud sentences that describe how a slope can affect the acceleration of an object.

⟳ Assess Understanding

Your Turn

Model Before students complete the activity, have them talk about the vocabulary terms from the lesson and how each one might be illustrated in the picture. Then have them follow the directions in the activity and mark the page as exactly as possible.

Talk and Write About It

On Their Own Encourage student groups to work together to complete the sentences if they have difficulty doing it on their own. Allow them to look back at the lesson for ideas if necessary.

Produce Language

On Their Own Have student pairs ask each other the Big Question and talk about how motion can be described before they begin to write.

Wrap Up

Table Talk Have students reflect on what they learned. Encourage students to build fluency by reading their writing in groups or to the class.

✔ **Learned** and applied vocabulary related to motion

✔ **Heard** statements about speed and how it is measured

✔ **Read** statements about how acceleration is different from speed or velocity

Lesson 11

Forces

Vocabulary force, newton, net force, friction, gravity, mass, weight

Materials a ball or a pencil, two books

 Science Background

- Force is described by both its strength and the direction in which it acts.

- An unbalanced force changes an object's motion. A balanced force does not affect the motion of an object.

- Friction is the force that two surfaces exert on each other when they rub against each other. Two factors that affect friction are the types of surfaces and how hard the objects are pushed together.

- Mass and distance affect the gravitational attraction between objects.

Frontload the Lesson

 How do objects react to being pushed or pulled?

Talk About It

Build Background As students review the picture of the zoo, direct the discussion so that all students discuss one element in the picture at a time.

Content and Language

Predict

Model Ask students to read the objectives aloud with you.

Guide Discussion Have students ask a question about one of the objectives. Then ask students to predict whether they will be able to answer their own question after going through the lesson.

Forces

 Big Question How do objects react to being pushed or pulled?

You will . . .
- Talk about different ways that force is described.
- Identify different kinds of forces.
- Use terms related to force.

Talk About It

Look at the picture of the zoo. How are objects, people, and animals moving? How are they being pushed or pulled? Talk about it with a partner.

Predict

Look at the Big Question and the "You will . . ." statements at the top of the page. Describe what you think you are going to learn in this lesson.

I think I am going to learn about . . .

Leveled Instruction

Early Beginner Ask students to repeat the word *newton* after you and to find a picture that contains an abbreviation for the unit (N).

Beginner Ask students to choose a picture from the lesson and use short phrases to describe whether a push or a pull is being shown.

Early Intermediate/Intermediate Ask students to describe the concept of *friction* in their own words. Invite them to find an illustrative example of it in the lesson.

Advanced/Transitioning Have students explain the concept of *net force* and give an example of it using complete sentences.

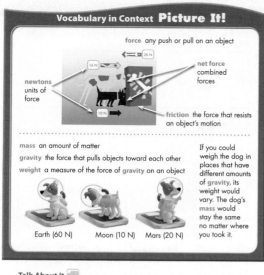

force any push or pull on an object

newtons units of force

net force combined forces

friction the force that resists an object's motion

mass an amount of matter

gravity the force that pulls objects toward each other

weight a measure of the force of gravity on an object

If you could weigh the dog in places that have different amounts of gravity, its weight would vary. The dog's mass would stay the same no matter where you took it.

Earth (60 N)   Moon (10 N)   Mars (20 N)

Talk About It

Work with a partner. Use the terms in the box above to complete the sentences.

1. Any push or pull is a . . . force.
2. Force is measured in units called . . . newtons.
3. All the forces acting on an object make up a . . . net force.
4. The force that pulls objects toward each other is . . . gravity.
5. How much matter an object has is its . . . mass.
6. How much an object weighs is its . . . weight.

Your Turn

Talk with a partner about the pictures in the Picture It box. Talk about ways that forces affect objects.

Academic Vocabulary

- Point out to students that the word *force* can be both a noun and a verb. The way it is used in science is usually a noun. Give the example *The force on the object is a pull.* Then give an example of the word as a verb, such as *I cannot force you to fall asleep.* Give students other examples of sentences that use *force* as a verb and a noun. Have students identify which part of speech is being used in each sentence.

- Tell students that the word *net* also has more than one meaning and that some can also be nouns. Explain that the word *net* as it is used in the lesson means a final, or end, result. *Net force* is the final force on an object after all forces have been considered. Ask students if they know another meaning of *net*. Explain that a butterfly net or a fishing net is a tool for catching something.

- Point out that the word *weight* is pronounced the same as the word *wait*, which means *to pause* or *stop*.

↻ Comprehensible Input

Vocabulary in Context: Picture It!

1. **Say the Term** Say each term slowly, artificially stressing each syllable. Have students repeat. Then say the term more naturally and have students repeat.

2. **Introduce Word Meaning** Connect each term to the visual that illustrates it.

3. **Demonstrate** Use gestures and visuals to demonstrate each term. For example, use books to demonstrate.

   - As you say the word *gravity* aloud, drop a book and explain that the force of gravity has pulled the book to the ground. Say, *On Earth this book weighs about a pound. On the moon there is less gravity, so the book would have less weight. However, the mass of the book would not change.*

   - Place a book on a desk and push it. Say, *I am applying a force to the book. I am pushing it. There is also a friction force from the book rubbing on the desk. The net force is the combination of the friction and the push and the gravity acting on the book. We can use newtons to measure any of these forces.*

4. **Apply** After all of the terms have been discussed, have students demonstrate understanding with Talk About It.

Talk About It

Guide Discussion Ask students to choose a term related to each picture in the Picture It section and use it in a sentence.

R T I Response to Intervention

If students have difficulty pronouncing the word *weight* as they read it from the book . . .

Then point out the silent *gh* sound and the *ei* vowel combination. Show other words with the same sound spelled the same way: *neighbor, sleigh, weigh.*

Your Turn

Guide Discussion Encourage students to talk about different ways that force affects objects. Invite them to apply a force to an object, such as rolling a ball or a pencil. Have them talk about that specific force and how the force affected the movement of the object.

Forces

⟳ Language Production

Do You Understand?

Comprehension Support Before students start the activity, have them talk about what is happening in each picture. Then have them decide how the science term relates to the picture.

Model Demonstrate how students can ask themselves questions to help them discuss the concepts pictured. Model some self-questioning, such as: *Is the skateboarder applying a force to the skateboard? I wonder: what force or forces might slow the skateboard down? What kind of force is working on the apple?*

Talk About It

Guide Discussion Have students work in groups if they have trouble completing the sentences. Remind students that they can refer to the pictures to help them answer the questions.

Your Turn

Guide Discussion Encourage students to talk about different examples of force in the classroom. Have them explain that a force is a push or a pull and give specific examples and demonstrations. Be sure that they understand that a *net force* is the total of all forces acting on an object.

Talk about what is happening in each picture. Use the word shown beside the picture as you describe it.

①	friction
②	gravity
③	mass
④	net force

Talk About It
Talk with a partner. Complete the sentences.
1. The dogs are pushing with a . . . of 10 N. net force
2. The pull of gravity is different on the Moon than on . . . Earth or other planets.
3. The elephant has a greater . . . than the man. mass
4. The ground resists the skateboard's motion with a force called . . . friction.

Your Turn
Work with a partner. Talk about how you think an object's mass might combine with force to affect motion.

44   Lesson 11

Leveled Language Proficiency

Students at each proficiency level should be able to perform the following tasks.

Listening/Speaking

Early Beginner/Beginner Gesture or point in response to oral directions. Use a word or a short phrase in response to questions about what *motion* is.

Early Intermediate/Intermediate Respond to a description of *distance* by finding pictures in the lesson that could illustrate an object that has gone a certain distance. Use a short phrase to explain how the picture illustrates distance.

Advanced/Transitioning Participate in a discussion about force. Use complete and complex sentences to explain the difference between velocity and acceleration.

Your Turn

Draw a line to match each definition and term. Then write a sentence using the term.

1 measure of the force of gravity on an object	mass	Sentences will vary.
2 unit used to measure force	weight	Sentences will vary.
		Sentences will vary.
3 measure of the amount of matter in an object	newton	

Write a sentence or two about the forces in the picture below.

Sentences will vary.

Sentences will vary.

Talk and Write About It

Complete the statements about force on objects.

1 Mass is a measure of matter. Weight is a measure of _gravity on an object_.

2 Newtons measure _force on an object_.

3 Net force is _all the forces acting on an object added together_
the sum of all the forces acting on an object.

Produce Language

Write one example of an object reacting to a force.

Forces 45

Leveled Language Proficiency

Students at each proficiency level should be able to perform the following tasks.

Reading/Writing

Early Beginner/Beginner Locate words that describe forces. Draw and label pictures to show examples of different kinds of forces.

Early Intermediate Read to find a reference to gravity. Write short phrases to describe the key vocabulary terms in this lesson.

Intermediate Comprehend phrases that describe net force. Write a description of how a net force can be measured.

Advanced/Transitioning Read aloud sentences that describe how an object slows down with friction. Write about a real-life example of friction.

Assess Understanding

Your Turn

Model Before students start the activity, explain that they may match up the definitions first, or they may write the sample sentences first. Before students write a sentence or two that goes with the boy in the wheelchair, ask partners to talk about the picture together. Pair advanced or transitioning students with early or beginning students to discuss the scene.

Talk and Write About It

On Their Own Have students work in pairs or small groups to complete the sentences. Remind them that the answers are not always one-word answers but that some will be phrases or long clauses that must make sense in the sentence.

Produce Language

On Their Own Have student pairs reread the Big Question. Then have them use their writing to talk about how objects react to pushes and pulls.

Wrap Up

Table Talk Have students reflect on what they learned. Encourage students to build fluency by reading their writing in groups or to the class.

✔ **Learned** and applied vocabulary related to forces

✔ **Spoken** statements about forces and how they are measured

✔ **Written** statements about how forces affect the motion of objects

Lesson 12

Newton's Laws of Motion

Vocabulary inertia, velocity, mass, acceleration, net force, action-reaction force

Materials a beach or playground ball, a toy car

Science Background

- Inertia is the tendency of an object to resist a change in motion.

- Newton's first law of motion states that an object at rest tends to stay at rest, and an object in motion at a constant velocity will keep moving at that velocity, unless a nonzero net force acts on the object.

- Newton's second law states that an object's acceleration depends on the object's mass and the net force acting on it.

- Newton's third law of motion states that if one object exerts a force on another object, then the second exerts a reaction force of equal strength in the opposite direction on the first object.

Frontload the Lesson

THE BIG ? What are Newton's three laws of motion?

Talk About It

Build Background As students review the picture of the dogs tugging on the rope, say words related to forces and motion, such as *push, pull, force,* and *motion.*

Content and Language

Predict

Model Read the objectives aloud. Explain that Newton was a scientist and mathematician who had many ideas about forces and motion.

Guide Discussion Encourage students to ask a question about one of the objectives.

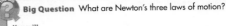

Big Question What are Newton's three laws of motion?

You will . . .
- Differentiate Newton's three laws of motion.
- Describe how forces act on moving objects.
- Use terms related to Newton's three laws of motion.

Talk About It

Look at the picture of the dogs. The brown dog pulls. The tan dog pulls back.

What are the forces in the picture? Talk about what might happen.

Predict

Look at the Big Question and the "You will . . ." statements at the top of the page. Describe what you think you are going to learn in this lesson.

I think I am going to learn about . . .

46 Lesson 12

Leveled Instruction

Early Beginner Ask students to repeat as you say the word and definition for *inertia.* Provide students with a real-world example, such as a swing that does not move until a force moves it.

Beginner Read one of Newton's laws to students and ask them to identify which one is being read.

Early Intermediate/Intermediate Ask students to describe the concept of *inertia* in their own words. Invite them to find the definition in the lesson and use it to form their own sentence.

Advanced/Transitioning Challenge students to describe each of Newton's laws. Have them use their own words and respond in complete sentences.

Vocabulary in Context Picture It!

The horse's speed in a certain direction is its **velocity**.

mass amount of matter

action-reaction forces

net force total of forces

inertia Objects keep moving or stay still unless a force causes a change.

acceleration any change in speed or direction

Talk About It
Work with a partner. Use the pictures in the box above to finish the sentences.

1. The bike's change in speed is its . . . **acceleration.**
2. The boy keeps moving when the bike stops because of . . . **inertia.**
3. The total forces of both dogs pushing the box is the . . . **net force.**
4. When a ball hits the ground and bounces back up, it shows . . . **action-reaction forces.**
5. All the matter in an object is the object's . . . **mass.**

Your Turn
Talk with a partner about the pictures in the Picture It box. Talk about examples of forces acting on the objects in your classroom. Include objects at rest as well as in motion.

Newton's Laws of Motion **47**

Academic Vocabulary

- Discuss the term *at rest* as it is used in Newton's first law of motion. Explain that the words are used to mean *an object that is not moving.* Reword Newton's laws by replacing the term. Say, *An object that is not moving will tend to remain not moving.*

- Review particular terms used in Newton's laws that students may have trouble with. For example, make sure students understand the meaning of *opposite* as the reverse, or as different as two things can be. Review other words used in the laws, such as *constant, nonzero net force,* and *exert.*

- Tell students that one type of law tells people how to behave, such as "Stop at a red light." Explain that in science, a law is a statement that describes how something always happens.

↻ Comprehensible Input

Vocabulary in Context: Picture It!

1. **Say the Term** Say each term slowly, artificially stressing each syllable. Have students repeat. Then say the term more naturally and have students repeat.

2. **Introduce Word Meaning** Connect each term to the visual that illustrates it.

3. **Demonstrate** Use gestures and visuals to demonstrate. For example:

   - Give real-life examples of inertia. For example, place an eraser or pencil at the side of a desk and explain that the object will stay at rest. Then push it off the desk. Explain that you applied a force. You made the object move.

   - Roll a ball along the floor and explain that it also shows inertia. It will continue to roll unless something stops it.

   - Push an object with both hands together. Explain that the net force is the combined forces of both hands, i.e., the total of all forces acting on the object.

4. **Apply** After all of the terms have been discussed, have students demonstrate understanding with Talk About It.

Talk About It

Guide Discussion Ask students to choose a term related to each picture in the Picture It box and use it in a sentence.

RTI Response to Intervention

If students have difficulty decoding the word *inertia* . . .

Then point out the *ti* in the word. Explain that the *ti* makes a *sh* sound. Ask students to discuss other words in which *ti* sounds like *sh*, such as the words *motion* and *acceleration.*

Your Turn

Guide Discussion Encourage students to talk about times they have noticed examples of each box.

Newton's Laws of Motion

↻ Language Production

Do You Understand?

Comprehension Support Before students start the activity, you may want to introduce the actual wording of each of Newton's three laws. Use the notes provided in Science Background to either read each law aloud or first write and then read each law for students. Encourage students to ask questions and to give examples, but tell them not to worry if they don't understand the meanings just yet. Explain that they can use the pictures and activities in this lesson to begin to understand these laws of motion.

Model Demonstrate how students can think about each question to help them answer it. Ask, *What happens if I push or pull on a spring? What happens if nothing pushes or pulls it? I remember that any push or pull is a force. So a force must act on the spring to make it move.*

Talk About It

Guide Discussion Have students work in groups. If they have trouble completing the sentence frames, remind them to look at the pictures in Picture It! If necessary, model connecting the pictures to key terms such as *acceleration* and *mass*.

Your Turn

Guide Discussion Circulate among pairs. Make sure that students understand that the dogs are pushing on the box with a net force of 26 Newtons.

A Closer Look

Word Parts As students realize that *action* and *reaction* are related, ask them to give examples of an *action* and *reaction* in real life.

Do You Understand?

Answer the questions to help think about Newton's laws.

	Newton's First Law
	What would happen if you pushed down on this spring? The spring would bounce upwards.
	Newton's Second Law
	Which takes more force to push? three carts
	Newton's Third Law
	What happens when one side goes down? The other side goes up.

Talk About It
Talk with a partner. Complete the sentences.
1. An object's speed in a certain direction is called the object's . . . velocity.
2. When a spring exerts a force on the ground, and the ground exerts the same force back, the forces are called . . . action-reaction forces.
3. Objects stay at rest or in motion because of . . . inertia.

Your Turn
Work with a partner. Look at the picture of the dogs in Picture It! Talk about what is happening.

> **A Closer Look**
>
> **Word Parts** Underline any prefixes or suffixes in the words below. What three-letter base word do both words share?
> - action
> - reaction   They both share the base word *act*.

Leveled Language Proficiency

Students at each proficiency level should be able to perform the following tasks.

Listening/Speaking

Early Beginner/Beginner Gesture or point in response to questions about motion. Draw a simple diagram in response to questions about what *inertia* is.

Early Intermediate Respond to a description of Newton's first law by finding pictures in the lesson that could illustrate it. Use short phrases to explain how the picture illustrates the law.

Intermediate Listen to a description of Newton's second law. Paraphrase what is being said using complete sentences.

Advanced/Transitioning Understand a description of different kinds of forces. Use complete and complex sentences to explain what Newton's third law states.

Your Turn

Newton's first law says that an object at rest will remain at rest unless acted upon by an unbalanced force. In the box below, draw a picture that shows this.

> Answer will depend on drawing.

Newton's second law says that an object's acceleration depends on its mass and the force acting on it. Draw a picture that shows how an object's acceleration depends on force.

> Answer will depend on drawing.

Newton's third law says that if one object exerts a force on another object, the second object pushes back with the same force. Draw a picture that shows this.

> Answer will depend on drawing.

Talk and Write About It

Complete the statements below to summarize Newton's three laws of motion.

1. An object at rest does not move unless <u>a force acts on it</u>.
2. An object's acceleration depends on its <u>mass and net force</u>.
3. For every action, there is an equal but opposite <u>reaction</u>.

Produce Language

Write what you have learned about each of Newton's laws. Use as many of the vocabulary terms as you can.

_____
_____
_____
_____

Leveled Language Proficiency

Students at each proficiency level should be able to perform the following tasks.

Reading/Writing

Early Beginner/Beginner Locate words that describe the motion of objects. Draw pictures to show examples of inertia and action-reaction forces.

Early Intermediate Read to find a reference to inertia. Write short phrases to describe the meaning of the term.

Intermediate Comprehend phrases that describe each of Newton's laws. Write a description of each law.

Advanced/Transitioning Read aloud sentences that describe each of Newton's laws. Write about real-life examples of Newton's laws of motion.

Assess Understanding

Your Turn

Model Before students start the activity, explain that they will be reading each of Newton's laws and then drawing a picture to illustrate the law. If necessary, model completing the activity on the board. Challenge students to choose a different subject for each of their illustrations.

Talk and Write About It

On Their Own Have students work in groups if they have trouble completing the sentence starters. Remind them that the answers might either be one-word answers or a full phrase.

Produce Language

On Their Own Have student pairs use their writing to present one of Newton's laws of motion to the class. They might want to create a poster, do a demonstration, or list an example or two, to illustrate the summary.

Wrap Up

Table Talk Have students reflect on what they learned. Encourage students to build fluency by reading their writing in groups or to the class.

✔ **Learned** and applied vocabulary related to Newton's laws

✔ **Spoken** statements about inertia and how it applies to everyday objects

✔ **Written** statements about Newton's three laws of motion

Lesson 13

Momentum

Vocabulary momentum, law of conservation of momentum, free fall, satellite, centripetal force, orbit

Materials 12-inch strings, metal washers, toy ball

 Science Background

- Momentum is the product of the mass and the velocity of an object. It has magnitude and direction (a vector quantity).

- When the acceleration of an object is caused solely by gravity, the object is said to be in free fall.

- Satellites in orbit around Earth continuously fall toward Earth, but because Earth is curved they travel around it.

Momentum

 Big Question What are *momentum* and *free fall*?

You will . . .
- Explain how moving objects have momentum.
- Relate the motion of free fall to the force of gravity.
- Use terms related to momentum and free fall.

Talk About It

Look at the picture. What will happen if you hold the string with your hand and swing the metal washer in a circle? Make a prediction. Then try it.

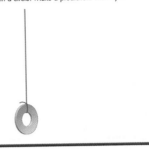

Predict
Look at the Big Question and the "You will . . ." statements at the top of the page. Describe what you think you are going to learn in this lesson.

I think I am going to learn about . . .

50   Lesson 13

 Frontload the Lesson

What are momentum and free fall?

Talk About It

Build Background Provide students with a 12-inch piece of string with a washer tied to one end of it. Have them first hold the string and washer in one hand. Then have them predict what will happen if they swing the washer around. **CAUTION:** Be sure students move to a safe distance from each other. Then have them try swinging the washer in a circle to demonstrate centripetal force.

Content and Language

Predict

Model Read the objectives aloud. As students repeat after you, correct any mispronunciations.

Guide Discussion Ask students to choose one of the objectives and ask their own question about it.

Leveled Instruction

Early Beginner Ask students to point to the word *momentum* in the lesson. Then ask them to point to pictures that illustrate the concept.

Beginner Provide sentence starters for students to create definitions of vocabulary terms in the lesson.

Early Intermediate/Intermediate Ask students questions about momentum and free fall that require them to answer in a complete sentence.

Advanced/Transitioning Have students model complete and complex sentences to compare the concepts of free fall and centripetal force.

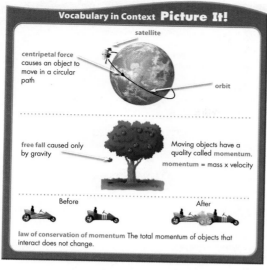

Vocabulary in Context **Picture It!**

satellite

centripetal force causes an object to move in a circular path

orbit

free fall caused only by gravity

Moving objects have a quality called momentum.

momentum = mass × velocity

Before

After

law of conservation of momentum The total momentum of objects that interact does not change.

Talk About It

Work with a partner. Use the pictures above to complete the sentences.

1. When an object accelerates only because of gravity, it is in . . . free fall.
2. When you multiply the mass of a moving object times its velocity, you get the object"s . . . momentum.
3. The idea that the total momentum of interacting objects is unchanged is called the law of . . . law of conservation of momentum.
4. A force that moves objects in a circular path is . . . centripetal force.
5. A curved path around an object in space is an . . . orbit.
6. An object that moves in orbit around another object is a . . . satellite.

Your Turn

Talk with a partner about the pictures in the Picture It box. Talk about the difference between objects in free fall and objects in orbit.

Momentum **51**

Academic Vocabulary

- When discussing the idea of *free fall*, point out to students that the word *free* has another meaning that does not have to do with science and forces. Explain that *free* also means "without costing money." Use sample sentences that present the term in both contexts and ask students to identify when one means "without costing money."

- When discussing the concept of *momentum* and how to calculate it, be sure to write the formula on the board: momentum = mass × velocity. Then express the equation in words as you point to each part: *momentum equals mass times velocity*. Explain to students that a mathematical equation can also be expressed as an English sentence.

↻ Comprehensible Input

Vocabulary in Context: Picture It!

1. **Say the Term** Say each term slowly, artificially stressing each syllable. Have students repeat. Then say the term more naturally and have students repeat.

2. **Introduce Word Meaning** Connect each term to the visual that illustrates it.

3. **Demonstrate** Use gestures and visuals to demonstrate.

   - As you say the word *centripetal*, point to the picture of the satellite orbit and trace your finger around the orbit. Say, *The word part centri means "around the center." How is the satellite moving around the center?*

   - Roll a ball and talk about its momentum.

   - Drop the ball and explain that the only force acting on the ball is gravity. So the ball is in free fall. Gravity is causing the ball to accelerate.

4. **Apply** After all of the terms have been discussed, have students demonstrate understanding with Talk About It.

Talk About It

Guide Discussion Ask students to look back at the pictures and use the terms to describe the pictures.

RTI Response to Intervention

If students have difficulty decoding the word *centripetal* . . .

Then remind students that the letter *c* can sound like a *k* or an *s*. In the word *centripetal*, it sounds like an *s*. Also, the *al* sounds more like *ul*. Say, *The word trip is in* centripetal. Then, say the whole word several times naturally and have students repeat.

Your Turn

Guide Discussion Encourage students to discuss each term one at a time and then compare the terms using sentence frames such as *Free fall is not like centripetal force, because* . . .

Momentum

Language Production

Do You Understand?

Comprehension Support Before students start the activity, point out that they will not be finding the momentum of each car in the Do You Understand section. They will be making sure they understand what each part of the equation for momentum means. Review the abbreviations for units of measure with students. Have students work in pairs.

Model Demonstrate how students can ask themselves questions to help them do the activity. Say, *Which part of the equation tells about the amount of matter in the car? How is mass measured? Which tells about how fast AND in what direction the car is moving? How is velocity measured?*

Talk About It

Guide Discussion Read the statements aloud with students as they work together to complete the sentences.

Your Turn

Guide Discussion Have students read aloud their written equations.

A Closer Look

On Their Own Remind students that they can try to find the meanings of unknown words by looking at smaller parts of the words.

Do You Understand?

1. In the pictures below, circle the numbers or letters showing the mass of each car.
2. Underline the numbers or letters showing velocity of each car.
3. Make a box around the numbers or letters showing the momentum of each car.

$$4\text{m/s} \times \boxed{100\text{ kg}} = \boxed{400\text{ kg} \cdot \text{m/s}}$$

$$2\text{m/s} \times \boxed{100\text{ kg}} = \boxed{200\text{ kg} \cdot \text{m/s}}$$

Talk About It
Complete the sentences.

1. The mass of the cars is measured in . . . kilograms.
2. The velocity of the cars is measured in . . . per . . . meters; second.
3. To calculate momentum, multiply mass times . . . velocity.
4. An object that does not have velocity cannot have . . . momentum.

Your Turn
Work with a partner. Compare your answers. Rewrite the equation for each car's momentum using words.

> **A Closer Look**
>
> **Word Parts** Underline the word part below that means "center."
> • centripetal force

Leveled Language Proficiency

Students at each proficiency level should be able to perform the following tasks.

Listening/Speaking

Early Beginner/Beginner Gesture or point in response to questions about centripetal force. Use a word or a short phrase in response to questions about what momentum is.

Early Intermediate Use short phrases to respond to questions about free fall. Tell about what causes the free fall of an object.

Intermediate Follow oral directions with little to no help. Explain in complete sentences how centripetal force works

Advanced/Transitioning Follow oral directions independently. Use complete and complex sentences to explain how to calculate the momentum of an object.

Your Turn

Write *free fall* or *centripetal force* for each picture.

free fall

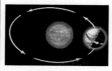
centripetal force

centripetal force

free fall

Talk and Write About It 📷 ✏️

Complete the statements.

1. An object in free fall accelerates because of <u>gravity</u>.
2. If you drop an object from your hand, the object is in <u>free fall</u>.
3. Objects stay in orbit in space because of <u>centripetal force</u>.
4. Centripetal force moves an object in a <u>circular path</u>.

Produce Language

Write about what you learned in this lesson. Use the word *momentum* in your answer.

_____

_____

_____

_____

Momentum **53**

Leveled Language Proficiency

Students at each proficiency level should be able to perform the following tasks.

Reading/Writing

Early Beginner/Beginner Locate words that describe momentum. Draw pictures to show an object in free fall and an object moving with centripetal force.

Early Intermediate Read to find a reference to centripetal force. Write short phrases to describe what *centripetal force* means.

Intermediate Comprehend phrases that describe an object in free fall. Write a description of what *free fall* means.

Advanced/Transitioning Read sentences that describe how to calculate the momentum of an object. Write a complete and original sentence that shows how to calculate the momentum of an object in a real-life situation.

↻ Assess Understanding

Your Turn

Model As students complete the activity, have them discuss what is happening in each picture. Then have students ask themselves, "What kind of force causes this kind of momentum?" Their answer to the question should be either *free fall* or *centripetal force*.

Talk and Write About It

On Their Own Encourage student groups to use the questions to help them begin a discussion about the difference between free fall and centripetal force.

Produce Language

On Their Own Have student pairs both write and talk about ways that an object can have momentum. Also ask them to talk about how momentum can be measured.

Wrap Up

Table Talk Have students use the Big Question to reflect on what they learned. Encourage students to build fluency by reading their writing in groups or to the class.

✔ **Learned** and applied vocabulary related to momentum

✔ **Heard** statements about how momentum can be calculated

✔ **Read** statements about differences and similarities between centripetal force and free fall

Lesson 14

Simple Machines

Vocabulary work, machine, input force, output force, mechanical advantage, efficiency, simple machine, inclined plane, wedge, screw, lever, fulcrum, pulley, wheel and axle

materials screw, plastic knife, spoon

 Science Background

- Work is done when a force is exerted on an object and that object moves. The amount of work is equal to the input force multiplied by the distance the object moves.

- A machine makes work easier by changing the amount, distance, or direction of the input force.

- The mechanical advantage of a machine is the ratio of output force to input force.

- The efficiency of a machine is equal to the output work divided by the input work, multiplied by 100 percent.

Frontload the Lesson

How do machines make it easier to do work?

Talk About It

Build Background Ask students to preview the images of simple machines in the Picture It box.

Content and Language

Predict

Model Read the objectives aloud and have students repeat after you. Then summarize the objectives in your own words.

Guide Discussion Write the objectives on the board. Have student volunteers identify key terms for each objective.

Simple Machines

 Big Question How do machines make it easier to do work?

You will . . .
- Identify and describe the different types of simple machines.
- Explain ways that a machine can make work easier.
- Use the scientific definition of the word *work*.

Talk About It

Imagine that you just won a new television. It is too heavy for you to lift, and there is no one around to help you carry it. How can you get the television into your house?

Talk with a partner. Discuss some tools and machines that might help you move the television.

Predict
Look at the Big Question and the "You will . . ." statements at the top of the page. Describe what you think you are going to learn in this lesson.

I think I am going to learn about . . .

54   Lesson 14

Leveled Instruction

Early Beginner/Beginner Provide tangible examples of common simple machines (such as a screw, a plastic butter knife, or a spoon). Demonstrate how each machine can make work easier.

Early Intermediate/Intermediate Encourage students to connect this material with their own experiences. Have students brainstorm a list of simple machines that they have used and keep it throughout the lesson. As they learn more, have students explain the work they do with each machine, and how the machine helps them.

Advanced Help students understand *mechanical advantage* and *efficiency* by reviewing mathematical concepts with them.

Transitioning Have students keep a short journal about their experiences with simple machines as they go through the lesson. Ask them to share their writing with the class.

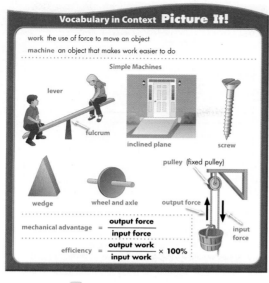

Vocabulary in Context Picture It!

work the use of force to move an object

machine an object that makes work easier to do

Simple Machines

lever

fulcrum

inclined plane

screw

pulley (fixed pulley)

wedge

wheel and axle

output force

input force

$$\text{mechanical advantage} = \frac{\text{output force}}{\text{input force}}$$

$$\text{efficiency} = \frac{\text{output work}}{\text{input work}} \times 100\%$$

Talk About It

Work with a partner. Use the words in the box above to finish these sentences.

1. To make work easier, you can use a . . . **machine.**
2. A simple machine with a fulcrum is a . . . **lever.**
3. Instead of using the stairs leading to a door, you might use a ramp, which is one kind of . . . **inclined plane.**
4. Your push or pull on a machine, such as a fixed pulley, is the . . . **input force.**
5. The push or pull the machine applies to an object is the . . . **output force.**

Your Turn

You have been asked to move a teacher's desk. Talk with a partner about how the machines in the Picture It box might help. Draw your plan.

Simple Machines **55**

Academic Vocabulary

- The word *exert* is frequently used when talking about force. Explain that *exert* means "to use or apply force". Demonstrate by pushing or pulling an object," and saying, *I am exerting force on this object. I am applying a force to the object. I am using force to push or to pull the object.*

- The mechanical advantage and the efficiency of machines both use ratios. Write the word *ratio* on the board and pronounce it, pointing out the *sh* sound. Explain that a ratio is a way to compare numbers. Demonstrate by writing ratios to compare items in the classroom. For example, write a desk-to-student ratio, a window-to-room ratio, or a coat-to-sleeve ratio.

- Remind students that an *advantage* is a benefit or a gain. Point out common examples, such as, *Studying hard gives you an advantage when you take a test.*

- Cognates are words that have the same or similar roots and meanings in two languages. Have students share any vocabulary terms they recognize as cognates to words in their first languages. For example, in Spanish *máquina* is a cognate for *machine* and *eficacia* is a cognate for *efficiency.*

↻ Comprehensible Input

Vocabulary in Context: Picture It!

1. **Say the Term** Say each term slowly, artificially stressing each syllable. Have students repeat. Then say the term more naturally and have students repeat.

2. **Introduce Word Meaning** Connect each term to the visual that illustrates it.

3. **Demonstrate** Use gestures and visuals to demonstrate.

   - Hold up items such as a screw, a knife, or a spoon, and demonstrate how they are used to do work—that is, how they help apply force to move an object or objects.

   - As you demonstrate, remind students that machines are used to change force, distance, or direction. Describe these changes as you model the use of each object.

   - Help students distinguish a wedge from an inclined plane by pointing out that a wedge often has two sloped surfaces, while an inclined plane has just one.

4. **Apply** After all the terms have been discussed, have students demonstrate understanding with Talk About It.

Talk About It

Guide Discussion Read the sentence starters for students. Point out that they will use words from the Picture it box to complete each sentence.

RTI Response to Intervention

If students have difficulty pronouncing the different *ch* sounds of *machine* and *mechanical* . . .

Then remind students that *-e* and *-i* after a consonant often result in a soft sound, while other vowels tend to create a hard sound.

Your Turn

Guide Discussion As a class, brainstorm words that describe a change in force, direction, or distance for students to use as they describe how to move the desk. (Useful words include *turn, up, down, push, pull,* and *under.*)

Simple Machines

Language Production

Do You Understand?

Comprehension Support Before students start the activity, review the different types of simple machines and their parts. Encourage students to think of familiar examples of simple machines. For example, an axe is a wedge; a wheelbarrow is a lever; a doorknob is a wheel and axle. Extend the search into magazines and textbook illustrations, such that students become more familiar with the six types of simple machines and find references for drawing these types. Have students consider how each machine works as they draw.

Model Ask questions to help students label the important parts of the machines. Say, *What do we call the part around which a lever rotates? Which is the wheel? Which is the axle? What is the rope of the pulley wrapped around?*

Talk About It

Guide Discussion Read the sentences aloud with students. Have them use their pictures and labels to help them complete the sentences.

Your Turn

Guide Discussion Circulate around the room to listen as students tell how the machines work. Provide help as needed.

A Closer Look

On Their Own Have students work in pairs. Model by giving examples of how the word *work* is used with its everyday meaning and with its scientific meaning. For sample sentences, using the scientific meaning, students may want to look in a classroom science book to find ideas.

Do You Understand?

Draw each of these simple machines. Label the important parts.

Lever	Wheel and Axle
Pulley	**Wedge**

Student drawings will vary widely, but should reflect the drawings in the Picture It box.

Talk About It
Complete the sentences.

1. A fulcrum is part of a machine called a . . . lever.
2. If you turn an axle, it will turn the part of the machine called the. . . wheel.
3. A wheel attached in a fixed location is a fixed . . . pulley.
4. A machine you use to push things apart is a . . . wedge.
5. The push you exert on a lever is the. . . input force.
6. When you use any of these machines, you are doing . . . work.

Your Turn
Work with a partner. Tell how each machine you have drawn does work.

> **A Closer Look**
>
> **Multiple Meanings** In everyday life, you do *work* when you have a job. In science, you do *work* when you use force to make an object move.
>
> Talk with a partner about different kinds of work that you do. Decide which kinds are "everyday work" and which kinds are "work" in the scientific meaning. (HINT: Some work may be both kinds.)

Leveled Language Proficiency

Students at each proficiency level should be able to perform the following tasks.

Listening/Speaking

Early Beginner/Beginner Point to each type of simple machine after hearing an oral description. State the name of each simple machine in response to a picture of it.

Early Intermediate Respond with hand gestures or short phrases to questions about simple machines. Give examples of everyday uses of simple machines.

Intermediate Follow directions for using simple machines. Explain in complete sentences how various simple machines make work easier.

Advanced/Transitioning Respond to complex oral directions for calculating mechanical advantage and efficiency. Use details to explain to a partner how to calculate mechanical advantage and efficiency.

Your Turn

1. Write the name of each simple machine in Figure 1.
2. In Figures 2 and 3, label the arrow in each picture as either **input force** or **output force**

1. pulley
2. input force — output force
3. inclined plane — input force — output force

3. On a separate sheet of paper, draw a person using a lever to do work. Identify the input force and the output force in your drawing.

Talk and Write About It

Complete the statements about machines and work.

1. A pulley is one type of simple <u>machine</u>
2. Mechanical advantage is equal to the output force divided by <u>the input force</u>
3. A lever moves around a fixed point, called the <u>fulcrum</u>
4. An example of a lever, other than a seesaw, is <u>Sample answers:</u> <u>spoon, crowbar, scissors</u>

Produce Language

Choose two simple machines. Write about how they make work easier.

_____
_____
_____
_____
_____

Simple Machines   **57**

Leveled Language Proficiency

Students at each proficiency level should be able to perform the following tasks.

Reading/Writing

Early Beginner/Beginner Match pictures of simple machines with written names. Label input force and output force on simple machines.

Early Intermediate Identify how simple machines make work easier by reading descriptions with illustrations. Write short paragraphs describing how simple machines make work easier.

Intermediate Interpret written information about work and machines with few visuals. Write explanations of how simple machines can be used to solve practical problems.

Advanced/Transitioning Infer details about work and simple machines from written descriptions. Write several paragraphs that compare and contrast various simple machines.

Assess Understanding

Your Turn

Model Before students start the activity, review the academic vocabulary term *figure,* as "any picture or diagram, appearing in text." Explain that the word *text,* is an academic way of saying "writing in print," such as a book or magazine. Introduce the abbreviation *Fig.* Explain that calling graphics *Figure 1, 2,* etc., allows readers to quickly find them. Have students brainstorm different types of figures and share any other meanings they know for this word. Then read the directions aloud. Remind students that they will be identifying input and output force for simple machines. If necessary, review the meanings of these vocabulary terms.

Talk and Write About It

On Their Own Have students work with a partner to complete the sentences. If they have difficulty thinking of an example of a lever, suggest that they think about everyday things that move around a fixed point. Give students examples of common levers—such as a spoon, a shovel, a paint-can opener—that they might draw for the second part of the activity.

Produce Language

On Their Own Read aloud the Big Question on the first page of the lesson. Point out that machines make work easier by changing the amount, distance, or direction of the input force. Have students discuss each machine with a partner. Then have them choose two machines and write about how they make work easier. Have students use specific examples from everyday life in their responses.

Wrap Up

Table Talk Have students reflect on what they learned. Encourage students to build fluency by reading their writing in groups or to the class.

✔ **Learned** ways that simple machines make work easier

✔ **Spoken** names of different types of simple machines

✔ **Read** definitions of *mechanical advantage* and *efficiency* of a machine, written as ratios

Lesson 15

Forms of Energy

Vocabulary energy, mechanical energy, potential energy, kinetic energy, energy transformation, law of conservation of energy, thermal energy, electrical energy, nuclear energy, electromagnetic energy, chemical energy

Materials 2 tennis balls, pictures that show different forms of energy, 1 rubber band, 1 book, a classroom electrical device (computer, lights, radio, etc.), 1 magnet

Science Background

- Energy is the ability to do work or cause change.

- Potential energy is energy that is stored as a result of the position or shape of an object. Kinetic energy is the energy of an object due to its motion. Mechanical energy is associated with the motion and position of an object.

- Forms of energy associated with the particles in objects include nuclear, thermal, electrical, electromagnetic, and chemical energy.

Frontload the Lesson

What are different forms of energy?

Talk About It

Build Background Have students work with a partner, taking turns dropping the balls and watching them bounce. Emphasize that objects can have different amounts of energy.

Content and Language

Predict

Model Read the objectives aloud. Relate them to familiar examples.

Guide Discussion Have students chorally read the objectives with you before they say what they think they will learn in the lesson.

Forms of Energy

 Big Question What are different forms of energy?

You will . . .
- Identify different forms of energy.
- Understand how energy can be transformed.
- Learn about the law of conservation of energy.
- Use key terms related to energy.

Talk About It

Energy is the ability to do work or cause change.
1. Hold one ball high.
2. Hold another ball low.
3. Let both balls fall.

Talk about why one ball bounces more. How do you think energy affects the bounce?

Predict
Look at the Big Question and the "You will . . ." statements at the top of this page. Describe what you think you are going to learn in this lesson.

I think I am going to learn about . . .

Leveled Instruction

Early Beginner/Beginner Provide students with pictures related to different types of energy or energy transformations. Ask students to point to the word or words in a list corresponding to the pictures.

Early Intermediate/Intermediate Describe a simple type of energy transformation. Have students draw or act out their example.

Advanced Demonstrate a simple type of energy transformation. Ask students to use complete sentences to describe the energy transformation.

Transitioning Provide students with examples of various types of energy transformation. Ask them to identify and write a description of the energy transformation in each example.

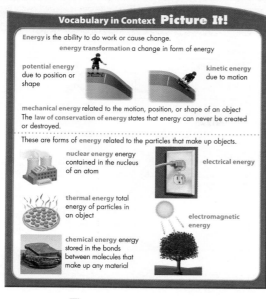

Energy is the ability to do work or cause change.

energy transformation a change in form of energy

potential energy due to position or shape

kinetic energy due to motion

mechanical energy related to the motion, position, or shape of an object

The **law of conservation of energy** states that energy can never be created or destroyed.

These are forms of energy related to the particles that make up objects.

nuclear energy energy contained in the nucleus of an atom

electrical energy

thermal energy total energy of particles in an object

electromagnetic energy

chemical energy energy stored in the bonds between molecules that make up any material

Talk About It

Work with a partner. Use the terms in the box above to finish the sentences.

1. Energy stored in chemical bonds, such as in food, is called . . . **chemical energy.**
2. Energy stored in an atom's nucleus is called . . . **nuclear energy.**
3. As an object falls, it loses potential energy and gains . . . **kinetic energy.**
4. A change from one form of energy to another form is called an . . . **energy transformation.**
5. The law that states that energy cannot be created or destroyed is . . . **law of conservation of energy.**

Your Turn

Talk with a partner about the terms in the Picture It box. What other pictures could you use to illustrate each term?

Academic Vocabulary

- Explain that in everyday life the word *energy* has a related but much broader meaning than it does in science. Ask students how the everyday meaning might help them remember the science meaning.

- Students may think the word *chemical* refers only to materials such as fertilizers, cleaning fluids, or solutions in beakers. Use the pictures in the lesson to emphasize to students that *chemical energy* refers to the energy stored in chemical bonds in the molecules that make up any material.

- Encourage students to find words in other lessons in this book that are similar to the vocabulary terms here. For example, *thermal* is similar to the word *thermometer*; both terms are related to heat. *Nuclear* is similar to the word *nucleus*.

- Have students share any vocabulary terms they recognize as cognates to words in their first languages. For example, in Spanish, the word *energía* is a cognate for *energy* and *química* is a cognate for *chemical*.

↻ Comprehensible Input

Vocabulary in Context: Picture It!

1. **Say the Term** Say each term slowly, artificially stressing each syllable. Have students repeat. Then say the term more naturally and have students repeat.

2. **Introduce Word Meaning** Connect each term to the visual that illustrates it.

3. **Demonstrate** Use gestures and visuals to demonstrate. For example:

- Stretch a rubber band and carefully point it away from all students toward a nearby wall. Say *potential energy*. Release the rubber band. As it moves through the air, say *kinetic energy*. Have a volunteer describe the difference.

- Point to a book placed near the edge of a shelf and say *potential energy*. Tip the book off the shelf. As it is falling, say *kinetic energy*.

- Turn on one of the electrical devices in the room (the lights, computer, radio, etc.) and say *electrical energy*.

4. **Apply** After all the terms have been discussed, have students demonstrate understanding with Talk About It.

Talk About It

Guide Discussion Ask students to use the terms from the Picture It box to answer the questions. Help them relate difficult concepts, such as energy conservation and energy transformation, to the pictures.

RTI Response to Intervention

If students have difficulty reading and understanding the word *transformation* . . .

Then have students write the word and circle the word parts, emphasizing that the root word *form* is a clue to the word's meaning, "the process of changing form."

Your Turn

Guide Discussion Emphasize that more than one form of energy may be associated with an object or process. For example, the mechanical energy of moving teeth helps break down food, enabling the chemical energy to be released during digestion.

Forms of Energy

↻ Language Production

Do You Understand?

Comprehension Support Review the pictures with students. Explain that each of the pictures relates to at least one form of energy listed. Ask questions and provide information to guide students' thinking about these relationships. For example, make sure that students understand that the cooling towers are part of a nuclear power plant. Explain how energy from nuclear processes is used to produce electrical energy at the plant, and how water heated by the process is cooled in the tower.

Model Demonstrate how students can analyze each picture to determine the type of energy it represents. Say, *What is the boy doing?* (running) *Running is a way of moving. What type of energy does a moving object have?*

Talk About It

Guide Discussion Read each question aloud with students. If students have difficulty, guide them to look at the pictures in the activity and the Picture It box to help answer each question.

Your Turn

Guide Discussion Listen to students as they compare the lines they drew. Help them with vocabulary they need to justify their answers.

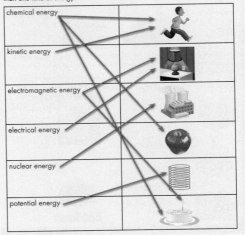

Do You Understand?

Each picture shows an example of energy. Draw a line (or lines) from the picture to the type (or types) of energy it shows. Some pictures show more than one kind of energy.

chemical energy
kinetic energy
electromagnetic energy
electrical energy
nuclear energy
potential energy

Talk About It
Work with a partner to answer the questions.
1. Which type of energy is stored in an atom's nucleus? nuclear
2. Energy comes from the sun in waves. Which type is it? electromagnetic
3. What is one type of energy your body has when you are walking? kinetic, mechanical
4. Which type of energy is stored in food? chemical

Your Turn
Talk with a partner about the lines to the pictures. Are your answers the same? Talk about why you drew each line.

60   Lesson 15

Leveled Language Proficiency

Students at each proficiency level should be able to perform the following tasks.

Listening/Speaking

Early Beginner/Beginner Point to pictures that relate to various types of energy in response to oral descriptions. Repeat the name of each type of energy after hearing it.

Early Intermediate Identify everyday examples of energy transformations based on oral descriptions. Say the name of different types of energy to complete sentence starters.

Intermediate Act out examples of energy transformations in response to oral instructions. Describe orally what happens in different types of energy transformation, after reading or hearing a description.

Advanced/Transitioning Complete tasks related to energy transformation in response to multi-step oral instructions. Discuss and give examples of energy and energy transformations in everyday life.

Your Turn

Use the pictures to help you complete each sentence.

Potential energy in the ball changes to _kinetic_ energy.	
Chemical energy in the battery changes to _electrical_ energy in the wires.	
As the temperature of the water increases, so does the water's _thermal energy_.	

Talk and Write About It 💬 ✏️

Complete the statements about forms of energy.

1. Reactions in the sun cause energy to change from nuclear energy to _electromagnetic energy_.
2. You can give a spring potential energy by _squeezing it_.
3. A moving bike has both _kinetic energy_ and _mechanical energy_.

Produce Language

Write about some ways energy can change form.

_____

_____

_____

In Other Words →

The	table	lists different forms of energy.
	chart	
	graphic organizer	

Leveled Language Proficiency

Students at each proficiency level should be able to perform the following tasks.

Reading/Writing

Early Beginner/Beginner Read and understand single words identifying different forms of energy. Label pictures of different forms of energy.

Early Intermediate/Intermediate Read labeled pictures and diagrams and relate them to teacher and student demonstrations. Complete simple sentence starters by writing the names of different types of energy.

Advanced/Transitioning Differentiate multiple meanings of energy-related terms. Write descriptions about personal experiences with different types of energy and energy transformations.

↻ Assess Understanding

Your Turn

Model Explain to students that they should complete the sentence that describes the energy transformation in the picture beside it. Demonstrate by drawing students' attention to the picture of the bouncing ball. Explain that energy changes from one form to another as the ball bounces. Read the sentence beside the picture. Guide students in talking about the type of energy that would best complete the sentence.

Talk and Write About It

On Their Own Encourage students to talk about each statement before completing it in writing. If they have difficulty, point them toward places in the lesson that show the same (or similar) examples of the energy types in question.

Produce Language

On Their Own Have pairs of students read and talk about the Big Question at the start of the lesson. Then have them discuss what they've learned about ways energy can change form, before writing their answers. If desired, call on volunteers to read the finished writing aloud.

In Other Words

Model Point out that a familiar meaning of *table* may be as "a piece of furniture." Then explain that, in science, *table* is used to mean "a way of presenting information, in rows and columns." Read the example sentence aloud for students and have them repeat it. Then ask, *What is another to way to say this? What is another word, or words, for* table? Encourage students to read the sentence aloud in turn, each time choosing a new highlighted word for the term *table*.

Wrap Up

Table Talk Have students reflect on what they learned. Encourage students to build fluency by reading their writing in groups or to the class.

✔ **Learned** names of different forms of energy

✔ **Spoken** statements about energy transformation

✔ **Heard** descriptions of energy conservation

Lesson 16

Thermal Energy and Heat

Vocabulary temperature, Celsius scale, Fahrenheit scale, Kelvin scale, absolute zero, convection, convection current, radiation, conduction, conductor, insulator, specific heat, thermal expansion

Materials two plastic cups for each small group of students; warm and cold tap water

 Science Background

- Temperature is a measure of the average kinetic energy of the particles in an object.
- Thermal energy is the total energy of an object's particles.
- Heat flows from warmer areas to cooler areas. The three methods of heat transfer are conduction, convection, and radiation.
- As the thermal energy of matter increases, its particles speed up, causing the pressure to increase and the heated material either to increase in volume or to disperse.

Frontload the Lesson

 How does heat flow from one object to another?

Talk About It

Build Background Provide each group with one cup filled with cold water and another cup with warm tap water. Say, *How does each hand feel holding the cup? Heat always moves from a warmer area to a cooler area.*

Content and Language

Predict

Model Read aloud the Big Question and the objectives as students listen. Demonstrate how to highlight key words.

Guide Discussion Have students discuss what they learned in the water activity before they make their prediction.

Thermal Energy and Heat

 Big Question How does heat flow from one object to another?

You will . . .
- Explain how temperature, thermal energy, and heat are related.
- Compare the three ways heat flows from one object to another.
- Understand and use key words related to thermal energy and heat.

Talk About It

Heat is the movement of thermal energy from one object to another.

Step 1 Hold a cup of cool water in one hand. Hold a cup of warm water in your other hand.

Step 2 Tell what you feel in each hand.

Step 3 Does heat move from the cup to your hand? Or does heat move from your hand to the cup? On the pictures above, draw arrows to show which way the heat moves in each case.

Predict
Look at the Big Question and the "you will . . ." statements at the top of the page. Describe what you think you are going to learn in this lesson.

I think I am going to learn about . . .

Leveled Instruction

Early Beginner Emphasize the direction of heat flow. Point to the different areas as you say *warmer* and *cooler*. Have students repeat the terms.

Beginner Use sentence frames to help students understand the concepts. Example: *Heat moves from . . . to . . .* (Sample: my hand; the water).

Early Intermediate Have students answer questions using simple sentences. Example: *When you hold a cup of cold water, how does the heat move? (The heat moves from your hand to the water.)*

Intermediate Instruct partners to communicate with each other during activities using questions and complete sentences. Encourage them to use new vocabulary terms related to heat transfer.

Advanced/Transitioning Ask students to give oral explanations of the heat transfer processes.

Vocabulary in Context Picture It!

temperature a measure of heat

Fahrenheit scale

Celsius scale

Absolute zero is the lowest temperature on the Kelvin scale.

specific heat the heat necessary to raise the temperature of a given substance by one degree Celsius.

requires less

requires more

thermal expansion an increase in volume because of an increase in temperature

Types of Heat Flow

convection the transfer of heat by the movement of currents

convection current a current caused by the rising of heated fluid and the sinking of cooled fluid

radiation the transfer of heat by electromagnetic waves

conduction the transfer of heat from one particle of matter to another

Insulators do not transfer heat well.

Conductors transfer heat well.

Talk About It

Work with a partner to complete the sentences.

1. Heat moves from a hot burner to a pan by . . . conduction.
2. On a hot day, the thermometer shows an increase in . . . temperature.
3. Hot water rises and cold water sinks by a type of heat flow called . . . convection, convection current.
4. Heat does not flow well through an . . . insulator.
5. Heat flows well through a . . . conductor.

Your Turn

Talk with a partner about different ways heat flows through objects. Then list three types of temperature scales. Use words from the Picture It box.

Academic Vocabulary

- Temperature is the measure of *average* kinetic energy of the moving particles in an object. Thermal energy is the *total* measure of kinetic energy of moving particles in an object. Two objects may have the same temperature, but one object may have more thermal energy if it has more particles in it.

- Make sure students do not confuse the word *transfer* with the word *transformation*. Demonstrate that *transfer* refers to flow, or movement. The energy moves from one object to another, or it moves from one area to another. *Transformation* refers to energy changing from one form to another.

- Point out that the scales *Fahrenheit, Celsius,* and *Kelvin* were all named after the scientists who developed them. Review the meaning of *scale,* as "a standard by which to measure."

- The terms *conductor* and *insulator* are also used to describe the ability of a material to conduct electricity. Although the concepts are different, materials that are good electrical conductors are often good thermal conductors.

↻ Comprehensible Input

Vocabulary in Context: Picture It!

1. **Say the Term** Say each term slowly, artificially stressing each syllable. Have students repeat. Then say the term more naturally and have students repeat.

2. **Introduce Word Meaning** Connect each term to the visual that illustrates it.

3. **Demonstrate** Use gestures and visuals to demonstrate. For example,

   - When teaching *thermal expansion,* represent the particles of a material by drawing a group of circles on the board. Label the drawing *cooler.*

   - Nearby, draw a group with the same number of circles, except have these spread out. Label this group *warmer.*

   - Explain your drawing. Tell students that it shows how thermal expansion occurs because the particles gain energy and spread apart.

4. **Apply** After all the terms have been discussed, have students demonstrate understanding with Talk About It.

Talk About It

Guide Discussion Have students look back at the pictures in the Picture It box. Ask them to use the terms to complete the sentences.

RTI Response to Intervention

If students have difficulty with *Celsius* and *Fahrenheit* . . .

Then write the terms on the board and ask students to tell which scale they are familiar with. Have students discuss the differences in the scales with each other.

Your Turn

Guide Discussion Have students look at the drawings in the Picture It box to guide their responses.

Thermal Energy and Heat

↻ Language Production

Do You Understand?

Comprehension Support Read the instructions aloud. If students are having difficulty, suggest that they look back at the Picture It box for review.

Model Hold up a copy of the lesson page, and demonstrate how students should draw arrows to indicate the direction of the convection current in the water.

Talk About It

Guide Discussion Read the sentences aloud and have students repeat after you. If they have difficulty determining an answer, provide them with two or more options. For example, *Heat moves from the cast iron burner to the metal pot by . . . conduction, convection, or radiation?*

Your Turn

Guide Discussion When describing heat transfer, help students follow the steps of the process. If they have difficulty, ask questions such as, *What happens first? What happens next?*

A Closer Look

On Their Own Have students work in pairs to complete this word study activity. Generate other examples for them, using the words *radiate/radiation,* and *insulate/insulator.*

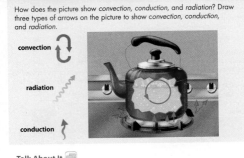

Do You Understand?

How does the picture show *convection, conduction,* and *radiation*? Draw three types of arrows on the picture to show *convection, conduction,* and *radiation.*

convection

radiation

conduction

Talk About It
Complete the sentences.
1. A metal pot conducts heat well, so it is a good . . . conductor.
2. Heat moves from warmer areas to . . . cooler areas.
3. The Fahrenheit and Celsius scales measure . . . temperature.
4. Heat moves out from the flame by a type of heat flow called . . . radiation.
5. Heat moves from metal to metal by a type of heat flow called . . . conduction.
6. Heat moves through the water in the pot by a type of heat flow called . . . convection.

Your Turn
Talk with a partner. Tell about heat transfer in the picture of the pot.

A Closer Look

Word Forms *Conducts, conduction,* and *conductor* are all forms of the word *conduct.*

Fill in the sentences below with the correct form of *conduct.*
1. Copper is a material that _____ conducts _____ heat well.
2. Through _____ conduction _____, heat flows from object to object.
3. You would not want to touch a heated _conductor_, such as a metal object.

Leveled Language Proficiency

Students at each proficiency level should be able to perform the following tasks.

Listening/Speaking

Early Beginner/Beginner Respond to oral questions about heat flow diagrams by pointing to correct parts of visual displays. Correctly say *conductor* or *insulator* when describing different materials.

Early Intermediate Identify everyday examples of conductors and insulators based on oral descriptions. Use simple sentences to describe conduction, convection, and radiation.

Intermediate Understand and apply oral descriptions of heat transfer processes. Use complex sentences to describe conduction, convection, and radiation.

Advanced/Transitioning Understand descriptions contrasting temperature and thermal energy and their relationships to kinetic energy. Effectively communicate abstract ideas about heat transfer processes.

Your Turn

1. Write *conduction*, *convection*, or *radiation* on the line next to each type of heat transfer.

conduction

convection

radiation

2. Circle the part of the drawing that shows an insulator.

Talk and Write About It

Complete the sentences.

1. The three types of temperature scales are <u>Celsius, Fahrenheit, and Kelvin scales</u>.

2. The increase in volume of a heated object is called <u>thermal expansion</u>.

3. The lowest temperature on the Kelvin scale is <u>absolute zero</u>.

4. Water heats slowly because it has a high <u>specific heat</u>.

5. A material that does not conduct heat well is called an <u>insulator</u>.

Produce Language

Write about how heat flows through objects. Use as many vocabulary terms as you can.

_____

_____

_____

_____

_____

_____

_____

Thermal Energy and Heat **65**

Leveled Language Proficiency

Students at each proficiency level should be able to perform the following tasks.

Reading/Writing

Early Beginner/Beginner Correctly read and understand simple labels related to heat transfer processes and conductors and insulators. Copy one- or two-word labels onto diagrams.

Early Intermediate Identify heat transfer processes from written descriptions. Formulate questions about heat transfer.

Intermediate Read and understand questions related to different methods of heat transfer. Write simple sentences comparing conduction, convection, and radiation.

Advanced Infer relationships between temperature and heat transfer from written descriptions. Use complex sentences to describe conduction, convection, and radiation.

Transitioning Apply information from written descriptions of heat transfer processes to other situations. Produce short paragraphs describing heat transfer in everyday situations.

Assess Understanding

Your Turn

Model Before students start the activity, draw a simple diagram on the board to review the processes of convection, conduction, and radiation. Have students repeat each of the three terms after you.

Talk and Write About It

On Their Own Read the sentences aloud with students. Then have them talk about each sentence with a partner before attempting to answer them. Provide guidance for any science concepts as needed.

Produce Language

On Their Own Before students write their answers, have them review the Big Question. They should then look back through the lesson and talk about what they have learned with a partner. Remind them to use the Picture It box for help with difficult vocabulary terms.

Wrap Up

Table Talk Have students reflect on what they learned and build fluency by reading their writing in groups or to the entire class.

✔ **Learned** and applied vocabulary related to temperature and thermal energy

✔ **Spoken** statements about heat transfer processes

✔ **Written** sentences about how an increase in thermal energy affects different materials and objects

Electricity

Vocabulary electric force, electric field, static electricity, conduction, induction, polarization, electric current, electric circuit, voltage, resistance, Ohm's law, series circuit, parallel circuit, power, short circuit, grounded

Materials balloon, wool fabric, sink faucet with trickle of cold or lukewarm water

Science Background

- An electric field surrounds every charged object. An electric force causes like charges to repel each other and unlike charges to attract each other.

- A charged object can attract an uncharged material by polarization. The charged object causes electrons within atoms of the uncharged material to have a slight positive charge at one end and a slight negative charge at the other end.

Frontload the Lesson

How does electric current flow?

Talk About It

Build Background Distribute materials to each small group of students in turn, or demonstrate the activity for them as they answer the questions. Help students see how the water is pulled toward the negatively charged balloon.

Content and Language

Predict

Model Read the objectives aloud. Use what students discussed in the Talk About It to further explain the objectives.

Guide Discussion Students can preview the lesson by looking at the pictures to help them make predictions.

Electricity

Big Question How does electric current flow?

You will . . .
- Discuss the different ways electric charges flow between objects.
- Compare and contrast different electrical circuits.
- Use key terms related to static electricity and electric current.

Talk About It

When either positive (+) or negative (–) electric charges build up on an object, the object has an overall positive or negative charge. Then it can push or pull on other objects with an electric force.

Step 1 Rub a balloon with wool.

Step 2 Hold the balloon near a slow stream of water. Tell what happens to the water.

Step 3 Turn the balloon around. What happens to the water now?

Tell why you think the balloon affected the water the way it did.

Predict
Listen as your teacher reads the Big Question and the "You will . . ." statements at the top of the page. Describe what you think you are going to learn in this lesson.

I think I am going to learn about . . .

Leveled Instruction

Early Beginner/Beginner Have students use small colored sticky notes with + and – signs to demonstrate the buildup or motion of charge as they learn the terms *static electricity, conduction, induction, polarization,* and *electric current.*

Early Intermediate Help students construct simple sentences to describe how different parts of an electric circuit work.

Intermediate Provide students with opportunities to apply the language they have learned by asking *how* and *why* questions related to electricity. For example, ask, *How is a series circuit different from a parallel circuit?*

Advanced/Transitioning As students work through the lesson, help them use complex sentences to contrast *conduction, induction,* and *polarization.*

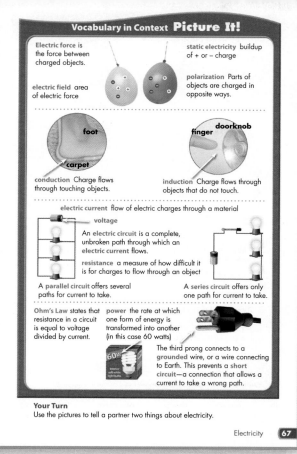

Vocabulary in Context Picture It!

Electric force is the force between charged objects.

static electricity buildup of + or – charge

electric field area of electric force

polarization Parts of objects are charged in opposite ways.

foot

carpet

conduction Charge flows through touching objects.

finger doorknob

induction Charge flows through objects that do not touch.

electric current flow of electric charges through a material

voltage

An **electric circuit** is a complete, unbroken path through which an **electric current** flows.

resistance a measure of how difficult it is for charges to flow through an object

A **parallel circuit** offers several paths for current to take.

A **series circuit** offers only one path for current to take.

Ohm's Law states that resistance in a circuit is equal to voltage divided by current.

power the rate at which one form of energy is transformed into another (in this case 60 watts)

The third prong connects to a **grounded** wire, or a wire connecting to Earth. This prevents a **short circuit**—a connection that allows a current to take a wrong path.

Your Turn
Use the pictures to tell a partner two things about electricity.

Electricity **67**

Academic Vocabulary

- Remind students that they can learn about the meaning of many words by looking at the base word. For example, the base word of *resistance* is *resist,* which means "to oppose something." The base word of *polarization* is *polar.* You can relate this to Earth's geographic poles, which are on opposite sides of Earth.

- Words that describe placement and direction are important for understanding many concepts related to electricity and electric circuits. Guide students in demonstrating the meanings of the terms *between, toward, away from, along, surrounded by,* and *through.*

- Have students share any vocabulary terms they recognize as cognates to words in their first languages. For example, in Spanish, *eléctrico* is a cognate for *electric* and *estática* is a cognate for *static.*

↻ Comprehensible Input

Vocabulary in Context: Picture It!

1. **Say the Term** Say each term slowly, artificially stressing each syllable. Have students repeat. Then say the term more naturally and have students repeat.

2. **Introduce Word Meaning** Connect each term to the visual that illustrates it.

3. **Demonstrate** Use gestures and visuals to demonstrate each term.

4. **Apply** After all the terms have been discussed, have students demonstrate understanding with Talk About It.

Talk About It

Guide Discussion Before students start their independent discussion, check for understanding with the following sentence starters:

1. *Charge is pulled to one side of a molecule by* . . . (polarization).

2. *The measure of how difficult it is for charges to flow through an object is called* . . . (resistance).

3. *The force between charged objects is called* . . . (electric force).

4. *If a circuit is connected to Earth it is* . . . (grounded).

5. *A buildup of charge on an object is* . . . (static electricity).

6. *The rate at which a light bulb uses electrical energy is its* . . . (power).

RTI Response to Intervention

If students have difficulty with the suffix *-ion* . . .

Then explain that it refers to naming an action, or giving a verb a noun form. For example, an object becomes polarized when *polarization* occurs.

Your Turn

Guide Discussion Listen as students discuss the pictures. Ensure they use correct terms to describe the flow of electric current. Make sure they notice the differences in the circuits.

Electricity

↻ Language Production

Do You Understand?

Comprehension Support Divide the class into groups of two or three. Have groups discuss each picture before deciding which of the two words best describes it. Provide help as needed with word meanings and pronunciations.

Model Ask questions that guide students in choosing the correct term that relates to each picture. For example, say, *The comb has a negative charge. How does this charge affect the bits of paper?*

Talk About It

Guide Discussion Read each sentence aloud. Then have students repeat and finish each sentence. Encourage students to discuss the answers with group members.

Your Turn

Guide Discussion If students have difficulty answering the question, discuss the meanings of the words *series* and *parallel*. Help students model the meanings by lining up items such as chairs or toothpicks in a series or in parallel form. Then help them relate the terms to circuits.

A Closer Look

On their Own Have students work in pairs to complete the word study activity. They should provide one sentence for each word in an everyday context. Extend the activity by challenging them to provide a sentence for each word in the scientific context of electricity. Then have students brainstorm examples of other words that have multiple meanings.

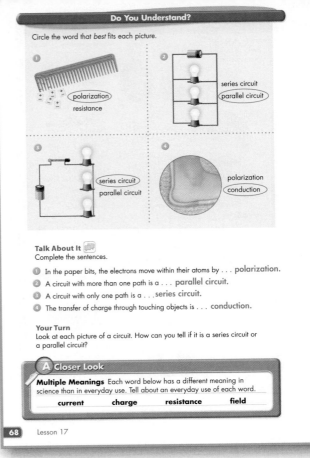

Do You Understand?

Circle the word that *best* fits each picture.

1. polarization / resistance
2. series circuit / parallel circuit
3. series circuit / parallel circuit
4. polarization / conduction

Talk About It
Complete the sentences.

1. In the paper bits, the electrons move within their atoms by . . . polarization.
2. A circuit with more than one path is a . . . parallel circuit.
3. A circuit with only one path is a . . . series circuit.
4. The transfer of charge through touching objects is . . . conduction.

Your Turn
Look at each picture of a circuit. How can you tell if it is a series circuit or a parallel circuit?

A Closer Look

Multiple Meanings Each word below has a different meaning in science than in everyday use. Tell about an everyday use of each word.

current	charge	resistance	field

Leveled Language Proficiency

Students at each proficiency level should be able to perform the following tasks.

Listening/Speaking

Early Beginner/Beginner Point to the corresponding picture when terms related to electricity are spoken aloud. Tell about electric circuits by pointing to different parts and using one or two spoken words.

Early Intermediate Match spoken phrases with pictures of conduction, induction, and polarization. Interact with partners by asking simple questions about electrical processes.

Intermediate Identify pictures of conduction, induction, and polarization based on oral descriptions. Compare series and parallel circuits using spoken phrases.

Advanced/Transitioning Analyze pictures related to static electricity and current electricity, based on oral descriptions. Use complex sentences to describe the sequence of events involved in conduction, induction, and polarization.

Your Turn
Use the vocabulary terms to label each picture.

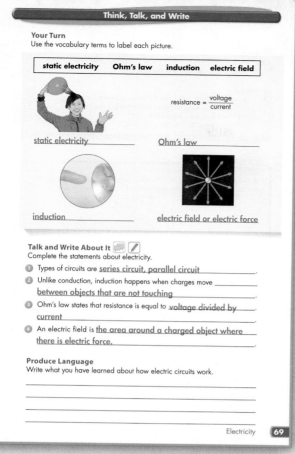

| static electricity | Ohm's law | induction | electric field |

$$resistance = \frac{voltage}{current}$$

static electricity

Ohm's law

induction

electric field or electric force

Talk and Write About It
Complete the statements about electricity.

1. Types of circuits are <u>series circuit, parallel circuit</u>.
2. Unlike conduction, induction happens when charges move <u>between objects that are not touching</u>.
3. Ohm's law states that resistance is equal to <u>voltage divided by current</u>.
4. An electric field is <u>the area around a charged object where there is electric force.</u>

Produce Language
Write what you have learned about how electric circuits work.

_____
_____
_____
_____

Leveled Language Proficiency

Students at each proficiency level should be able to perform the following tasks.

Reading/Writing

Early Beginner/Beginner Read labels related to electrical processes and circuits. Write one or two words to describe an electrical process or circuit.

Early Intermediate Match written terms with pictures of conduction, induction, polarization, and circuits. Formulate and write wh- questions about electrical circuits.

Intermediate Follow written directions for activities related to electricity. Use simple sentences to write about electrical processes and circuits.

Advanced/Transitioning Analyze written information about electrical processes and circuits. Write summaries of electrical concepts and processes, using complex sentences.

↻ Assess Understanding

Your Turn

Model Remind students to use vocabulary terms they have used when talking about and labeling the pictures. For example, point to the picture of the electric charge. Say, *This is an electric charge. What do the lines mean?*

Talk and Write About It

On Their Own Have students work with a partner to discuss and answer the questions. Provide help with pronouncing and spelling unfamiliar words.

Produce Language

On Their Own Have students complete this activity according to their language ability. For beginning students, ask questions that allow them to answer with just one or two words. Have advanced students provide complex answers. Advanced students might also provide a written explanation of electric circuits using the vocabulary terms.

Wrap Up

Table Talk Have students reread the Big Question to reflect on what they learned and build fluency by reading their writing in groups or to the entire class.

✔ **Learned** how to describe electric circuits

✔ **Spoken** words related to electricity

✔ **Written** labels for *conduction, induction,* and *polarization*

Lesson 18

Magnetism

Vocabulary magnet, magnetism, magnetic pole, magnetic force, magnetic field lines, compass, magnetic field, magnetic declination

Materials two bar magnets, paper clips

Science Background

- The magnetic field around a magnet is strongest at its poles.

- A magnet can attract iron and several other types of metal. When a magnet is brought close to iron, the magnetic force causes groups of atoms in the iron to align so that the iron itself becomes magnetized.

- The tip of a compass needle is a magnetic north pole. A compass needle points toward Earth's North Pole because the magnetic pole near there is actually a south magnetic pole.

↻ Frontload the Lesson

What is magnetism?

Talk About It

Build Background Distribute the magnets to pairs or small groups. Read the directions aloud and have volunteers demonstrate each action. Be sure that students understand the questions.

↻ Content and Language

Predict

Model Read aloud the objectives as students follow along. Model reading the Big Question aloud and using it to make a prediction about the lesson or to set a purpose for reading.

Guide Discussion Have students generate their own questions about magnets and magnetism.

Magnetism

 Big Question What is magnetism?

You will . . .
- Label magnetic poles and the forces between them.
- Describe the magnetic field lines around a magnet.
- Discuss how a compass works.
- Use key terms to describe magnetism.

Talk About It

A **magnet** exerts a force on every other magnet. Look at the magnets your teacher gives you. Follow the steps below. Discuss the questions.

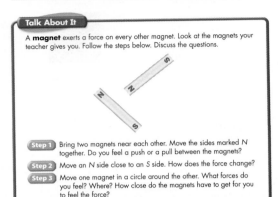

Step 1 Bring two magnets near each other. Move the sides marked *N* together. Do you feel a push or a pull between the magnets?

Step 2 Move an *N* side close to an *S* side. How does the force change?

Step 3 Move one magnet in a circle around the other. What forces do you feel? Where? How close do the magnets have to get for you to feel the force?

Predict
Look at the Big Question and the "You will . . ." statements at the top of the page. Describe what you think you are going to learn in this lesson.

I think I am going to learn about . . .

Leveled Instruction

Early Beginner/Beginner Have students use magnets or pictures of magnets to demonstrate comprehension of the vocabulary.

Early Intermediate/Intermediate Students should be able to respond to questions about magnets with simple sentences. Help students expand their vocabulary by providing examples of adverbs they can add to their sentences. (e.g., Say, *These magnets repel strongly.*)

Advanced/Transitioning Students should be able to produce detailed explanations of concepts in magnetism. Provide opportunities for advancement by asking questions that require students to relate concepts or make inferences. (e.g., Say, *What kind of magnetic force must the North Pole have to attract the north pole of a compass magnet?*)

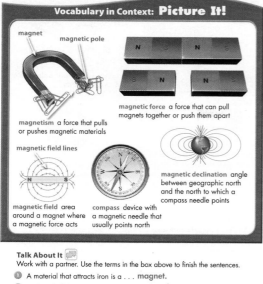

Vocabulary in Context: **Picture It!**

magnet

magnetic pole

magnetism a force that pulls or pushes magnetic materials

magnetic force a force that can pull magnets together or push them apart

magnetic field lines

magnetic field area around a magnet where a magnetic force acts

compass device with a magnetic needle that usually points north

magnetic declination angle between geographic north and the north to which a compass needle points

Talk About It

Work with a partner. Use the terms in the box above to finish the sentences.

1. A material that attracts iron is a . . . magnet.
2. Each end of a magnet is a . . . magnetic pole.
3. The push or pull between magnets is a . . . magnetic force.
4. The area where a magnetic force acts is a . . . magnetic field.
5. A device with a magnetic needle that spins is a . . . compass.
6. The push or pull force of a magnet on magnetic materials is . . . magnetism.
7. Lines that show a magnetic field's direction are . . . magnetic field lines.
8. The angle between where a compass points and geographic north is the . . . magnetic declination.

Your Turn

Look at the pictures above. Use the vocabulary terms to tell a partner about each picture.

Magnetism 71

Academic Vocabulary

- Focus on word forms in this lesson: *magnet, magnetism, magnetic.* Help students understand that *magnet* and *magnetism* are nouns. *Magnetic* is an adjective that describes anything related to a magnet. *Magnetism* is the force between magnetic materials.

- Make sure students understand the terms *like* and *unlike* that are used to describe the poles of a magnet. Draw magnets on the board with like and unlike poles facing, and help students describe the poles as like or unlike.

- Cognates are words that have the same or similar roots and meanings in two languages. Have students share any vocabulary terms they recognize as cognates to words in their native languages. For example, in Spanish *magnetismo* is a cognate for *magnetism, magnético* is a cognate for *magnetic,* and *declinación* is a cognate for *declination.*

↻ Comprehensible Input

Vocabulary in Context: Picture It!

1. **Say the Term** Say each term slowly, artificially stressing each syllable. Have students repeat. Then say the term more naturally and have students repeat.

2. **Introduce Word Meaning** Connect each term to the visual that illustrates it.

3. **Demonstrate** Use gestures and visuals to demonstrate. For example:

   - As you say the word *magnetism,* hold up a bar magnet. Say, *The magnet has a magnetic force. It attracts some metals like iron.*

   - Point out some paper clips. Say, *The paper clips contain iron. The magnet attracts the paper clips.*

   - As you pick up paper clips with the magnet, say *magnetism.*

4. **Apply** After all the terms have been discussed, have students demonstrate understanding with Talk About It.

Talk About It

Guide Discussion Challenge students to try answering the questions in pairs before looking at the pictures and labels above. Then have students look back at the pictures in the Picture It! box to check their answers.

RTI Response to Intervention

If students have difficulty pronouncing *magnetism* . . .

Then explain that the *s* in the *-ism* suffix is pronounced like a *z.*

Your Turn

Guide Discussion Have students look at each picture and answer the question *What does it show?* Beginning students might answer by simply repeating one or two words. Suggest adjectives to help more advanced students use complex descriptions. e.g., (*close, far: The field lines are closer at the pole.*)

Magnetism

↻ Language Production

Do You Understand?

Comprehension Support Make sure students understand that *N* stands for *north* and *S* stands for *south*. Read aloud the instruction line for each picture. If students have difficulty, suggest that they look back at the Picture It box.

Model Emphasize the vocabulary terms as you discuss each picture. Have students repeat the terms after you. For example, point to the picture of the magnet and compass. Say *magnetic declination,* and have students repeat. Say, *Draw an arrow to show where the magnetic declination is* and have students repeat. If students are unsure of what to do, point to the field lines in the Picture It box and say, *magnetic declination.*

Talk About It

Guide Discussion Read each statement aloud. If students are unsure how to complete the sentence, point to the corresponding picture. For extra help, you can provide answer options. For example, say, *A compass needle points toward a magnet's . . . north pole or south pole?*

Your Turn

Guide Discussion Have students look back at the Picture It box and the Do You Understand? pictures. Review the vocabulary terms. Then have students plan their answers before answering verbally.

In Other Words

Model Point out that *instrument* is a more formal way to say *tool* or *device*. Read the example sentence aloud for students. Then ask, *What is another way to say this? What is another word, or words, for* instrument? Encourage students to read the sentence aloud in turn, each time choosing a new highlighted word for the term *instrument*. Then have students brainstorm scientific instruments. Clarify any confusion over multiple meanings by listing musical instruments in a separate category.

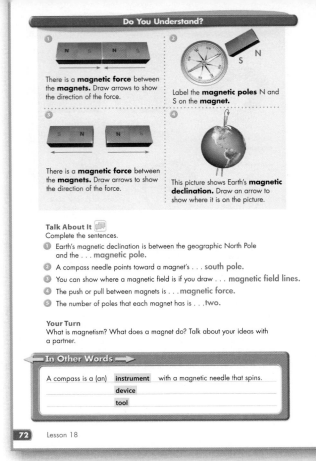

Do You Understand?

① There is a **magnetic force** between the **magnets.** Draw arrows to show the direction of the force.

② Label the **magnetic poles** N and S on the **magnet.**

③ There is a **magnetic force** between the **magnets.** Draw arrows to show the direction of the force.

④ This picture shows Earth's **magnetic declination.** Draw an arrow to show where it is on the picture.

Talk About It
Complete the sentences.
① Earth's magnetic declination is between the geographic North Pole and the . . . magnetic pole.
② A compass needle points toward a magnet's . . . south pole.
③ You can show where a magnetic field is if you draw . . . magnetic field lines.
④ The push or pull between magnets is . . . magnetic force.
⑤ The number of poles that each magnet has is . . . two.

Your Turn
What is magnetism? What does a magnet do? Talk about your ideas with a partner.

→ In Other Words →

A compass is a (an) | instrument | with a magnetic needle that spins.
| device |
| tool |

Leveled Language Proficiency

Students at each proficiency level should be able to perform the following tasks.

Listening/Speaking

Early Beginner/Beginner Point to pictures or use simple gestures to answer questions about magnets. Use one or two words to describe magnets and magnetism.

Early Intermediate Follow multistep oral directions for labeling magnetic poles and magnetic field lines. Ask simple questions about magnets and magnetism.

Intermediate Exhibit comprehension of oral descriptions related to magnets and magnetic properties by using complete sentences during discussions.

Advanced/Transitioning Comprehend complex explanations of magnetic declination. Participate fully in discussions of magnetic properties of materials.

Your Turn

Write the term from the box that best describes each part of the picture.

magnet	magnetic field lines	magnetic poles

magnet

magnetic poles

N

S

magnetic field line or magnetic field

Talk and Write About It

Complete the statements about magnets and magnetism.

1. Magnetic force is the push or pull between two magnets .
2. Magnetic field lines show the magnetic field around a magnet .
3. A compass tells which direction is north .
4. The angle between the North Pole and Earth's magnetic pole is its magnetic declination .
5. Each end of a magnet is a magnetic pole .

Produce Language

Write what you have learned about magnetism in this lesson. Use as many vocabulary terms as you can.

_____

_____

_____

_____

_____

_____

Leveled Language Proficiency

Students at each proficiency level should be able to perform the following tasks.

Reading/Writing

Early Beginner/Beginner Match pictures of magnets and magnetic concepts with words. Complete sentence starters with vocabulary related to magnetism.

Early Intermediate Follow written directions for activities about magnets. Write simple sentences to describe magnets and magnetism.

Intermediate Distinguish between similar written terms such as *magnetism* and *magnetic*. Use complex sentences to provide written descriptions of magnets and magnetic effects.

Advanced/Transitioning Understand complex ideas, such as *magnetic declination,* based on written descriptions. Use complex sentences to summarize concepts about magnets and magnetism.

Assess Understanding

Your Turn

Model Point out to students that they will write a vocabulary term on each line. For example, draw their attention to the arrow pointing to the magnetic field lines. Ask, *What are these?* If they are unsure what to write, have them look back at the Picture It box and choose the term that best fits.

Talk and Write About It

On Their Own Read each statement aloud and have students repeat after you. Have partners discuss each sentence and decide which word or words best completes it. Remind students to look at the pictures for help.

Produce Language

On Their Own Have students talk about magnetism and magnets with a partner. Encourage them to ask each other questions. Then have students write about what they have learned. Beginning students might write just one sentence, but advanced students should write one or two paragraphs.

Wrap Up

Table Talk Have students reflect on what they learned and build fluency by reading their writing in groups or to the entire class.

✔ **Learned** vocabulary related to magnets and magnetism

✔ **Heard** about magnetic declination

✔ **Written** a description of magnetism

Magnetic Force and Electromagnetism

Vocabulary electromagnetism, solenoid, electromagnet, galvanometer, electric motor, generator, electromagnetic induction, transformer, direct current, alternating current

Materials 10 index cards for each student

 Science Background

- A magnetic field surrounds any current-carrying wire. If the wire is wound into a coil, the net effect is a magnetic field that is like that of a bar magnet.

- An electric current produces a magnetic field because of electromagnetism. Electromagnetic induction is the process of generating an electric current from the motion of a conductor through a magnetic field.

- Most power plants produce alternating current (AC) rather than direct (DC).

 Frontload the Lesson

How are electricity and magnetism related?

Talk About It

Build Background Read each term aloud, allowing time for students to write and sort their cards. As they predict or infer new meanings, encourage them to use the Picture It box.

 Content and Language

Predict

Model Read the Big Question and the objectives aloud as students listen. Encourage questions about the lesson that students can "read to find out."

Guide Discussion Ask students to say the Big Question and the objectives with you. Have them tell what they think they will learn.

Magnetic Force and Electromagnetism

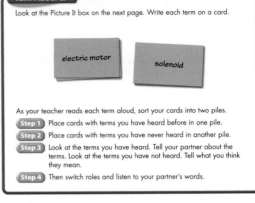

Big Question How are electricity and magnetism related?

You will . . .
- Explain how electricity and magnetism are related.
- Identify devices that use electromagnetism.
- Understand and use terms related to electromagnetism.

Talk About It

Look at the Picture It box on the next page. Write each term on a card.

electric motor

solenoid

As your teacher reads each term aloud, sort your cards into two piles.

Step 1 Place cards with terms you have heard before in one pile.

Step 2 Place cards with terms you have never heard in another pile.

Step 3 Look at the terms you have heard. Tell your partner about the terms. Look at the terms you have not heard. Tell what you think they mean.

Step 4 Then switch roles and listen to your partner's words.

Predict
Look at the Big Question and the "You will . . ." statements at the top of the page. Describe what you think you are going to learn in this lesson.

I think I am going to learn about . . .

Leveled Instruction

Early Beginner Ask students questions about electromagnetic devices using simple sentences, and allow students to answer with one or two words or by pointing to the correct answer.

Beginner Have students chorally read sentences about electromagnetic devices. Help students answer by choosing one of the vocabulary terms.

Early Intermediate/Intermediate Students should be able to read sentence starters with minimal help and complete the sentences with the correct terms. Provide guidance with pronunciation of unfamiliar terms, such as solenoid.

Advanced/Transitioning Provide opportunities for students to answer questions using complex sentences. Have students describe electromagnetism and electromagnetic induction orally or by writing paragraphs.

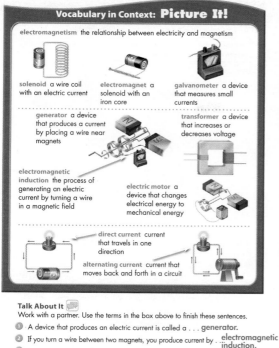

Vocabulary in Context: **Picture It!**

electromagnetism the relationship between electricity and magnetism

solenoid a wire coil with an electric current

electromagnet a solenoid with an iron core

galvanometer a device that measures small currents

generator a device that produces a current by placing a wire near magnets

transformer a device that increases or decreases voltage

electromagnetic induction the process of generating an electric current by turning a wire in a magnetic field

electric motor a device that changes electrical energy to mechanical energy

direct current current that travels in one direction

alternating current current that moves back and forth in a circuit

Talk About It

Work with a partner. Use the terms in the box above to finish these sentences.

1. A device that produces an electric current is called a . . . generator.
2. If you turn a wire between two magnets, you produce current by . . . electromagnetic induction.
3. You can increase or decrease the voltage of a current with a . . . transformer.
4. A device that uses current to turn an axle is an . . . electric motor.
5. A wire coil with an electric current in it it is a . . . solenoid.

Your Turn

Talk to your partner about the pictures. Tell whether each term relates to electricity, magnetism, or both.

Magnetic Force and Electromagnetism   **75**

Academic Vocabulary

- Point out the suffix *-meter* in *galvanometer*. Explain that *galvano-* means "electric current," and *-meter* means "a measuring device." Together they mean "a device that measures electric current."

- Draw students' attention to the suffixes *-or* in *generator* and *-er* in *transformer*. These suffixes change a verb to a noun. A generator is a device that generates electricity. A transformer is a device that transforms electricity.

- Discuss the meanings of *direct* and *alternating*. *Direct* means "in one direction." *Alternating* means "changing back and forth." Challenge students to use the words in a non-science context.

↻ Comprehensible Input

Vocabulary in Context: Picture It!

1. **Say the Term** Say each term slowly, artificially stressing each syllable. Have students repeat. Then say the term more naturally and have students repeat.

2. **Introduce Word Meaning** Connect each term to the visual that illustrates it.

3. **Demonstrate** Use gestures and visuals to demonstrate each term. For example:

   - As you say the term *electromagnetic induction*, point to the generator. Say, *The wire is a conductor. It moves through the magnetic field and begins to conduct electric current.*

   - Demonstrate with your hand how the armature of the generator moves between the magnets.

   - Say, *The magnetic field produces a current in the wire.* Demonstrate the back-and-forth motion of the alternating current.

4. **Apply** After all the terms have been discussed, have students demonstrate understanding with Talk About It.

Talk About It

Guide Discussion Have students look at the pictures in the Picture It box. Ask them to use the terms to answer the questions.

RTI Response to Intervention

If students have difficulty with the different "g" sounds of *galvanometer* and *generator* . . .

Then demonstrate the hard "g" sound often heard before *u, a,* or *o* and the soft "g" sound (like "j") often heard before *e, i,* or *y.*

Your Turn

Guide Discussion Help students identify the differences in the pictures. For example, a battery is a source of voltage for the motor, but a galvanometer measures the current produced by the generator.

↻ Language Production

Do You Understand?

Comprehension Support Lead the class in discussing each of the pictures. Then have students independently write the term that best describes each picture.

Model Guide students to identify the term that correctly labels each picture and to use correct language to describe the pictures. For example, point to the picture of the electric motor. Say, *Look at the axle in the picture. What is causing it to move?* (an electric current) *Where does the current come from?* (the battery)

Talk About It

Guide Discussion Read each sentence aloud. Then have students read them aloud with a partner. Instruct students to use the pictures to determine which device each sentence describes.

Your Turn

Guide Discussion Explain to students that each of the devices shown in the pictures either produces or uses electricity and magnetism. Have students discuss the pictures with a partner. Then have them construct one or more sentences to explain how electricity and/or magnetism relate to the picture. You might wish to have more advanced students write their descriptions as well as explain the relationship orally.

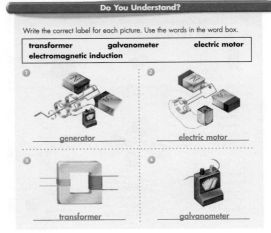

Do You Understand?

Write the correct label for each picture. Use the words in the word box.

transformer   galvanometer   electric motor
electromagnetic induction

① generator

② electric motor

③ transformer

④ galvanometer

Talk About It 💬
Complete the statements.
① You can increase or decrease the voltage of an electric current with a . . . transformer
② A device that uses an electric current to turn an axle is an . . . electric motor
③ You can measure small amounts of an electric current with a . . . galvanometer
④ You can produce an electric current with a . . . generator
⑤ The relationship between electricity and magnetism is called . . . electromagnetism

Your Turn
Look at each picture. Tell how each device relates to electricity or magnetism.

76   Lesson 19

Leveled Language Proficiency

Students at each proficiency level should be able to perform the following tasks.

Listening/Speaking

Early Beginner/Beginner Demonstrate comprehension of the vocabulary terms using pictures or actions in response to oral descriptions. Ask and respond to simple questions about electromagnetism and electromagnetic devices.

Early Intermediate Understand oral instructions for identifying electromagnetic devices. Retell simple descriptions of electromagnetic processes.

Intermediate Demonstrate understanding of oral descriptions of electromagnetism and electromagnetic induction. Use complex sentences to describe electromagnets, electric motors, and other electromagnetic devices.

Advanced/Transitioning Comprehend elaborate discussions of technical aspects of electromagnetic devices. Communicate fluently in group discussions about electromagnetism.

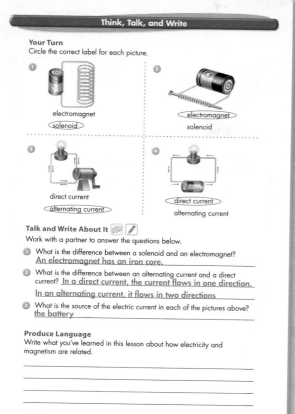

Your Turn

Circle the correct label for each picture.

1. electromagnet
   (solenoid)

2. (electromagnet)
   solenoid

3. direct current
   (alternating current)

4. (direct current)
   alternating current

Talk and Write About It

Work with a partner to answer the questions below.

1. What is the difference between a solenoid and an electromagnet?
   An electromagnet has an iron core.

2. What is the difference between an alternating current and a direct current? In a direct current, the current flows in one direction.
   In an alternating current, it flows in two directions

3. What is the source of the electric current in each of the pictures above?
   the battery

Produce Language

Write what you've learned in this lesson about how electricity and magnetism are related.

_____

_____

_____

_____

_____

Magnetic Force and Electromagnetism **77**

Leveled Language Proficiency

Students at each proficiency level should be able to perform the following tasks.

Reading/Writing

Early Beginner/Beginner Match pictures of electromagnetic devices with written captions. Write labels for electromagnetic devices.

Early Intermediate Apply knowledge of word forms to understand meanings of written words such as *electromagnet* and *transformer*. With a partner, write to describe pictures of electromagnetic devices.

Intermediate Follow written directions for analyzing electromagnetic devices. Write two or three complex sentences to describe the relationship of electricity and magnetism.

Advanced/Transitioning Infer details about electromagnetism and electromagnetic induction from written descriptions. Write detailed descriptions to analyze the relationship of electricity and magnetism.

↻ Assess Understanding

Your Turn

Model Engage students in discussing each of the pictures. Ask questions that prompt students to correctly use the vocabulary terms they have learned. For example, say, *Name parts of the circuit that you see.* (wire, battery) *What do the arrows mean?* (the direction of the current) *What type of current must it be?* (direct current)

Talk and Write About It

On Their Own Read the statements aloud with students. Instruct them to use the pictures as a guide in completing the sentences. Suggest that students look back at the Picture It box for extra help in completing the activity.

Produce Language

On Their Own Before students start the assignment, read aloud the Big Question: *How are electricity and magnetism related?* Remind students that each of the devices they have studied in this lesson involves electricity or magnetism. Some use electricity to produce magnetism, and others use magnetism to produce electricity. Suggest that students consider how the devices use electricity and magnetism when answering the question. First have students tell their answer to a partner, and then have them write their answer.

Wrap Up

Table Talk Have students reflect on what they learned and build fluency by reading their writing in groups or to the entire class.

✔ **Learned** how electricity and magnetism are related

✔ **Spoken** descriptions of electromagnetism and electromagnetic induction

✔ **Written** names of various electromagnetic devices

Lesson 20

Waves

Vocabulary wave, longitudinal wave, transverse wave, medium, vibration, amplitude, node, wavelength, frequency, reflection, refraction, diffraction

Materials rubber band, flashlight, mirror, glass of water, pencil, string, rope

Science Background

- Amplitude describes the height of a transverse wave from its center point to its crest or trough. Amplitude can also mean the maximum distance particles move from their rest position in a longitudinal wave.

- Wavelength describes the wave's length, and frequency describes a rate of how many waves pass a given spot within a given time. Speed describes how quickly a wave moves.

- In a wave, speed is equal to wavelength times frequency.

- Waves change direction by reflection, refraction, and diffraction.

↻ Frontload the Lesson

 What are the characteristics of waves?

Talk About It

Build Background Model how to make a wave with a jump rope or string. Ask students to talk about their experiences with ocean waves and vibrations.

↻ Content and Language

Predict

Model Read the Big Question and objectives aloud. As students repeat after you, point out that a wave has parts and acts in a certain way.

Guide Discussion Ask students to look at the objectives. Encourage them to point out the words they do not know, and to share questions they have about waves.

Waves

 Big Question What are the characteristics of waves?

You will . . .
- Identify the difference between amplitude and wavelength.
- Explain how waves can change direction or combine.
- Use terms related to waves and wavelengths.

Talk About It

Waves of energy travel in different ways. Sound energy and light energy both move in some kind of wave. How does the picture below remind you of ocean waves?

Step 1 Use a rope or string to make waves. How are your waves like ocean waves? How are they different?

Step 2 Make a humming sound. Feel your throat while you hum. What kind of energy is traveling through your throat and through the air when you hum?

Predict

Look at the Big Question and the "You will . . ." statements at the top of the page. Describe what you think you are going to learn in this lesson.

I think I am going to learn about . . .

Leveled Instruction

Early Beginner Ask students to find a picture in the lesson that illustrates the concept of *reflection*.

Beginner Ask students questions about how light waves move. Have them use a short phrase or sentence to describe what a *wavelength* is.

Early Intermediate/Intermediate Encourage students to work independently. Ask them to describe the meaning of the term *vibration* and give an example.

Advanced/Transitioning Invite students to use complete and complex sentences to describe the difference between *reflection* and *refraction*.

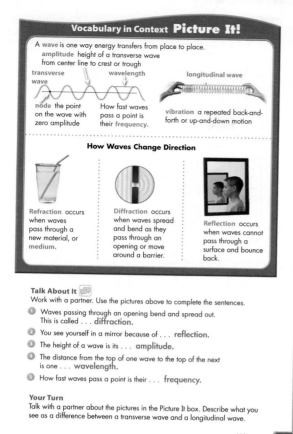

Vocabulary in Context Picture It!

A **wave** is one way energy transfers from place to place.
amplitude height of a transverse wave from center line to crest or trough

transverse wave

wavelength

longitudinal wave

node the point on the wave with zero amplitude

How fast waves pass a point is their **frequency**.

vibration a repeated back-and-forth or up-and-down motion

How Waves Change Direction

Refraction occurs when waves pass through a new material, or **medium**.

Diffraction occurs when waves spread and bend as they pass through an opening or move around a barrier.

Reflection occurs when waves cannot pass through a surface and bounce back.

Talk About It
Work with a partner. Use the pictures above to complete the sentences.

① Waves passing through an opening bend and spread out. This is called . . . **diffraction.**

② You see yourself in a mirror because of . . . **reflection.**

③ The height of a wave is its . . . **amplitude.**

④ The distance from the top of one wave to the top of the next is one . . . **wavelength.**

⑤ How fast waves pass a point is their . . . **frequency.**

Your Turn
Talk with a partner about the pictures in the Picture It box. Describe what you see as a difference between a transverse wave and a longitudinal wave.

Waves **79**

Academic Vocabulary

- Point out to students that there are many prefixes used in words associated with waves. A prefix is a word part that comes at the beginning of a word and changes the word's meaning. Point out the words *node* and *antinode*. The prefix *anti-* means "not." So, *antinode* means "not a node."

- The prefix *trans-* means "across." A *transverse wave* is one that goes across.

- The prefix *re-* means "again." The terms *resonance, reflection,* and *refraction* show how a wave moves again after it meets another wave or object.

↻ Comprehensible Input

Vocabulary in Context: Picture It!

1. **Say the Term** Say each term slowly, artificially stressing each syllable. Have students repeat. Then say the term more naturally and have students repeat.

2. **Introduce Word Meaning** Connect each term to the visual that illustrates it.

3. **Demonstrate** Use gestures and visuals to demonstrate each term. For example:

   - Point out the suffix *-ation* and the root word *vibrate*. Explain that to *vibrate* means "to move back and forth."

   - As you say the word *vibration*, use a rubber band to demonstrate how it can vibrate.

4. **Apply** After all of the terms have been discussed, have students demonstrate understanding with Talk About It.

Talk About It

Guide Discussion Ask students to look back at the terms in Talk About It. Encourage them to use the terms to describe the images in the Picture It box.

RTI Response to Intervention

If students have difficulty understanding the meaning of the word *diffraction* . . .

Then review the concept by saying that it is a process of bending light waves or other waves. It happens when light waves pass through a narrow space. The waves bend when they come out of the narrow space.

Your Turn

Guide Discussion Encourage students to discuss different types of waves (light, sound, water). Encourage them to complete the sentence frame for each type of wave: *One type of wave is . . .*

Waves

Language Production

Do You Understand?

Comprehension Support Provide students with the materials listed at the beginning of the lesson. They may want to use the flashlight and mirror to demonstrate reflection. They can use the glass of water and pencil to demonstrate refraction. They can also use the string to demonstrate vibration. Diffraction can be shown by shining the flashlight through a small space in their fist or in a piece of paper.

Model Demonstrate how students can ask themselves questions to help show each concept. Say, *What is reflection? How can use these materials to show this?*

Talk About It

Guide Discussion Read the statements aloud with students as they work together to complete the sentences. Then have students work with partners to compare their completed sentences. Finally, have volunteers read the completed sentences aloud to correct them. Where several students have added the wrong word, go back to the presentation of that item to make sure that the students understand it.

Your Turn

Guide Discussion Listen to students talk about how else they can use the materials to make light waves or sound waves. Remind them that sound waves can be made by making any kind of vibration, such as hitting an object against a desk or plucking a rubber band.

A Closer Look

On Their Own After pointing out each root word, ask students to say the suffix that all the words have in common. Explain that the suffix turns the roots from verbs into nouns.

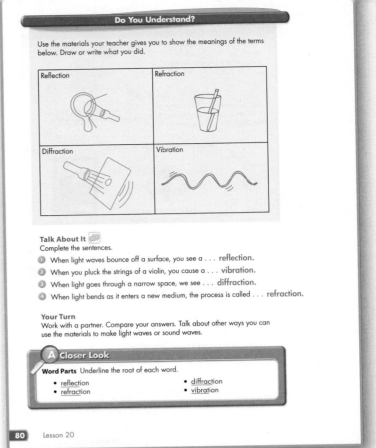

Do You Understand?

Use the materials your teacher gives you to show the meanings of the terms below. Draw or write what you did.

| Reflection | Refraction |
| Diffraction | Vibration |

Talk About It
Complete the sentences.
1. When light waves bounce off a surface, you see a . . . reflection.
2. When you pluck the strings of a violin, you cause a . . . vibration.
3. When light goes through a narrow space, we see . . . diffraction.
4. When light bends as it enters a new medium, the process is called . . . refraction.

Your Turn
Work with a partner. Compare your answers. Talk about other ways you can use the materials to make light waves or sound waves.

A Closer Look

Word Parts Underline the root of each word.
- reflection
- refraction
- diffraction
- vibration

Leveled Language Proficiency

Students at each proficiency level should be able to perform the following tasks.

Listening/Speaking

Early Beginner/Beginner Gesture or point in response to oral directions. Say aloud the words that describe the parts of a wave.

Early Intermediate Use hand gestures or short phrases to respond to questions. Explain what frequency is and what it has to do with waves.

Intermediate Follow oral directions with little to no help. Describe what nodes and antinodes are, and when they occur in a wave. Use complete sentences.

Advanced/Transitioning Follow oral directions independently. Using complete and complex sentences, explain the difference between frequency and resonance.

Your Turn

Match each term to the correct picture. Explain to a partner why the picture matches the word in each case.

refraction

nodes

reflection

Talk and Write About It ✏️
Complete the sentences.

1. A node is the point of a transverse wave where there is <u>no amplitude</u>.
2. Refraction occurs when light travels through <u>a new medium</u>.
3. You can see a reflection in <u>mirrors or other shiny surfaces</u>.

Produce Language
Write what you learned in this lesson about waves and how they move. Use as many vocabulary terms as you can.

_____

_____

_____

_____

_____

Waves 81

Leveled Language Proficiency

Students at each proficiency level should be able to perform the following tasks.

Reading/Writing

Early Beginner/Beginner Locate words that describe waves. Write words that tell how waves move.

Early Intermediate Read to find out the difference between *amplitude* and *wavelength*. Write an explanation that includes the terms *wave* and *vibration*.

Intermediate Use phrases that describe how waves change as they move through different mediums. Write complete sentences to explain what *refraction* is.

Advanced/Transitioning Read aloud sentences that describe *resonance*. Write complete and original sentences that describe what *resonance* is, and give an example.

↻ Assess Understanding

Your Turn

Model As students complete the activity, ask them to look at each picture and describe what is happening. Encourage them to explain what waves have to do with each picture. Explain that it sometimes helps to talk about the picture as they think about what it might illustrate.

Talk and Write About It

On Their Own Encourage student groups to use the questions to form their own sentences that explain how waves move.

Produce Language

On Their Own Have student pairs both write and talk about what they have learned about waves. Encourage them to describe what happens when waves change direction.

Wrap Up

Table Talk Have students reread the Big Question and revisit their predictions and/or any questions they raised at the beginning of the lesson as a way to reflect on what they learned. Encourage students to build fluency by reading their writing in groups or to the class.

✔ **Learned** and applied vocabulary related to waves

✔ **Spoken** statements about how waves move

✔ **Written** statements about what happens when waves change direction

Lesson 21

Sound

Vocabulary pitch, intensity, decibel (dB), Doppler effect

Materials (optional) tuning fork, bowl of water, audio or video that demonstrates the Doppler effect, string or cord

 Science Background

- Sound travels as a longitudinal wave. The pitch of a sound depends on the frequency of the sound wave.

- The loudness of a sound depends on the intensity, or energy, of the sound wave as it travels through the area where it is heard or measured.

- The Doppler effect occurs because the source of a sound is moving. The motion causes the waves either to get closer together (high frequency) or to spread out (low frequency).

Frontload the Lesson

 What factors affect the characteristics of sound?

Talk About It

Build Background Tell students that sound is energy in the form of vibrations. Demonstrate that sound travels in waves by hitting a tuning fork and placing it into a bowl of water. Explain that sound has many characteristics, such as loudness and pitch. Use your voice or an instrument to demonstrate.

Content and Language

Predict

Model Read the Big Question and objectives aloud. As students repeat after you, correct any mispronunciations.

Guide Discussion Ask students to say the objectives with you. Encourage them to use the sentence starter to say what they think they will learn.

Sound

 Big Question What factors affect the characteristics of sound?

You will . . .
- Explain pitch, loudness, and intensity.
- Describe the Doppler effect.
- Use key terms to describe sound.

Talk About It

Read these questions about sound. Talk about the pictures.
Which sounds are high pitched? Which sounds are low pitched?
Which sounds are quiet, or soft? Which sounds are loud?

Predict
Look at the Big Question and the "You will . . ." statements at the top of the page. Describe what you think you are going to learn in this lesson.

I think I am going to learn about . . .

Leveled Instruction

Early Beginner Have the students repeat the terms *quiet, loud, high-pitched,* and *low-pitched.* Help students make each type of sound and point to the appropriate pictures.

Beginner/Early Intermediate Provide sentence frames for students as they point to each picture. Example: *The ___ has a higher pitch than the ___. The ___ is louder than the ___.*

Intermediate Ask students to give examples of other sounds they know that are loud, soft, high-pitched, and low-pitched.

Advanced/Transitioning Ask students to give examples of sounds that are loud, soft, high- and low-pitched, and high- and low-intensity. Let them conclude that the high-intensity sounds are loud, and the low-intensity sounds are soft.

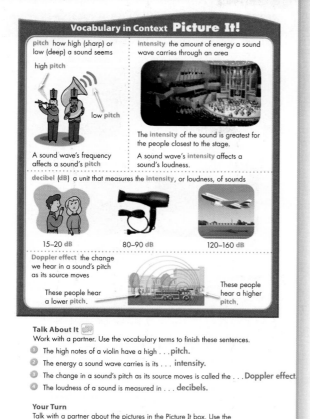

Vocabulary in Context **Picture It!**

pitch how high (sharp) or low (deep) a sound seems

high pitch

low pitch

A sound wave's frequency affects a sound's **pitch**

intensity the amount of energy a sound wave carries through an area

The **intensity** of the sound is greatest for the people closest to the stage.

A sound wave's **intensity** affects a sound's loudness.

decibel (dB) a unit that measures the **intensity**, or loudness, of sounds

15–20 dB   80–90 dB   120–160 dB

Doppler effect the change we hear in a sound's pitch as its source moves

These people hear a lower **pitch**.

These people hear a higher **pitch**.

Talk About It
Work with a partner. Use the vocabulary terms to finish these sentences.
1. The high notes of a violin have a high . . . **pitch**.
2. The energy a sound wave carries is its . . . **intensity**.
3. The change in a sound's pitch as its source moves is called the . . . **Doppler effect**.
4. The loudness of a sound is measured in . . . **decibels**.

Your Turn
Talk with a partner about the pictures in the Picture It box. Use the vocabulary terms to explain what you know about sound.

Sound   **83**

Academic Vocabulary

- The word *frequency* describes the rate at which sound waves occur in a given amount of time, with higher frequencies referring to higher rates. Students may benefit from briefly reviewing the previous lesson (Lesson 20) on the topic of "Waves."

- The word *Doppler* in the term *Doppler effect* refers to the Austrian scientist Christian Doppler, who discovered this phenomenon.

- Students may be familiar with the word *pitch* as a verb meaning "to throw a ball." Point out that this a multiple meaning word. Use the Frayer Model in the Resources section of the Student Book to teach the word *pitch*. Students can provide examples and non-examples of the word's meaning in relation to sound.

- The words *higher, lower, louder,* and *softer* have formed the comparative degree by adding the suffix *-er*. Demonstrate how the suffix is added to the roots and how this changes the meaning.

- The terms *loudness* and *intensity* are closely related. The *intensity* of sound influences how *loud* the sound seems.

↻ Comprehensible Input

Vocabulary in Context: Picture It!

1. **Say the Term** Say each term slowly, artificially stressing each syllable. Have students repeat. Then say the term more naturally and have students repeat.

2. **Introduce Word Meaning** Connect each term to the visual that illustrates it.

3. **Demonstrate** Use gestures and visuals to demonstrate each term. For example:

   - Demonstrate high- and low-pitched sounds. Use the picture to point out that a high-pitched sound has sound waves that travel at a higher frequency, so the lines in the picture are drawn close together.

   - To explain *intensity*, have students stand close to the source of a sound and then move away.

   - Demonstrate sounds to compare *decibel* levels. Point out to students that a 10-dB increase represents a tenfold increase in intensity. For example, a 30-dB sound is 100 times more intense than a 10-dB sound.

   - Play audio or video of a race car, moving siren, or other moving sound to show the *Doppler effect*.

4. **Apply** After each term has been discussed, have students demonstrate understanding with Talk About It.

Talk About It

Guide Discussion Ask students to look back at the pictures and terms in Talk About It to answer each question.

RTI Response to Intervention

If students have difficulty pronouncing *decibel* . . .

Then explain that *c* has an *s* sound when it comes before *i*.

Your Turn

Guide Discussion Ask students to use the Picture It terms to discuss what they know about sound. Have them describe factors that affect sound. Give examples, as needed, to help guide the discussion.

Sound

⟳ Language Production

Do You Understand?

Comprehension Support Remind students that sound travels in waves. Explain the relationship between sound waves and decibel level. Tell students that decibel level measures loudness. A loud sound has more energy.

Model Read the instructions and the terms in the box aloud. Allow students to complete the activity as independently as possible, assisting as needed. Remind them that they can look back at the Picture It box, or look at Lesson 20, if necessary, for help.

Talk About It

Guide Discussion Read the sentences aloud with students as they work to complete them. Have students refer to the pictures in the Do You Understand activity. Ask them to describe the sounds pictured, using their own words as well as the vocabulary terms.

Your Turn

Guide Discussion Listen to student discussions and help them correct any mistakes or misunderstandings as needed. Encourage students to use the vocabulary terms in their discussions and to draw diagrams to demonstrate their points. Circulate during discussions and alert particular students who make an instructive or original comment that they will be called on later to share it with the class.

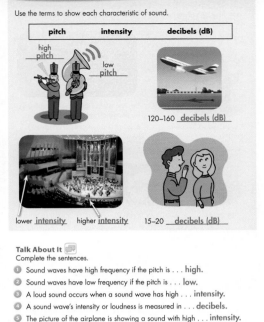

Do You Understand?

Use the terms to show each characteristic of sound.

| pitch | intensity | decibels (dB) |

high pitch
low pitch

120–160 <u>decibels (dB)</u>

lower <u>intensity</u>   higher <u>intensity</u>   15–20 <u>decibels (dB)</u>

Talk About It
Complete the sentences.
1. Sound waves have high frequency if the pitch is . . . high.
2. Sound waves have low frequency if the pitch is . . . low.
3. A loud sound occurs when a sound wave has high . . . intensity.
4. A sound wave's intensity or loudness is measured in . . . decibels.
5. The picture of the airplane is showing a sound with high . . . intensity.
6. The picture of the boy whispering shows a sound with low . . . intensity.

Your Turn
Work with a partner. Talk about different musical instruments you have heard. What were some characteristics of the sounds produced by each instrument?

Leveled Language Proficiency

Students at each proficiency level should be able to perform the following tasks.

Listening/Speaking

Early Beginner/Beginner Correctly identify a picture in response to spoken key vocabulary. Repeat vocabulary terms in response to oral directions.

Early Intermediate Demonstrate sounds with appropriate characteristics in response to spoken key vocabulary. Explain pitch using short spoken phrases and sentences.

Intermediate Follow oral directions with little to no help. Use complete spoken sentences to describe how sound intensity varies as a sound wave travels from its source.

Advanced/Transitioning Follow oral directions and complete tasks independently. Use complete and complex sentences along with examples to explain the Doppler effect.

Think, Talk, and Write

Your Turn

Work with a group. Make sounds to demonstrate each characteristic. Write to tell what you did.

1. High pitch Answers will vary widely. Check student
2. Low pitch _____ demonstrations.
3. High intensity _____
4. Low intensity _____
5. High decibel level _____
6. Low decibel level _____

Talk and Write About It 💬 ✏️
Complete the sentences.

1. A low note is a sound with a low pitch .
2. A soft sound is a sound with low intensity .
3. If you are near the source of a sound you will hear it louder because its intensity is higher .
4. Some sounds I've heard that have a low decibel level are: Sample answers: whispering, soft music, keyboarding .
5. Some sounds I've heard that have a high decibel level are: Sample answers: a plane taking off, a fire truck, loud music .

Produce Language
Write about what you learned in this lesson about characteristics of sound. Use as many vocabulary terms as you can.

_____
_____
_____
_____
_____

◀ **In Other Words** ▶

Air temperature is a **factor** that affects the speed of sound.
condition

Leveled Language Proficiency

Students at each proficiency level should be able to perform the following tasks.

Reading/Writing

Early Beginner/Beginner Identify, read, and write key vocabulary terms related to the characteristics of sound.

Early Intermediate Read and write key vocabulary terms and use them in simple phrases. Write short phrases to describe the characteristics of sound.

Intermediate Read and paraphrase descriptions of the characteristics of sound. Use key vocabulary terms in complete sentences to describe the factors that affect sound's pitch and intensity.

Advanced/Transitioning Read aloud sentences related to sound. Write complete, complex sentences, with examples, about pitch, intensity, and the Doppler effect.

Assess Understanding

Your Turn

Model Have students perform this activity outdoors or in some isolated indoor location, so that the activity does not disrupt students and teachers in other classrooms. Read the instructions and choose one term to model.

Talk and Write About It

On Their Own Provide help in reading each of the sentences. Encourage students to think about all of the possible answers as they complete each sentence.

In Other Words

Model Read the example sentence aloud for students and have them repeat it. Then ask, *What is another way to say this? What is another word, or words, for* factor? Have students take turns reading the sentence aloud, choosing one of the two yellow-highlighted words to fill in the space each time. Then have students suggest their own sentences that use the word *factor*.

Produce Language

On Their Own Have student groups both talk and write about what they've learned about sound and the factors that affect sound's characteristics. Encourage students to use as many vocabulary terms as possible.

Wrap Up

Table Talk Have students reflect on the Big Question and what they learned. Encourage students to build fluency by reading their writing in groups or to the class.

✔ **Learned** and applied vocabulary related to decibels and the loudness of sound

✔ **Spoken** statements about the differences between pitch and intensity

✔ **Written** statements describing the Doppler effect

Lesson 22

Electromagnetic Waves

Vocabulary polarized light, photoelectric effect, photon, electromagnetic spectrum, radio waves, microwaves, infrared rays, ultraviolet rays, X-rays, gamma rays, electromagnetic wave, visible light

Materials jump rope, radio

Science Background

- An electromagnetic wave is made up of vibrating electric and magnetic fields that move through space or some medium at the speed of light.

- In some ways, electromagnetic waves behave like waves. In other ways, electromagnetic waves behave like particles.

- The electromagnetic spectrum is made up of radio waves, microwaves, infrared rays, visible light, ultraviolet rays, X-rays, and gamma rays.

Frontload the Lesson

What are the characteristics and uses of electromagnetic waves?

Talk About It

Build Background Display a radio and turn it on. Tune in several stations. Explain that the radio's antenna receives electromagnetic waves from each radio station.

Content and Language

Predict

Model Read the Big Question and the objectives aloud and have students repeat. As students repeat after you, point out that the lesson is about *electromagnetic waves*.

Guide Discussion Ask students to look at the objectives. Invite them to ask a question they hope to answer as they read the lesson.

Big Question What are the characteristics and uses of electromagnetic waves?

You will . . .
- Recognize that electromagnetic waves act like both waves and particles.
- Describe the parts of the electromagnetic spectrum.
- Use terms related to the electromagnetic spectrum.

Talk About It

Do you listen to the radio? What is your favorite radio station?

When you listen to a radio, watch TV, or heat popcorn in a microwave, you are using electromagnetic waves.

Predict
Look at the Big Question and the "You will . . ." statements at the top of the page. Describe what you think you are going to learn in this lesson.

I think I am going to learn about . . .

86 Lesson 22

Leveled Instruction

Early Beginner Ask students to find a picture in the lesson that illustrates the concept of the *photoelectric effect*.

Beginner Ask students questions about the electromagnetic spectrum. Have them use a short phrase or sentence to describe an *electromagnetic wave*.

Early Intermediate/Intermediate Have students work independently. Ask them to describe the meaning of the term *radio waves* and give an example.

Advanced/Transitioning Have students use complete and complex sentences to describe the different characteristics of *radio waves* and *gamma rays*.

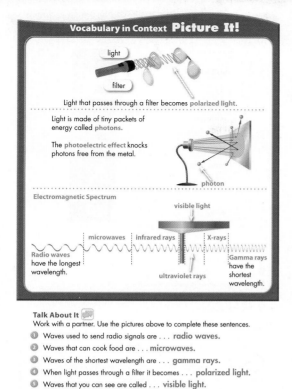

Vocabulary in Context **Picture It!**

light

filter

Light that passes through a filter becomes polarized light.

Light is made of tiny packets of energy called photons.

The photoelectric effect knocks photons free from the metal.

photon

Electromagnetic Spectrum

visible light

microwaves | infrared rays | X-rays

Radio waves have the longest wavelength.

ultraviolet rays

Gamma rays have the shortest wavelength.

Talk About It
Work with a partner. Use the pictures above to complete these sentences.
1. Waves used to send radio signals are . . . radio waves.
2. Waves that can cook food are . . . microwaves.
3. Waves of the shortest wavelength are . . . gamma rays.
4. When light passes through a filter it becomes . . . polarized light.
5. Waves that you can see are called . . . visible light.

Your Turn
Talk with a partner about the pictures above. Compare the wavelengths of the waves on the chart.

Electromagnetic Waves **87**

Academic Vocabulary

- Explain to students that some words in the lesson are made from two words. It is easier to tell the meaning by looking at the word parts. For example, *electro* and *magnetic* combine to make the word *electromagnetic*.

- In a similar way, the words *photo* and *electric* combine to make the word *photoelectric*. This word involves both light (photo) and electrons.

- Point out other words that combine two words or word parts, such as *microwaves* and *ultraviolet*.

⟳ Comprehensible Input

Vocabulary in Context: Picture It!

1. **Say the Term** Say each term slowly, artificially stressing each syllable. Have students repeat. Then say the term more naturally and have students repeat.

2. **Introduce Word Meaning** Connect each term to the visual that illustrates it.

3. **Demonstrate** Use gestures and visuals to demonstrate each term. For example:

   - Point out the parts of the word *electromagnetic*. Point out the prefix *electro-* and the suffix *-ic*. Also point out the root word *magnet*. Ask students to try to explain what the words mean together. (They describe something with both electric fields and magnetic fields.)

   - Use a jump rope to demonstrate wavelength, frequency, and energy. Have a volunteer hold one end while you move the other end in even pulses side to side across the floor or desk to produce waves of different wavelength, frequency, and energy.

4. **Apply** After all of the terms have been discussed, have students demonstrate understanding with Talk About It.

Talk About It

Guide Discussion Ask students to look back at the pictures in Talk About It. Ask them to use the terms in the Picture It box to describe the pictures.

RTI Response to Intervention

If students have difficulty pronouncing the multisyllabic terms in the lesson . . .

Then write the words on the board broken into either word parts or syllables. Pronounce each part separately and then blend them together. Have students repeat with you.

Your Turn

Guide Discussion Encourage students to discuss different waves in the electromagnetic spectrum and how they are used. Encourage them to complete a sentence frame such as *One kind of wave is . . . It is used to . . .*

Electromagnetic Waves

⟳ Language Production

Do You Understand?

Comprehension Support Before students begin the activity, have them review the pictures and talk about what they know about them. They may be more familiar with the X-ray, the radio, and the rainbow than the microwave. Invite students to talk about each picture before they try to match the pictures with the words in the left column.

Model Demonstrate how students can ask themselves questions to help them match each concept to a picture. Say, *What is visible light? What colors is it made of?*

Talk About It

Guide Discussion Read the statements aloud with students as they work together to complete them. Then have students work with partners to compare their completed sentences. Finally, have volunteers read the completed sentences aloud to correct them. Where several students have added the wrong word, go back to the presentation of that item to make sure that the students understand it.

Your Turn

Guide Discussion Listen to students explain the different kinds of waves. If needed, allow students to look through the lesson for examples of how each type of wave in the spectrum is used.

A Closer Look

On Their Own Have students work in pairs to complete this word study activity. Then have them suggest new examples of similar words. Remind students that they can try to find the meanings of unknown words by looking at smaller parts of words. Ask them to point out the smaller parts of each word on the list.

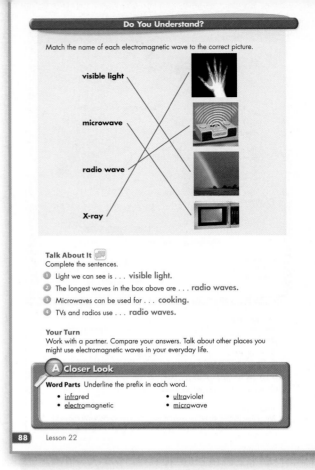

Do You Understand?

Match the name of each electromagnetic wave to the correct picture.

- visible light
- microwave
- radio wave
- X-ray

Talk About It 🖉
Complete the sentences.
1 Light we can see is . . . visible light.
2 The longest waves in the box above are . . . radio waves.
3 Microwaves can be used for . . . cooking.
4 TVs and radios use . . . radio waves.

Your Turn
Work with a partner. Compare your answers. Talk about other places you might use electromagnetic waves in your everyday life.

🔍 Ⓐ **Closer Look**

Word Parts Underline the prefix in each word.
- infrared
- electromagnetic
- ultraviolet
- microwave

Leveled Language Proficiency

Students at each proficiency level should be able to perform the following tasks.

Listening/Speaking

Early Beginner/Beginner Gesture or point in response to oral directions. Say words that describe the parts of the electromagnetic spectrum.

Early Intermediate/Intermediate Follow oral directions with little to no help. Use complete sentences to describe the characteristics of microwaves.

Advanced/Transitioning Follow oral directions independently. Using complete and complex sentences, explain characteristics of and uses for all of the waves in the electromagnetic spectrum.

Your Turn

The number of waves that pass a point each second is the frequency. Radio waves have the lowest frequency. Gamma rays have the highest frequency.

Look at the words in the word bank. Write the name of the electromagnetic waves in order of their frequency. Start with the lowest frequency as number 1.

gamma rays	X-rays	radio waves
microwaves	infrared rays	visible light
ultraviolet rays		

1 <u>radio waves</u>   2 <u>microwaves</u>   3 <u>infrared rays</u>
4 <u>visible light</u>   5 <u>ultraviolet rays</u>   6 <u>X-rays</u>
7 <u>gamma rays</u>

Talk and Write About It
Complete the sentences.

1. Electromagnetic waves with the third-longest wavelength are <u>infrared rays</u>
2. Gamma rays have a wavelength that is <u>shortest</u>
3. Waves with the lowest frequency have the wavelength that is <u>longest</u>
4. The electromagnetic spectrum includes <u>radio waves, microwaves, infrared rays, visible light, ultraviolet light, X-rays, and gamma rays</u>

Produce Language
Write what you learned about electromagnetic waves. Use as many vocabulary terms as you can.

_____
_____
_____
_____
_____

Electromagnetic Waves **89**

Leveled Language Proficiency

Students at each proficiency level should be able to perform the following tasks.

Reading/Writing

Early Beginner/Beginner Locate words that describe electromagnetic waves. Write the names of different waves in the spectrum.

Early Intermediate Read to find out the difference between two types of waves in the electromagnetic spectrum. Write an explanation of the differences and include the name of each type of wave.

Intermediate Comprehend phrases that describe the uses of waves in the electromagnetic spectrum. Write complete sentences to describe how three types of waves are used.

Advanced/Transitioning Read aloud sentences that describe the characteristics and uses for waves in the electromagnetic spectrum. Write complete and original sentences that describe the wavelengths, frequency, and energy of the waves.

Assess Understanding

Your Turn

Model As students complete the activity, have them first review what they know and insert answers that they can figure out on their own. If they still are uncertain, allow them to look back through the lesson to get an idea of the order of waves in the electromagnetic spectrum.

Talk and Write About It

On Their Own Encourage student groups to use the questions to form their own sentences that explain waves in the electromagnetic spectrum.

Produce Language

On Their Own Have student pairs both write and talk about what they learned about electromagnetic waves. Encourage them to use complete sentences when possible.

Wrap Up

Table Talk Have students reflect on what they learned. Encourage students to build fluency by reading their writing in groups or to the class.

✔ **Learned** and applied vocabulary related to characteristics of electromagnetic waves

✔ **Spoken** statements about the electromagnetic spectrum

✔ **Written** statements about the uses of different kinds of electromagnetic waves

Lesson 23

Light and Color

Vocabulary transparent, translucent, opaque, primary color, secondary color, complementary color, pigments

Materials colored pencils: magenta, cyan, yellow

 Science Background

- An opaque object is the color of the light it reflects.

- A transparent or translucent object is the color of the light it transmits.

- If the three primary colors of light are combined in equal amounts, they produce white light.

- If the three primary colors of pigment are combined in equal amounts, they produce black pigment.

Light and Color

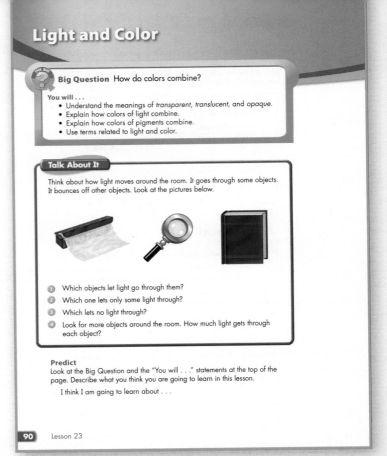

Big Question How do colors combine?

You will . . .
- Understand the meanings of *transparent, translucent,* and *opaque.*
- Explain how colors of light combine.
- Explain how colors of pigments combine.
- Use terms related to light and color.

Talk About It

Think about how light moves around the room. It goes through some objects. It bounces off other objects. Look at the pictures below.

1. Which objects let light go through them?
2. Which one lets only some light through?
3. Which lets no light through?
4. Look for more objects around the room. How much light gets through each object?

Predict
Look at the Big Question and the "You will . . ." statements at the top of the page. Describe what you think you are going to learn in this lesson.

I think I am going to learn about . . .

90   Lesson 23

Frontload the Lesson

 How do colors combine?

Talk About It

Build Background Use the pictures on the page to begin a class discussion about light. After discussing the pictures, look at other objects in the room. Discuss whether they let light through them or not.

Content and Language

Predict

Model Read the Big Question and objectives aloud. As students repeat after you, explain that the lesson is about both light and color. Explain that color and light are related to each other.

Guide Discussion Ask students to choose one of the objectives and ask a question about it. Model rephrasing a question as a statement, beginning with the sentence frame on the student page.

Leveled Instruction

Early Beginner Ask students to find a picture in the lesson that shows a *pigment.*

Beginner Ask students questions about how light can pass through objects. Have them use the terms *transparent, translucent,* and *opaque* to describe the objects.

Early Intermediate/Intermediate Have students work independently. Ask them to describe the meaning of the term *complementary colors.*

Advanced/Transitioning Have students use complete and complex sentences to describe the difference between primary colors and secondary colors of light and pigments.

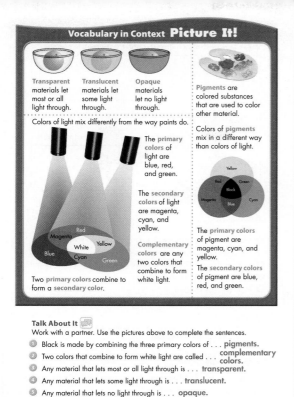

Vocabulary in Context **Picture It!**

Transparent materials let most or all light through.

Translucent materials let some light through.

Opaque materials let no light through.

Pigments are colored substances that are used to color other material.

Colors of light mix differently from the way paints do.

The primary colors of light are blue, red, and green.

The secondary colors of light are magenta, cyan, and yellow.

Complementary colors are any two colors that combine to form white light.

Colors of pigments mix in a different way than colors of light.

The primary colors of pigment are magenta, cyan, and yellow.

The secondary colors of pigment are blue, red, and green.

Two primary colors combine to form a secondary color.

Talk About It

Work with a partner. Use the pictures above to complete the sentences.

1. Black is made by combining the three primary colors of . . . **pigments.**
2. Two colors that combine to form white light are called . . . **complementary colors.**
3. Any material that lets most or all light through is . . . **transparent.**
4. Any material that lets some light through is . . . **translucent.**
5. Any material that lets no light through is . . . **opaque.**

Your Turn

Talk with a partner about the pictures in the Picture It box. Tell how light changes when it strikes different objects in the room.

Light and Color **91**

Academic Vocabulary

- Point out the word part *trans-* in the vocabulary terms *transparent* and *translucent.* Explain that *trans-* means "across," "over," or "beyond." Light moves through and beyond a transparent object.

- Point out that the word *primary* means "first," and *secondary* means "second." A primary color is the first, or most basic, type of light or pigment. A secondary color is made by combining two primary colors. Remind students that primary and secondary colors are different in the cases of light and pigment.

- Students may have heard the word *compliment* as meaning something good said about someone or something. Point out that this word has an *i* in the middle. Explain that the root of *complementary* is *complement*, which has an *e* in the middle, a part that completes something.

↻ Comprehensible Input

Vocabulary in Context: Picture It!

1. **Say the Term** Say each term slowly, artificially stressing each syllable. Have students repeat. Then say the term more naturally and have students repeat.

2. **Introduce Word Meaning** Connect each term to the visual that illustrates it.

3. **Demonstrate** Use gestures and visuals to demonstrate each term. For example:

   - As you say the word *transparent*, point to a window, a drinking glass, or another transparent object in the room.

   - Next, point to the term *translucent* and point to a translucent object. You might fog up a pair of eyeglasses with your breath, or steam up a glass, holding it near a stream of hot tap water.

   - As you introduce primary and secondary colors, explain that some color wheels or paint sets may label colors differently—with red, yellow, blue as the primary colors. The important distinction for any set of primary pigment colors is that they are not a blend of other colors, and that, when mixed evenly, they combine to make black.

   - If available, display color wheels or examples of pigments, such as paints, inks, food coloring, or clothing dye.

Talk About It

Guide Discussion Ask students to look back at the Picture It box as they complete the sentences.

R T I Response to Intervention

If students have difficulty pronouncing the word *opaque* . . .

Then write the word on the board, and underline the last three letters. Explain that this spelling comes from French. The *qu* has a *k* sound, and the *e* is silent.

Your Turn

Guide Discussion Encourage students to discuss different ways light can react with objects. Have them complete a sentence frame such as, *When light hits the . . . it . . .*

Color and Light

↻ Language Production

Do You Understand?

Comprehension Support Read the instructions with students. Review the objects. Review with students what *translucent, transparent,* and *opaque* mean before they begin to classify the objects.

Model Demonstrate how students can ask themselves questions to help them classify the objects. Say, *Can I see through an empty glass? Can I see clearly through frosted glass? Is it blurry when I look through it?*

Talk About It

Guide Discussion Read the sentences aloud with students as they work together to complete them. Then have students work with partners to compare their completed sentences. Finally, have volunteers read the completed sentences aloud to correct them. Where several students have added the wrong word, go back to the presentation of that item to make sure that the students understand it.

Your Turn

Guide Discussion Listen to partners name other objects that are transparent, translucent, or opaque. If they classify the objects incorrectly, help them ask themselves questions to obtain the correct answer.

In Other Words

Model Read the example sentence aloud for students and have them repeat it. Then ask, *What is another way to say this? What is another word, or words, for* distinguish? Have students take turns reading the sentence aloud, choosing one of the yellow-highlighted words or phrases to fill in the space each time. Then have students suggest their own sentences that use the word *distinguish*. As an example, point them to the "You will . . ." statements (the lesson objectives) at the start of the lesson.

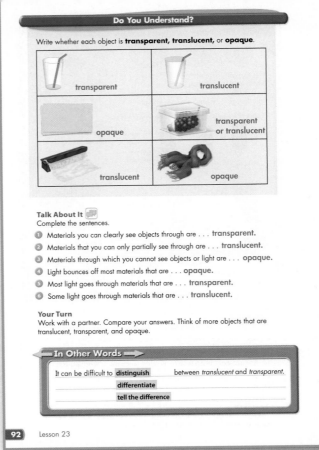

Do You Understand?

Write whether each object is **transparent, translucent,** or **opaque.**

transparent	translucent
opaque	transparent or translucent
translucent	opaque

Talk About It
Complete the sentences.

1. Materials you can clearly see objects through are . . . transparent.
2. Materials that you can only partially see through are . . . translucent.
3. Materials through which you cannot see objects or light are . . . opaque.
4. Light bounces off most materials that are . . . opaque.
5. Most light goes through materials that are . . . transparent.
6. Some light goes through materials that are . . . translucent.

Your Turn
Work with a partner. Compare your answers. Think of more objects that are translucent, transparent, and opaque.

⇐ In Other Words ⇒

It can be difficult to **distinguish** between *translucent* and *transparent.*
differentiate
tell the difference

Leveled Language Proficiency

Students at each proficiency level should be able to perform the following tasks.

Listening/Speaking

Early Beginner/Beginner Gesture or point in response to oral directions. Say the terms *transparent, translucent,* and *opaque* in relation to materials.

Early Intermediate Use hand gestures or short phrases to respond to spoken questions. Orally explain what happens to light as it passes through a translucent material.

Intermediate Follow oral directions with little to no help. Use complete spoken sentences to tell what happens when light strikes opaque objects.

Advanced/Transitioning Follow oral directions independently. Explain, using complete and complex spoken sentences, how objects of different materials react when light strikes them.

Your Turn

Use the colored pencils your teacher gives you. Mix cyan, yellow, and magenta to make each color below.

Mix pigments to make **red**.	Mix pigments to make **green**.
( )	( )
I mixed <u>magenta</u> and <u>yellow</u> .	I mixed <u>yellow</u> and <u>cyan</u> .

Mix pigments to make **blue**.	Mix pigments to make **black**.
( )	( )
I mixed <u>magenta</u> and <u>cyan</u> .	I mixed <u>magenta</u> <u>yellow</u> and <u>cyan</u> .

Talk and Write About It 🗨 ✏

Complete the statements about pigments and light.

1. The primary colors of pigment are <u>magenta, yellow, and cyan</u> .
2. When two primary colors combine, the result is a <u>secondary color</u> .
3. Black pigment is made by combining <u>magenta, yellow, and cyan</u> equally.
4. The result of all colors of light combining is <u>white light</u> .

Produce Language

Write what you learned about light and color in this lesson. Use as many vocabulary terms as you can.

_____

_____

_____

_____

Light and Color **93**

Leveled Language Proficiency

Students at each proficiency level should be able to perform the following tasks.

Reading/Writing

Early Beginner/Beginner Locate words that describe light and color. Write the names of the primary colors of light.

Early Intermediate Read to find out how colors of light combine to form white light. Write short phrases that explain what happens as colors of light are mixed.

Intermediate Comprehend phrases that describe pigment. Explain how the color black is made from colors of pigment.

Advanced/Transitioning Read aloud sentences that compare light and pigment. Explain, in a written paragraph, the differences between the two.

Assess Understanding

Your Turn

Model Before beginning the activity, pass out colored pencils that are yellow, cyan, and magenta. Model how to fill in the circles on the page with an even amount of shading for each pencil, using the same amount of pressure for each color. Remind students that pigments must be mixed equally and evenly to make the requested colors. If you do not have access to pencils in these colors, have students look at the pigment diagram in the Picture It box and find the result of each combination.

Talk and Write About It

On Their Own Encourage groups to use the questions to form their own sentences that explain how light and pigments are different.

Produce Language

On Their Own Have pairs both write and talk about what they learned about light and color. Encourage them to describe how colors of light mix.

Wrap Up

Table Talk Have students reflect on The Big Question and what they learned. Encourage students to build fluency by reading their writing in groups or to the class.

✔ **Learned** and applied vocabulary related to light and color

✔ **Spoken** statements about how light can mix to make colors

✔ **Written** statements about how colors of pigment and light are different

Lesson 24

Reflection and Refraction

Vocabulary regular reflection, diffuse reflection, plane mirror, virtual image, concave mirror, optical axis, focal point, convex mirror, refraction, concave lens, convex lens

Materials mirror, glass of water, flashlight, pencil, prism, plane mirrors, spoon

Science Background

- Regular reflection occurs when parallel rays of light hit a smooth surface. You see a clear image. Diffuse reflection occurs when parallel rays of light hit an uneven surface. The image is unclear or missing.

- When light rays enter a new medium at an angle, the change in speed causes the rays to bend, or be refracted.

 Big Question What are reflection and refraction?

You will . . .
- Understand the difference between regular and diffuse reflections.
- Describe what causes light rays to refract.
- Use terms related to reflection and refraction.

Talk About It

What happens when you look in a mirror?

1. What do you see?
2. Why do you see it?
3. Talk about what happens when light hits a surface that is *reflective*—mirrored or mirror-like.

As a group, use the materials your teacher gives you to discover what happens when light hits different surfaces. Talk about what you see.

Predict
Look at the Big Question and the "You will . . ." statements at the top of the page. Describe what you think you are going to learn in this lesson.

I think I am going to learn about . . .

94   Lesson 24

Frontload the Lesson

 What are reflection and refraction?

Talk About It

Build Background Review safety guidelines and distribute the following to small groups: glasses of water, flashlights, pencils, plane mirrors, spoons, and prisms. Let students experiment with the materials for a few minutes.

Content and Language

Predict

Model Read the Big Question and the objectives aloud. Then have students read them chorally.

Guide Discussion Ask students to choose one of the objectives and ask a question about it. Record their questions on the board.

Leveled Instruction

Early Beginner Ask students to find a picture in the lesson that shows a *reflection*.

Beginner Ask students questions about mirrors. Have them use the terms *convex* and *concave* to describe two types of mirrors.

Early Intermediate/Intermediate Have students work independently. Ask them to explain the meaning of the term *refraction*.

Advanced/Transitioning Have students prepare a presentation for the class comparing and contrasting regular reflection and diffuse reflection. Encourage them to include a demonstration, a diagram, and a verbal summary of each phenomenon.

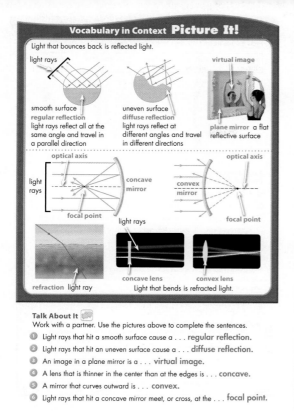

Vocabulary in Context Picture It!

Light that bounces back is reflected light.

light rays

smooth surface
regular reflection
light rays reflect all at the same angle and travel in a parallel direction

uneven surface
diffuse reflection
light rays reflect at different angles and travel in different directions

virtual image

plane mirror a flat reflective surface

optical axis

light rays

concave mirror

focal point

optical axis

convex mirror

focal point

light rays

concave lens

convex lens

refraction light ray

Light that bends is refracted light.

Talk About It

Work with a partner. Use the pictures above to complete the sentences.

1. Light rays that hit a smooth surface cause a . . . regular reflection.
2. Light rays that hit an uneven surface cause a . . . diffuse reflection.
3. An image in a plane mirror is a . . . virtual image.
4. A lens that is thinner in the center than at the edges is . . . concave.
5. A mirror that curves outward is . . . convex.
6. Light rays that hit a concave mirror meet, or cross, at the . . . focal point.

Your Turn

Tell a partner about different ways that light reflects.

Reflection and Refraction **95**

Academic Vocabulary

- Point out that the rays of light hitting each surface are parallel light rays. Demonstrate *parallel* by drawing parallel lines and explaining that they never touch each other. Students will also use this term in math class.

- Explain that a virtual image is an image that only seems to exist. Students may have heard the term *virtual* applied to computer-based activities or experiences.

- Point out that *plane* is a multiple-meaning word. It can mean "a flat, smooth surface," as in a *plane mirror*, and it can be a short version of *airplane*. It also has a homophone, *plain*, which also has multiple meanings. Be sure students understand that the meaning of *plane mirror* is not "an airplane mirror," but rather "any mirror that is a flat surface." Show them the illustration of a hand mirror on the first page of the lesson as an example. Review any examples students have encountered of the term *plane* used in geometry or other mathematics.

- Cognates are words that have the same or similar roots and meanings in two languages. Have students share any vocabulary terms they recognize as cognates to words in their first languages.

↻ Comprehensible Input

Vocabulary in Context: Picture It!

1. **Say the Term** Say each term slowly, artificially stressing each syllable. Have students repeat. Then say the term more naturally and have students repeat.

2. **Introduce Word Meaning** Connect each term to the visual that illustrates it.

3. **Demonstrate** Use gestures and visuals to demonstrate each term. For example:

   - As you say the word *concave*, point to a picture of a concave lens or concave mirror such as a spoon. Then demonstrate the act of forming the shape of a bowl or curve. Say, *A concave mirror curves in like a bowl.*

   - As you say the word *convex*, point to a picture of a convex lens or mirror, such as the reverse side of the spoon. Then, with your hands, demonstrate the shape.

4. **Apply** After all of the terms have been discussed, have students demonstrate understanding with Talk About It.

Talk About It

Guide Discussion Ask students to look back at the pictures. Ask them to use the terms to describe the pictures.

RTI Response to Intervention

If students have difficulty distinguishing *reflection* and *refraction* . . .

Then write the words on the board and underline the middle syllable in each. Review and compare the pronunciations of the words with students. Have students write the words on cards, then practice listening by holding up the cards as you say the words aloud.

Your Turn

Guide Discussion Encourage students to discuss how a reflection is made and how light is refracted. Remind them that mirrors use light to make reflections. Encourage them to complete a sentence frame such as *A reflection is made when . . . Light is refracted when . . .*

Reflection and Refraction

↻ Language Production

Do You Understand?

Comprehension Support Read the directions and the terms in the box aloud with students. Review the meanings of *concave*, *convex*, and *plane* as they relate to mirrors and lenses.

Model Demonstrate the process of matching a term with a picture. Say, *The first term in the box is* concave mirror. *What does a concave mirror look like? I'll find the picture that shows it.*

Talk About It

Guide Discussion Have students work with a partner to complete the statements. Remind them to refer to the Picture It box on the previous page and to the completed activity above for help.

Your Turn

Guide Discussion Circulate among the student pairs as they discuss. Listen to partners describe what happens to light in concave and convex mirrors or lenses. Point out that if they can see their reflection in a spoon, the back of the spoon is a convex mirror and the front of the spoon is a concave mirror. Encourage them to examine the Picture It box for help. As you listen, inform certain students that you will call on them later to share their responses. Then lead a class discussion of students' ideas.

A Closer Look

On Their Own Have students work in pairs to complete this word study activity. Discuss the variations in word meanings, and ask volunteers to share the sentences they wrote. If time allows, extend the activity by having students complete a copy of the Frayer Model in the Resources section of the Student Book.

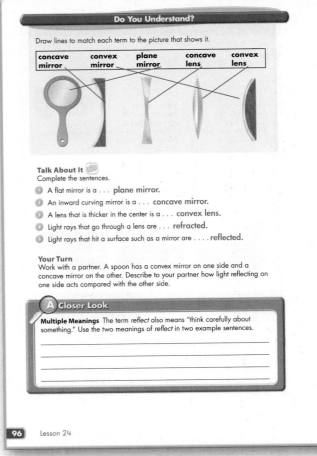

Do You Understand?

Draw lines to match each term to the picture that shows it.

| concave mirror | convex mirror | plane mirror | concave lens | convex lens |

Talk About It
Complete the sentences.

1. A flat mirror is a . . . plane mirror.
2. An inward curving mirror is a . . . concave mirror.
3. A lens that is thicker in the center is a . . . convex lens.
4. Light rays that go through a lens are . . . refracted.
5. Light rays that hit a surface such as a mirror are . . . .reflected.

Your Turn
Work with a partner. A spoon has a convex mirror on one side and a concave mirror on the other. Describe to your partner how light reflecting on one side acts compared with the other side.

A Closer Look

Multiple Meanings The term *reflect* also means "think carefully about something." Use the two meanings of *reflect* in two example sentences.

_____

_____

_____

Leveled Language Proficiency

Students at each proficiency level should be able to perform the following tasks.

Listening/Speaking

Early Beginner/Beginner Gesture or point in response to oral directions. Say words that describe the terms *mirror* and *lens*.

Early Intermediate Use short phrases to respond to questions. Tell in conversation what happens when you view an image in a convex mirror.

Intermediate Follow oral directions with little to no help. Using complete spoken sentences, tell where the focal point of a concave mirror is.

Advanced/Transitioning Follow oral directions independently. Explain, using complete and complex spoken sentences, why an image looks different when reflected by a concave mirror than when reflected by a convex mirror.

Your Turn

Draw a circle around the pictures that show **refraction**. Draw a square around the pictures that show **reflection**.

Talk and Write About It

Complete the sentences.

1. Refraction happens when _light bends_ .
2. As light travels through different materials, or mediums, the rays may bend, or _refract_ .
3. Light can refract when it passes through _glass_ or _water_ .
4. Light rays reflected from a concave mirror meet at _the focal point_ .
5. Some types of mirrors are _plane mirrors, convex mirrors, and concave mirrors_ .

Produce Language

Write what you learned about reflection and refraction. Use as many vocabulary terms as you can.

Reflection and Refraction **97**

Leveled Language Proficiency

Students at each proficiency level should be able to perform the following tasks.

Reading/Writing

Early Beginner/Beginner Locate words that describe refraction. Copy terms to identify pictures.

Early Intermediate Read to find out what refraction is. Write short phrases that explain how light refracts as it passes through different mediums.

Intermediate Comprehend phrases and sentences that describe illustrations showing reflection and refraction. Write sentences to explain some differences between convex and concave lenses.

Advanced/Transitioning Read aloud sentences that compare reflection and refraction. Write paragraphs to explain the difference between reflection and refraction.

↻ Assess Understanding

Your Turn

Model Remind students that refraction occurs when light passes through a lens or other material. Reflection occurs when light bounces off a mirror or other surface. Remind students that refraction means "the bending of light."

Talk and Write About It

On Their Own Encourage student groups to use the example statements as a springboard to write one or more of their own sentences that explain refraction.

Produce Language

On Their Own Have student pairs write and talk about what they learned about reflection and refraction. Encourage them to describe lesson topics in their own words.

Wrap Up

Table Talk Have students reflect on the Big Question and what they learned. Encourage students to build fluency by reading their writing in groups or to the class.

✔ **Learned** and applied vocabulary related to concave and convex lenses

✔ **Spoken** statements about the difference between reflection and refraction

✔ **Written** statements describing ways that light reflects off differently shaped mirrors and refracts as it passes through different mediums

APPENDIX

STEM Topics

Resource Pages for Physical Science appear following the STEM lessons.

Technology and Engineering

Vocabulary technology, brainstorming, engineer, constraint, prototype, trade-off, troubleshooting, risk-benefit analysis, patent

Science Background

- Technology includes any objects that people use, such as a computer, a fork, and a chair. Technology also includes applications of scientific ideas that people use which are not objects, such as the Internet.

- The steps for designing technology include identifying a need, researching the problem, designing a solution, building a prototype, troubleshooting and redesigning, and communicating the solution.

Technology and Engineering

 Big Question What is technology, and how does it affect our lives?

You will . . .
- Identify different types of technology.
- Describe how an engineer designs new technology.
- Use key words related to the design and use of technology.

Talk About It

Technology is the practical application of knowledge to solve problems.

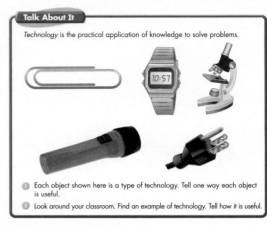

1. Each object shown here is a type of technology. Tell one way each object is useful.
2. Look around your classroom. Find an example of technology. Tell how it is useful.

Predict
Look at the Big Question and the "You will . . ." statements at the top of the page. Describe what you think you are going to learn in this lesson.

I think I am going to learn about . . .

98   STEM Appendix Lesson 1

Frontload the Lesson

What is technology, and how does it affect our lives?

Talk About It

Build Background Point out that technology includes objects as well as applications of scientific ideas that are not objects. Have students talk to a partner about the ways objects in the pictures are useful. For each example of technology that students identify ask, *Why can we call this technology? How is it useful?*

Content and Language

Predict

Model Read the objectives aloud to the class. Discuss the meanings of academic terms, such as *describe, design,* and *identify.*

Guide Discussion Draw students' attention to the Big Question and read it aloud. Have students look ahead at pictures in the lesson to make their predictions.

Leveled Instruction

Early Beginner/Beginner After introducing vocabulary terms, show students photographs of various engineering scenarios. Say a word, such as *prototype*, and guide students to an example.

Early Intermediate/Intermediate Have small groups of students demonstrate vocabulary by role-playing. For example, after discussing the meaning of *brainstorming*, students can demonstrate the term by discussing the design of a new type of skateboard.

Advanced/Transitioning Relate vocabulary to concepts by having small groups perform a simple task. For example, ask students to combine simple objects, such as a rubber band, a toothpick, and a paper clip, to make a useful tool. At different steps in the process, encourage students to use terms such as *technology, brainstorming, trade-off,* and *troubleshooting.*

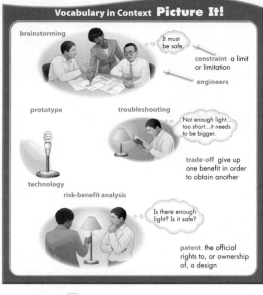

Vocabulary in Context **Picture It!**

brainstorming

It must be safe.

constraint a limit or limitation

engineers

prototype

troubleshooting

Not enough light... too short...it needs to be bigger.

trade-off give up one benefit in order to obtain another

technology

risk-benefit analysis

Is there enough light? Is it safe?

patent the official rights to, or ownership of, a design

Talk About It

Work with a partner. Use the words in the box above to finish these sentences.

1. A person who uses technology to solve problems is an . . . engineer.
2. Talking in a group about ideas for solving a problem is . . . brainstorming.
3. Anything that limits a design is a . . . constraint.
4. A model of a new invention or new technology is a . . . prototype.
5. When you identify flaws or errors in a design you are . . . troubleshooting.

Your Turn

Talk with a partner about engineering. What happens when engineers design a new technology. Use sequence words and the words in the Picture It box.

Technology and Engineering **99**

Academic Vocabulary

- Remind students that the suffix *-ing* indicates that something is in progress. Point out the forms *brainstorm* and *troubleshoot*. The vocabulary terms *brainstorming* and *troubleshooting* are referring to the process that is happening as new technology is being developed.

- Write the words *technology, technological,* and *technical* on the board. Point out that *technology* refers to applying science to solve a problem or make something useful. The term *technological* describes things related to technology. *Technical* refers to a detailed way of describing or doing something.

- Have students use clues such as their knowledge of the terms *design, engineer,* and *technology,* to predict the meaning of the term *engineering.* Point out that the words *engineer* and *engineering* can be used as both a noun and a verb. Give examples of each use. *Engineering* means "the process of designing, planning, and building."

Comprehensible Input

Vocabulary in Context: Picture It!

1. **Say the Term** Say each term slowly, artificially stressing each syllable. Have students repeat. Then say the term more naturally and have students repeat.

2. **Introduce Word Meaning** Connect each term to the visual that illustrates it.

3. **Demonstrate** Use gestures and visuals to demonstrate each term. For example:

   - As you say the word engineer, point to one of the people looking at the table. Say, *The engineers are brainstorming. They talk about their ideas for the design.*

   - Point to a computer or television in your room. Say, *This uses a lot of electricity, but it is helpful in teaching. Paying more for electricity in order to get better lessons for the students is a trade-off.* Ask students if they have ever had problems with a cell phone. Ask, *What do you do if your cell phone doesn't work?* As students give their responses, point out that they are troubleshooting the problem.

4. **Apply** After all the terms have been discussed, have students demonstrate understanding with Talk About It.

Talk About It

Guide Discussion Have students look back at the pictures in the Picture It box. Ask them to use the terms to answer the questions.

RTI Response to Intervention

If students have difficulty with the idiomatic word *troubleshooting* . . .

Then write the words *trouble* and *shoot* on the board. Say each word individually and have students repeat. Talk about the meanings of the individual words. Then explain that *troubleshooting* means "problem solving."

Your Turn

Guide Discussion Ask questions that help students understand steps in the design process. For example, ask, *What happens first?* (brainstorming) *What happens next?* (make a prototype)

Technology and Engineering

↻ Language Production

Do You Understand?

Comprehension Support First have students tell what each picture shows, and then ask questions to help students connect it to the vocabulary term. For example, say, *A cell phone is something that an engineer uses, but many other people also use cell phones. What is a cell phone an example of? Which word can I most closely relate to the cell phone?* Have students circle the word that *best* relates to the picture.

Model Demonstrate questions students might ask themselves about the pictures to determine the correct answer. Say, *What does the picture show? What does each word mean? Which word best tells about the picture?*

Talk About It

Guide Discussion Have students review the terms in the Do You Understand box. Read each sentence aloud with students. Then have them complete it using the word that fits best.

Your Turn

Guide Discussion Have partners check to ensure they both have circled the same words. Then ask students to take turns summarizing a term orally. While one partner gives a term's definition or clue, the other partner should identify the word that *best* describes what they hear.

A Closer Look

On Their Own Have students work in pairs to complete this word study activity. Then have them look back at the Picture It box and identify two other vocabulary terms that are made of smaller words. Help students identify and clarify the meanings of *troubleshooting and trade-off* in a similar way.

Do You Understand?

Circle the word in each box that *best* tells what the picture shows.

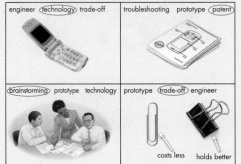

| engineer (technology) trade-off | troubleshooting prototype (patent) |
| (brainstorming) prototype technology | prototype (trade-off) engineer |

costs less | holds better

Talk About It

Talk with a partner. Complete the sentences.

1. A phone and a fan are types of . . . technology.
2. When designing new technology, cost can be a . . . constraint.
3. An activity in which people think of new ideas is called . . . brainstorming.
4. A document that gives an inventor rights to a design is a . . . patent.
5. Giving up one benefit in order to have another is a . . . trade-off.
6. Analyzing and fixing problems in a design is called . . . troubleshooting.

Your Turn

Work with a partner. Look at the words you circled above. Tell a partner what they mean using your own words.

> **A Closer Look**
>
> **Compound Words** Circle the two words that make up the word *brainstorm*. Tell what each of the words means. How do they contribute to your understanding of the word?

Leveled Language Proficiency

Students at each proficiency level should be able to perform the following tasks.

Listening/Speaking

Early Beginner/Beginner Find pictures in the lesson that relate to vocabulary words students hear. Say new vocabulary aloud after identifying the picture.

Early Intermediate/Intermediate Respond to simple oral instructions, such as *Show what an engineer does. Show how to brainstorm.* Use complete sentences to orally respond to questions about technology.

Advanced Distinguish between related terms, such as *trade-off and constraint*, based on oral descriptions. Use simple sentences to orally describe pictures related to the design of technology.

Transitioning Make inferences about consequences of different types of technology based on oral descriptions of problems. Discuss the steps of designing technology.

Your Turn

Engineering new technology requires several steps. If all goes well, it is roughly a seven-step process.

1. Identify a need.
2. Research the Problem.
3. Design a solution.
4. Evaluate constraints and make trade-offs.
5. Build a model.
6. Troubleshoot and redesign.
7. Communicate the solution.

With a partner, write a number (or numbers), 1 through 7, below each term in the box. Show which step in the design process each term describes.

prototype	engineers	brainstorm	patent
5	1-7	3,4,6	7

Talk and Write About It

Complete the statements about technology.

1. Some examples of technology are _pen, lamp, clock_ .
2. An engineer works to _design new technology_ .
3. Before manufacturing, engineers first make a model called a **prototype**.
4. A car must be safe. Safety is a design _constraint_ .
5. If you troubleshoot a design, you think about _problems that it has_ .

Produce Language

Write a sentence that tells what technology is. Then name two kinds of technology you use each day. Tell how they help you.

_____
_____
_____
_____

Technology and Engineering **101**

Leveled Language Proficiency

Students at each proficiency level should be able to perform the following tasks.

Reading/Writing

Early Beginner/Beginner Match written vocabulary terms with pictures related to technology and its design. Label pictures related to technology.

Early Intermediate Follow along with text that is read aloud by a teacher or another student. Complete sentences with words or phrases related to technology.

Intermediate Answer questions about technology design in response to written descriptions. Use details to write short descriptions of technology and ways they use it.

Advanced/Transitioning Infer meanings of words and concepts, such as *technology, prototype*, and *risk-benefit analysis*, based on recognition of word forms and word parts. Use complex sentences to produce detailed descriptions of the engineering process and technology design.

Assess Understanding

Your Turn

Model Point out to students that number one shows the first thing that happens when an engineer designs new technology, and number seven shows the last. Have students look at the Picture It box for visual support. Model how to find a logical match between terms and steps of the design process. For example, say, *Does an engineer do all of these steps? Yes. So, I'll write the numbers 1 through 7 below the word* engineers.

Talk and Write About It

On Their Own Have students take turns reading the sentence starters aloud with a partner. Then have them work individually to write their responses. Encourage pairs to compare their answers.

Produce Language

On Their Own Before students write their answers, read the Big Question aloud and discuss it. Ask students to think about what they do both at school and at home to find two examples of technology that they use each day.

Wrap Up

Table Talk Have students reflect on what they learned. Encourage students to build fluency by reading their writing in groups or to the class.

✔ **Learned** what technology is and how it affects our lives

✔ **Spoken** statements about designing technology

✔ **Written** names of different steps in the design of technology

Lesson 2

Measurement

Vocabulary metric system, SI, mass, weight, volume, meniscus, density, estimate, accuracy, precision

Materials all optional: metric balance, graduated cylinders, various balls of the same size but different densities (such as foam balls, rubber balls, ping-pong balls, wooden balls, or marbles), metric rulers, bathroom scale, and/or spring scale

Science Background

- Scientists use the International System of Units, or SI (from the French *Système International d'Unités*), for measurement.

- SI is a version of the metric system. The metric system is a measurement system based on the number 10.

- A standard system of measurement makes it easier for scientists to compare data and communicate with each other about their results.

Frontload the Lesson

Why is a standard system of measurement important in science?

Talk About It

Build Background Pass out the metric rulers, and encourage pairs to take measurements of items found on or near their desks. Ask students about things they measure at home and in school.

Content and Language

Predict

Model Read the objectives aloud. Pause to explain or to demonstrate key terms, such as *measurement.*

Guide Discussion Encourage students to think about the Big Question as they predict what they are going to learn in the lesson.

 Big Question Why is a standard system of measurement important in science?

You will . . .
- Describe and use the International System of Units (SI) and the metric system.
- Explain why scientists use the International System of Units.
- Use terms related to measurement.

Talk About It

Look at the pictures below. What might you measure with each object?

Talk with a partner about the things you measure every day.

Predict
Look at the Big Question and the "You will . . ." statements at the top of the page. Describe what you think you are going to learn in this lesson.

I think I am going to learn about . . .

102 STEM Appendix Lesson 2

Leveled Instruction

Early Beginner Have students point to pictures and use gestures to answer questions. Label what each tool measures and display the tools in the room to help students visualize the vocabulary terms.

Beginner Keep a list of key terms on the board for students to refer to when answering questions about measurement.

Early Intermediate/Intermediate Encourage students to respond to questions about measurement with complete sentences and examples from everyday life.

Advanced/Transitioning Have these students partner with beginner students. Encourage them to model how they think about, talk about, and write about what they do to take different kinds of measurements.

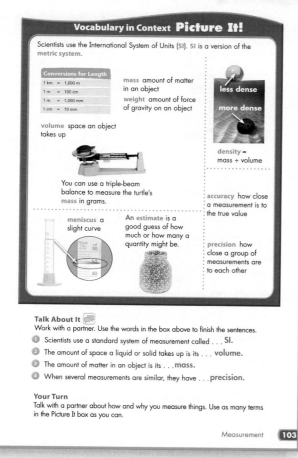

Academic Vocabulary

- Explain that students may have heard the word *density*. For example, *population density* refers to how many people live within a measured area.

- Write the word *accuracy* on the board. Explain that *accuracy* is formed from the word *accurate*, which means "without error" or "true."

- Since the metric unit to measure force is Newtons, students may be puzzled by the fact that many scales provide "weight" in grams. What the scales are really providing is a comparison to how much a certain amount (in grams) of mass weighs while under the pull of Earth's gravity. Explain that in science class, measures of grams and kilograms will quantify mass, not weight.

Cultural Consideration

If students are from other countries, they may be familiar with the metric (SI) system. Encourage these students to show other students such things as the relationship between millimeters, centimeters, and meters. Encourage all students to start "thinking metric," and discourage them from trying to convert metric to units.

⟳ Comprehensible Input

Vocabulary in Context: Picture It!

1. **Say the Term** Say each term slowly, artificially stressing each syllable. Have students repeat. Then say the term more naturally and have students repeat.

2. **Introduce Word Meaning** Connect each term to the visual that illustrates it.

3. **Demonstrate** Use gestures and visuals to demonstrate each term. For example:

   - Pour water into a graduated cylinder. Point to the meniscus and have a volunteer read the volume measurement. Pour some water out and have a volunteer tell the new volume, reading at the bottom of the meniscus.

   - Pass out balls of similar size but varying densities. Have students order them from least to greatest density.

   - Demonstrate how to use a metric balance to measure mass. Explain that mass is how much matter an object has.

   - Demonstrate how to weigh an object on a scale. Explain that weight is a measure of force that tells how much gravity pulls down on an object.

4. **Apply** After each term has been discussed, have students demonstrate understanding with Talk About It.

Talk About It

Guide Discussion Have students use the terms in the Picture It box to name the objects you used in your demonstrations.

R T I Response to Intervention

If students have difficulty pronouncing the word *precision* . . .

Then remind students that *ci* can form a soft sound. Point out other words that have the soft *ci* sound (*cinema, cider*).

Your Turn

Guide Discussion As students converse, provide support. Elicit prior experience. Suggest resources. Ask questions that partners can answer together.

Measurement

↻ Language Production

Do You Understand?

Comprehension Support Before students begin, read the directions aloud with them. Have volunteers read each question aloud. Explain to students that they will write the answer on the line.

Model Demonstrate how you might answer the first question. Say, *I see the plant. A ruler is next to it to help measure the height. The top of the plant aligns with the number 4 on the ruler. So the plant is 4 centimeters in height.*

Talk About It

Guide Discussion Read the sentences aloud with students as they work together to complete each one.

Your Turn

Guide Discussion Ask students to place two items from their book bag on their desk. Hold a book and a notebook in each hand. Say, *The book seems heavier than the notebook. I could put the items on a scale to find out which weighs more. If they are the same size, then the heavier one must have the greatest density.*

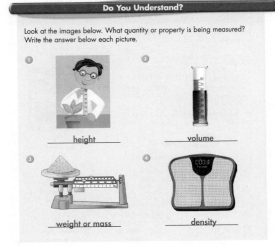

Do You Understand?

Look at the images below. What quantity or property is being measured? Write the answer below each picture.

① height   ② volume

③ weight or mass   ④ density

Talk About It 💬
Talk with a partner. Complete the sentences.

① Scientists use a standard system of measurement called . . . the metric system; SI.
② A graduated cylinder is used to measure . . . volume.
③ When you divide an object's mass by its volume, you are finding the object's . . . density.
④ A triple-beam balance is used to measure . . . mass.
⑤ A measurement of the pull of gravity on something is its . . . weight.
⑥ The curved upper surface of the liquid in a graduated cylinder is called a . . . meniscus.

Your Turn
Talk to a partner about the objects in your backpack, or book bag. Tell how you can measure each object. Point out which objects weigh most and which have the greatest and least density.

104   STEM Appendix Lesson 2

Leveled Language Proficiency

Students at each proficiency level should be able to perform the following tasks.

Listening/Speaking

Early Beginner/Beginner Gesture or point in response to to oral directions. Ask and respond to spoken questions about measurement, including volume, mass, and weight.

Early Intermediate Accurately follow simple oral directions. Respond to spoken questions about mass, density, volume, and weight using short phrases or simple sentences.

Intermediate Listen to vocabulary terms and then explain their meaning. Participate in limited discussions with phrases and simple sentences comparing the concepts of accuracy and precision.

Advanced/Transitioning Follow multiple-step oral directions. Use extended discourse to explain concepts related to accuracy, precision, density, mass, and weight.

Your Turn
Write or circle to complete each item.

Give an estimate of how many marbles are in the jar.	Which object has greater density?	Maya wanted to measure 2 cm of ribbon. Did her measurement have accuracy?
Sample: about 500	the stone	yes
Circle the SI units of measure. 2 centimeters 5 kilometers 6 inches 12 meters 25 feet 17 millimeters 301 yards	Circle the meniscus. How much water is in the cylinder? 44 ml	Circle the image that shows greater volume.

Talk and Write About It
Complete the statements about measurements.

1. An example of an estimate is guessing how many people are at a concert.
2. A measurement is accurate if it is close to or is the targeted value.
3. Millimeters are used to measure the volume of a liquid.

Produce Language
Why is it important that scientists from different countries use the same system of measurement? Write your explanation.

_____
_____
_____
_____
_____

Measurement **105**

Leveled Language Proficiency

Students at each proficiency level should be able to perform the following tasks.

Reading/Writing

Early Beginner/Beginner Match pictures to corresponding terms. Create a word bank to use in writing, by listing words and phrases related to measurement.

Early Intermediate Read to find information about mass, weight, and volume. Write explanations using multiple sentences in a logical order.

Intermediate Connect written statements about measurements with prior experiences. Use details and examples to describe density, volume, mass, and weight.

Advanced/Transitioning Make inferences while reading about accuracy and measurement. Revise a piece of writing to ensure detail, focus, and clarity.

Assess Understanding

Your Turn

Model As students complete the activity, prompt student thinking with questions such as: *How can you estimate how many marbles are in the jar? What are some examples of SI units? How do you read a graduated cylinder?* After students have completed the activity, have volunteers share some of their answers. Encourage students to discuss how to make a good estimate, and what makes a number precise or accurate.

Talk and Write About It

On Their Own Call on volunteers to use their own words to define or give examples of some of the measurement terms from the lesson.

Produce Language

On Their Own Before students begin writing, have a class discussion about the Big Question. Ask students for examples of some of the things scientists study. Then brainstorm how measurement might be used in each case. Ask, *What might happen if the meaasurements are not accurate? What might happen if the measurements were not given in standard units?*

Wrap Up

Table Talk As a way of answering the Big Question, have volunteers read aloud what they wrote for Produce Language. Have students reflect on what they learned. Encourage students to build fluency by reading their writing in groups or to the class.

✔ **Learned** and applied vocabulary related to measurements and measuring

✔ **Spoken** statements about mass, weight, volume, and density

✔ **Written** statements about accuracy and precision

Mathematics

Vocabulary significant figures, percent error, mean, median, mode, range, anomalous data, graph, linear graph, nonlinear graph, model

 Science Background

- *Significant figures* of a measurement consist of all measured digits and one estimated digit. When reading a number, all nonzero digits are significant. A zero is significant only if it is between two nonzero digits, such as 305, or if it is to the right of a nonzero digit *and* it is to the right of the decimal place. For example, 270 has two significant figures, but 27.0 has three significant figures.

- *Percent error* indicates how different a measured value is from a known value.

- The *range* is the difference between the greatest and least number in a set of data. The *mean* is the average number. The *median* is the middle number, and the *mode* is the number that appears most often.

 Frontload the Lesson

What math skills and tools do scientists use?

Talk About It

Build Background Call on students to share examples. Encourage students to look back at previous lessons for ideas.

Content and Language

Predict

Model Read each objective aloud. Explain that having a skill means being able to do something. A math tool is any method used to do mathematics.

Guide Discussion Read aloud the Big Question. Then have students tell what they think they will learn in the lesson, using the sentence starter.

Mathematics

 Big Question What math skills and tools do scientists use?

You will . . .
- Describe math skills scientists use to collect data.
- Identify math tools scientists use to analyze data.
- Understand and use key words related to math skills and tools used by scientists.

Talk About It

List three examples of how you use mathematics in your daily life.

①

②

③

Now list three things you learned in science class that scientists may have used mathematics to discover.

①

②

③

Talk with a partner about why you think math is important in science.

Predict
Look at the Big Question and the "You will . . ." statements at the top of the page. Describe what you think you are going to learn in this lesson.

I think I am going to learn about . . .

106 STEM Appendix Lesson 3

Leveled Instruction

Early Beginner/ Beginner When appropriate, offer simpler words to help students identify and use the vocabulary terms. For example, to tell about the *median* of data, students might say *middle* or they could say *line* for *linear*. Make a word wall of mathematics vocabulary terms and leave it up as a reference in your science or English language classroom.

Early Intermediate/Intermediate Provide verbal sentence frames for students to use in their descriptions of the vocabulary terms. After students complete a sentence frame, have them repeat the entire sentence.

Advanced/Transitioning As students describe the vocabulary terms, be sure to ask them for examples to support their descriptions. For example, when students talk about the mean, have them identify the mean of a set of data.

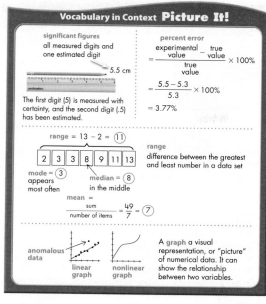

Your Turn
Talk with a partner about the numbers in the Picture It box. Tell how the vocabulary words relate to the numbers.

Academic Vocabulary

- Remind students that a *sum* is what you get when you add together a series of numbers, and a *difference* is what you get when you subtract.

- Point out to students that they may see the term *significant figures* written as *sig figs* or as *significant digits*.

- Make sure students understand the meanings of the terms *measured* and *estimated* when defining *significant figures*. Explain that finding the *estimate* means identifying a value that is probably close to the real value.

- Cognates are words that have the same or similar roots and meanings in two languages. Have students share any vocabulary terms they recognize as cognates to words in their first languages. In Spanish, for example, the word for *figure* is *figura*, and the word for *percent* is *porcentaje*.

↻ Comprehensible Input

Vocabulary in Context: Picture It!

1. **Say the Term** Say each term slowly, artificially stressing each syllable. Have students repeat. Then say the term more naturally and have students repeat.

2. **Introduce Word Meaning** Connect each term to the visual that illustrates it.

3. **Demonstrate** Use gestures and visuals to demonstrate each term. For example:

   - As you discuss different types of graphs, draw them on the board. Point out to students that an *anomalous data* point does not fall on the line or curve of the graph.

   - Put a set of data on the board, and work through it as a class to identify the *mean, median, mode,* and *range*. Talk about each.

4. **Apply** After all the terms have been discussed, have students demonstrate understanding with Talk About It.

Talk About It

Guide Discussion Before students start their independent discussions, check for understanding with the following sentence starters:

1. *How close an experimental value is to a true value is the . . .* (percent error.)

2. *The average of all numbers in a data set is the . . .* (mean.)

3. *The number that is most common in a data set is the . . .* (mode.)

4. *A graph that is a straight line is a . . .* (linear graph.)

5. *A graph that is not a straight line is a . . .* (nonlinear graph.)

R T I Response to Intervention

If students have difficulty saying *anomalous* . . .

Then say and talk about each syllable separately.

Your Turn

Guide Discussion Monitor students' descriptions, and provide clarification when necessary. If needed, provide additional data sets.

Mathematics

Language Production

Do You Understand?

Comprehension Support Tell students to read each answer choice before deciding which is best represented by the illustrations or examples.

Model Demonstrate how to ask questions that help choose the best answer. Say, *What does the graph look like?* (a line) *What does × 100% mean?* (percent) *What number in the data set is circled?* (the one in the middle; the median) Encourage students to ask themselves such questions to help them choose the correct term.

Talk About It

Guide Discussion Read the sentences aloud with students. Encourage students to use the graphs or numbers in the Do You Understand box to help them complete the sentences.

Your Turn

Guide Discussion If students have insufficient vocabulary to explain their choices, provide simple sentences that they can repeat. For example, when explaining the linear graph say, *It is a line.* For percent error say, *It is the difference divided by the real value.*

A Closer Look

On Their Own Have students work in pairs to complete this word study activity. Everyday meanings include "not nice" for *mean*, "fashion or method" for *mode*, and an "expanse" "stove" or "row of mountains" for a *range*.

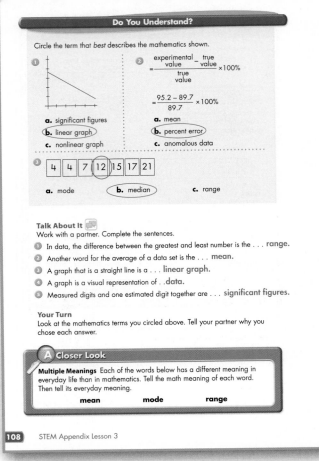

Leveled Language Proficiency

Students at each proficiency level should be able to perform the following tasks.

Listening/Speaking

Early Beginner/Beginner Draw a linear or nonlinear graph based on oral statements. Say numbers to demonstrate comprehension of key terms.

Early Intermediate Find *mean, median, mode,* and *range* based on an oral presentation of a data set. Use simple sentences to identify significant figures and types of graphs.

Intermediate Connect pictures and procedures to oral descriptions of the math skills and tools. Discuss the activities with a partner using detailed explanations.

Advanced/Transitioning Infer details about math skills based on detailed oral explanations. Give a detailed oral summary of how scientists use math in their work, using key terms without support.

Your Turn

5.6 cm	Draw a nonlinear graph.
centimeters	Place an anomalous data point on it.
Which is the estimated digit in the significant figures above? **.6**	Answer should show a curve on the graph with a data point that is not on the curve.

4   4   9   12   26

What is the mean? __11__
What is the mode? __4__
What is the range? __22__
What is the median? __9__

Talk and Write About It

Complete the statements about how math is used by scientists.

1. A low percent error means that the results of an experiment _____ __are accurate__
2. A nonlinear graph has a __curved line__ .
3. In a range of data, the median is found __in the middle__ .
4. To find the mean, you add the numbers in a data set and then __divide by the number of items in that set__ .
5. The range of a set of data is found by subtracting _____ __the least number from the greatest__
6. Compared to other data, an anomalous data point is _____ __very different__

Produce Language

Write about how scientists use math skills and tools in their work.

_____

_____

_____

_____

_____

Leveled Language Proficiency

Students at each proficiency level should be able to perform the following tasks.

Reading/Writing

Early Beginner Differentiate terms with the same beginning sounds, such as *mean*, *median*, and mode. Identify mathematics skills and tools by circling the correct labels.

Beginner Follow along with written text as the teacher reads it aloud. Complete sentence starters using one- or two-word responses about data sets, graphs, and other math terms.

Early Intermediate/Intermediate Answer questions about the terms *mean*, *median*, *mode* and *range* after reading descriptions and seeing examples. Write several sentences describing meanings of mathematics words.

Advanced/Transitioning Follow complex written instructions. Write detailed descriptions of mathematical concepts.

Assess Understanding

Your Turn

Model Read each question or instruction aloud. Reinforce learning by having students do a team "scavenger hunt" to find additional examples of the mathematical terms in math and science textbooks in the classroom.

Talk and Write About It

On Their Own Have partners read and discuss each sentence starter. Then have each student write the correct word or words to complete the sentences. Encourage students to review their responses with their partner after they finish. Have pairs discuss any discrepancy in their answers and correct their work as needed. Note that some variation among answers, due simply to word choice, is acceptable.

Produce Language

On Their Own Read the instructions aloud with students. Then review the Big Question with students. Remind students that a *skill* is something you are able to do, and a *tool* is any object or method that helps you do a task.

Wrap Up

Table Talk Have students reflect on what they learned and build fluency by reading their writing in groups or to the entire class.

✔ **Learned** to identify linear graphs, nonlinear graphs, and anomalous data

✔ **Spoken** statements about *mean*, *median*, *mode*, and *range* of data

✔ **Heard** descriptions of significant figures and percent error

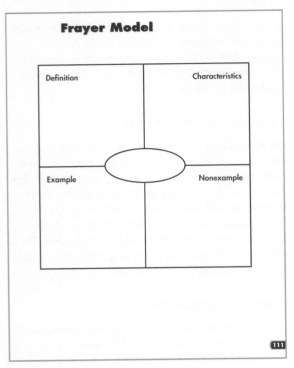

page 111

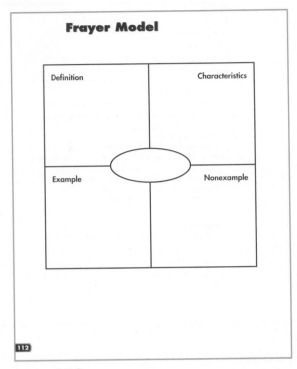

page 112

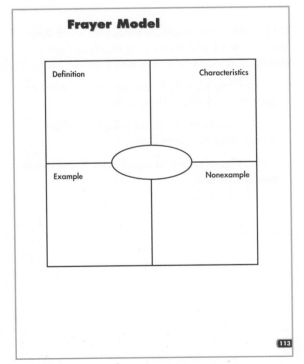

page 113

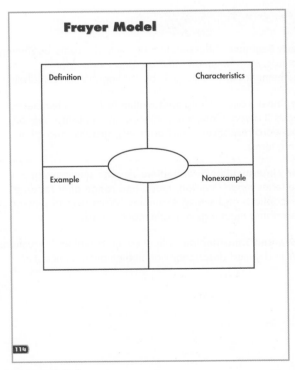

page 114

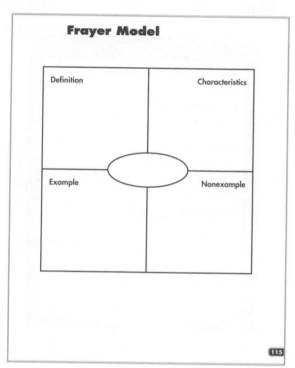

page 115

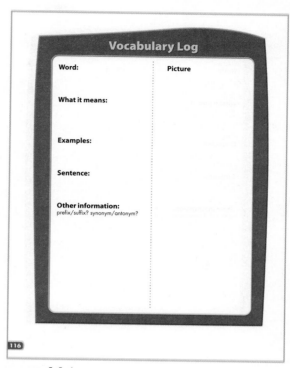

page 116

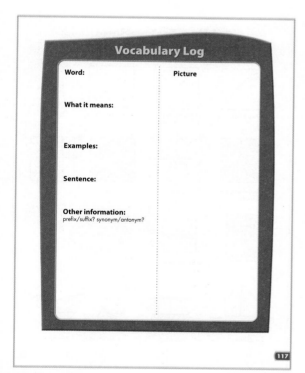

page 117

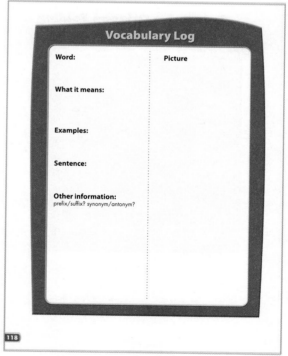

page 118

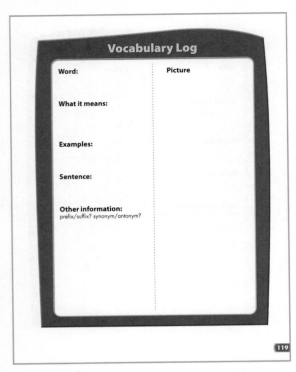

page 119

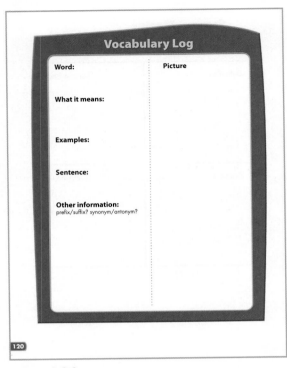

page 120

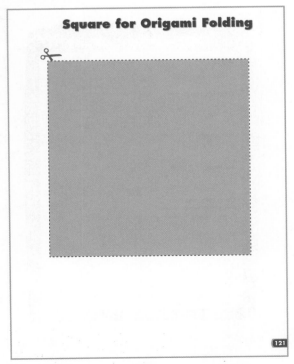

page 121

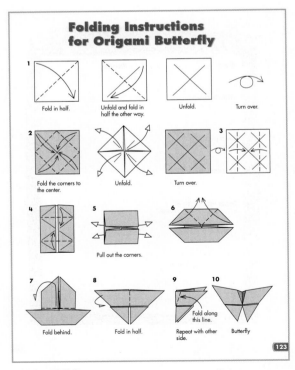

page 123

CREDITS

Illustrations

2, 3, 4 Greg Harris; **3, 26, 31, 32, 34, 35, 36, 50, 55, 57, 59, 62, 79, 94, 96, 97, 98, 99, 100, 103, 105** Kenneth Batelman; **5, 31, 40, 46, 47, 51, 54, 57, 58, 60** Nathan Jarvis; **6, 7, 8, 11, 12, 13, 18, 20, 21, 32, 35, 47, 48, 53, 59, 60, 61, 63, 64, 65, 66, 67, 68, 71, 86, 88, 90, 91, 92, 97, 98, 102, 104** Rob Schuster; **7, 71, 72, 75, 77, 104, 105** Peter Bull; **7, 38, 48, 55, 82, 98, 102, 104** Precision Graphics; **19, 20, 28, 30, 39, 59, 78, 79, 90, 92, 97** Steve McEntee; **21, 91, 97** Theresa Sakno; **39, 41** Fanny Mellet Berry; **42, 44, 45** Charlene Chua; **51, 69, 81** Stephen Durke; **53, 83, 84** Dave Cockburn; **60** Jonathan Massie; **69** Jonathan Williams; **82, 83, 84** Chris Reed; **104** Robin Boyer; **123** Reproduced with permission by Dover Publications from Easy Origami by John Montroll, October 1992./©Dover Publications.

Photographs

Every effort has been made to secure permission and provide appropriate credit for photographic material. The publisher deeply regrets any omission and pledges to correct errors called to its attention in subsequent editions.

Unless otherwise acknowledged, all photographs are the property of Pearson Education, Inc.

Photo locators denoted as follows: Top (T), Center (C), Bottom (B), Left (L), Right (R), Background (Bkgd)

Cover

Origami "Helicopter" designed and folded by Brian Chan, in handmade Origamido® paper by Richard L. Alexander and Michael G. LaFosse.

11 ivan kmit/Fotolia, volff/Fotolia; **19** Tom Mc Nemar/Fotolia; **20** Jupiter Images/Thinkstock; **30** Christopher Pattberg/iStockphoto, Drew Hadley/iStockphoto, Harun Aydin/iStockphoto, Photolibrary Group, Inc.; **31** Daniel Loiselle/iStockphoto;

58 ©AnutkaT/Shutterstock; **63** Comstock Images/Getty images/Thinkstock; **81** (T, CR) ©DK Images; **82** Steve Byland/Fotolia, Viorel Sima/Shutterstock; **83** artmim/Fotolia, Pavel Losevsky/Fotolia; **84** Pavel Losevsky/Fotolia; **87** EuToch/Fotolia; **88** Graham Prentice/Fotolia, Joseph Dudash/Fotolia, mario beauregard/Fotolia; **95** Jupiterimages/Thinkstock; **98** EuToch/Fotolia; **100** Zedcor Wholly Owned/Getty Images/Thinkstock; **103** Terex/Dreamstime LLC, Britvich/Dreamstime LLC, Chiyacat/Dreamstime LLC.

INDEX

INDEX, *cont.*

endoskeleton, L: 62–65
endotherm, L: 62–65
endothermic reaction, P: 30–33
energy, E: 6–9; P: 58–61
energy transformation, P: 58–61
engineer, E: 98–101; L: 98–101;
    P: 98–101
environmental science, L: 50–53
enzyme, L: 74–77
epicenter, E: 26–29
epidermis, L: 70–73
epiglottis, L: 74–77
epithelial tissue, L: 66–69
equator, E: 34–37
equinox, E: 78–81
erosion, E: 38–41, 42–45
esophagus, L: 74–77
estimate, E: 102–105;
    L: 102–105; P: 102–105
eukaryote, L: 6–9
eutrophication, E: 50–53
evaporation, E: 50–53, 66–69
evolution, L: 6–9, 34–37
excretion, L: 82–85
exoskeleton, L: 62–65
exothermic reaction, P: 30–33
external fertilization, L: 62–65
extinct, E: 30–33
extinction, L: 50–53
extrusion, E: 46–49
extrusive rock, E: 18–21

F

Fahrenheit scale, P: 62–65
fault, E: 22–25, 46–49
fermentation, L: 18–21
fertility (of soil), E: 38–41
fetus, L: 94–97
flagellum, L: 54–57
flood, E: 66–69

flower, L: 58–61
focal point, P: 94–97
focus, E: 26–29
foliated, E: 18–21
food chain, L: 46–49
food web, L: 46–49
force, E: 82–85; P: 42–45
fossil, E: 46–49; L: 34–37
fossil fuel, E: 74–77
fracture, E: 14–17
free fall, P: 50–53
frequency, P: 78–81
friction, P: 42–45
front, E: 70–73
fulcrum, P: 54–57
fungus, L: 54–57

G

galaxy, E: 94–97
gallbladder, L: 74–77
galvanometer, P: 74–77
gamma ray, P: 86–89
gas, P: 10–13
gas giants, E: 90–93
gene, L: 22–25
generator, P: 74–77
genetic disorder, L: 30–33
genetic engineering, L: 30–33
genetics, L: 22–25
genome, L: 30–33
genotype, L: 22–25
genus, L: 6–9
geocentric, E: 90–93
geode, E: 14–17
Geologic Time Scale, E: 46–49
geosphere, E: 6–9
geostationary orbit, E: 86–89
glacier, E: 42–45
gland, L: 66–69, 94–97

global warming, E: 74–77
globe, E: 34–37
Golgi apparatus, L: 10–13
gradualism, L: 34–37
grain, E: 18–21
graph, E: 106–109; L: 106–109;
    P: 106–109
gravity, E: 82–85; P: 42–45
greenhouse effect, E: 62–65
greenhouse gases, E: 74–77
grounded, P: 66–69
groundwater, E: 42–45
group, P: 14–17
gymnosperm, L: 58–61

H

habitat, L: 38–41
hair follicle, L: 70–73
half-life, E: 46–49; P: 18–21
heart, L: 78–81
heliocentric, E: 90–93
hemisphere, E: 34–37
hemoglobin, L: 78–81
herbivore, L: 46–49
heredity, L: 22–25
heterotroph, L: 18–21
heterozygous, L: 22–25
homeostasis, L: 6–9, 66–69
homologous structures, L: 34–37
homozygous, L: 22–25
hormone, L: 94–97
host, L: 54–57
hot spot, E: 30–33
humidity, E: 66–69
humus, E: 38–41
hurricane, E: 70–73
hybridization, L: 30–33
hydrosphere, E: 6–9
hypothalamus, L: 94–97
hypothesis, E: 2–5; L: 2–5; P: 2–5

INDEX, *cont.*

plankton, E: 54–57

plasma, L: 78–81

plate, E: 22–25

plate tectonics, E: 22–25

platelet, L: 78–81

polar, E: 70–73

polar bond, P: 26–29

polar zone, E: 74–77

polarization, P: 66–69

polarized light, P: 86–89

pollen, L: 58–61

pollination, L: 58–61

pollution, L: 50–53

polyatomic ion, P: 22–25

population, L: 38–41

population density, L: 38–41

pore, L: 70–73

potential energy, P: 58–61

power, P: 66–69

precipitate, P: 30–33

precipitation, E: 50–53, 66–69

precision, E: 102–105; L: 102–105; P: 102–105

predation, L: 42–45

pressure, P: 10–13

primary color, P: 90–93

primary succession, L: 42–45

prime meridian, E: 34–37

probability, L: 22–25

producer, L: 46–49

product, P: 30–33

prokaryote, L: 6–9

protein, L: 26–29

protist, L: 54–57

proton, P: 14–17

prototype, E: 98–101; L: 98–101; P: 98–101

pulley, P: 54–57

punctuated equilibrium, L: 34–37

Punnett square, L: 22–25

Q

qualitative observation, E: 2–5; L: 2–5; P: 2–5

quantitative observation, E: 2–5; L: 2–5; P: 2–5

quasar, E: 94–97

R

radial symmetry, L: 62–65

radiation, E: 10–13, E: 62–65; P: 62–65

radio wave, P: 86–89

radioactive decay, E: 46–49; P: 18–21

radioactivity, P: 18–21

rain gauge, E: 66–69

range, E: 106–109; L: 106–109; P: 106–109

reactant, P: 30–33

reactivity, P: 18–21

recessive allele, L: 22–25

rectum, L: 74–77

red blood cell, L: 78–81

reference point, P: 38–41

reflection, P: 78–81

reflex, L: 90–93

refraction, P: 78–81, 94–97

regular reflection, P: 94–97

relative age, E: 46–49

remote sensing, E: 86–89

renewable resource, L: 50–53

replacement, P: 30–33

replication, L: 18–21

reservoir, E: 50–53

resistance, P: 66–69

response, L: 66–69

retina, L: 90–93

reverse fault, E: 26–29

revolution, E: 78–81

ribosome, L: 10–13, 26–29

Ring of Fire, E: 30–33

risk-benefit analysis, E: 98–101; L: 98–101; P: 98–101

rock cycle, E: 18–21

rocket, E: 86–89

rotation, E: 78–81

rover, E: 86–89

runoff, E: 42–45

S

S wave, E: 26–29

salinity, E: 54–57

satellite, E: 78–81, 86–89; P: 50–53

saturated solution, P: 34–37

saturated zone, E: 50–53

scale, E: 34–37

scattering, E: 62–65

scavenger, L: 46–49

scientific notation, E: 94–97

screw, P: 54–57

sea-floor spreading, E: 22–25

seamount, E: 54–57

secondary color, P: 90–93

secondary succession, L: 42–45

sediment, E: 18–21, 42–45

sedimentary rock, E: 18–21

seed, L: 58–61

selective cutting, L: 50–53

selectively permeable, L: 14–17

seismic waves, E: 10–13

seismogram, E: 26–29

seismograph, E: 26–29

selective breeding, L: 30–33

semiconductor, P: 18–21

sensory neuron, L: 90–93

series circuit, P: 66–69

sex chromosomes, L: 30–33

sex-linked gene, L: 30–33

sexual reproduction, L: 6–9

INDEX, *cont.*

shearing, E: 26–29

short circuit, P: 66–69

SI, E: 102–105; L: 102–105; P: 102–105

significant figures, E: 106–109; L: 106–109; P: 106–109

silica, E: 30–33

simple machine, P: 54–57

skeletal muscle, L: 70–73

skeleton, L: 70–73

slope, P: 38–41

small intestine, L: 74–77

smooth muscle, L: 70–73

soil, E: 38–41

soil conservation, E: 38–41

soil horizon, E: 38–41

solar eclipse, E: 82–85

solar flare, E: 90–93

solar system, E: 90–93

solar wind, E: 90–93

solenoid, P: 74–77

solid, P: 10–13

solstice, E: 78–81

solubility, P: 34–37

solute, P: 34–37

solution, E: 14–17; P: 34–37

solvent, P: 34–37

space probe, E: 86–89

space shuttle, E: 86–89

space spinoff, E: 86–89

space station, E: 86–89

species, L: 6–9, 34–37

specific heat, P: 62–65

spectrograph, E: 94–97

spectrum, E: 94–97

speed, P: 38–41

sphere, E: 6–9

spring tide, E: 82–85

stalactite, E: 42–45

stalagmite, E: 42–45

star, E: 78–81

static electricity, P: 66–69

stimulus, L: 66–69

stomach, L: 74–77

storm, E: 70–73

storm surge, E: 70–73

stratosphere, E: 58–61

streak, E: 14–17

stress, E: 26–29

striated muscle, L: 70–73

strike-slip fault, E: 26–29

subduction, E: 22–25

subjective, E: 2–5; L: 2–5; P: 2–5

subscript, P: 22–25

subsoil, E: 38–41

substance, P: 6–9

succession, L: 42–45

sunspot, E: 90–93

surface tension, P: 10–13

surface wave, E: 26–29

suspension, P: 34–37

sustainable use, L: 50–53

symbiosis, L: 42–45

symbol, E: 34–37

synapse, L: 90–93

synthesis, P: 30–33

system, E: 6–9

T

T cell, L: 86–89

technology, E: 98–101; L: 98–101; P: 98–101

telescope, E: 94–97

temperate zone, E: 74–77

temperature, E: 62–65; P: 62–65

tendon, L: 70–73

tension, E: 26–29

terrestrial planets, E: 90–93

texture, E: 18–21

thermal energy, E: 62–65; P: 58–61

thermal expansion, P: 62–65

thermometer, E: 62–65

thermosphere, E: 58–61

threatened species, L: 50–53

thrust, E: 86–89

thunderstorm, E: 70–73

tide, E: 82–85

topographic map, E: 34–37

topsoil, E: 38–41

tornado, E: 70–73

toxin, L: 86–89

trace fossil, E: 46–49

trachea, L: 82–85

trade-off, E: 98–101; L: 98–101; P: 98–101

trait, L: 22–25

transfer RNA, L: 26–29

transform boundary, E: 22–25

transformer, P: 74–77

translucent, P: 90–93

transparent, P: 90–93

transpiration, E: 50–53

transverse wave, P: 78–81

trench, E: 54–57

tributary, E: 50–53

triple bond, P: 26–29

tropical, E: 70–73

tropical zone, E: 74–77

troposphere, E: 58–61

troubleshooting, E: 98–101; L: 98–101; P: 98–101

tsunami, E: 54–57

tumor, L: 26–29

tundra, E: 74–77

U

ultraviolet ray, P: 86–89

umbra, E: 82–85

unconformity, E: 46–49

unicellular, L: 6–9

universe, E: 94–97

CREDITS

Photographs

Every effort has been made to secure permission and provide appropriate credit for photographic material. The publisher deeply regrets any omission and pledges to correct errors called to its attention in subsequent editions.

Unless otherwise acknowledged, all photographs are the property of Pearson Education, Inc.

Cover

Cover Art: Origami designed and folded by Brian Chan, in handmade Origamido® paper by Michael G. LaFosse and Richard L. Alexander.

PEARSON

Providing a Complete Solution for English Language Learners

Introduce the Research

Accelerating the Progress of English Language Learners

Noted author Jim Cummins, one of the most highly respected authorities on language acquisition, outlines five key principles for success with ELLs in the content area classroom in *Accelerating the Progress of English Language Learners*.

- Models building content-specific lessons using teaching strategies
- Summarizes current research and best practices
- Provides an overview of language proficiency levels
- Introduces the techniques used in sheltered instruction that can be further developed through SIOP training

Develop an Instructional Framework
The SIOP® Model

Developed by Dr. Jana Echevarría, Dr. MaryEllen Vogt, and Dr. Deborah Short, the Sheltered Instruction Observation Protocol (SIOP®) Model is an empirically validated approach for implementing effective sheltered content instruction for students acquiring the English language.

- Offers teachers a model for lesson planning and implementation that provides English learners access to grade-level content
- Includes instructional components and features that have been found to improve ELLs academic achievement
- Develops practical skills to collaborate, share, and implement robust lesson plans that include language and content objectives for ELLs
- Provides frameworks for implementing SIOP in both the elementary and secondary classrooms and across content areas

Apply in Practice
Pearson A+RISE®
Aligned Research-based Instructional Strategies for ELLs

Created by award-winning educator and author Evelyn Arroyo, A+Rise® Strategy Cards and Standards2Strategy™ (S2S) online resource empowers K-12 educators with just-in-time teaching strategies to build academic language for ELLs and all students across content areas.

- Features research-based instructional strategies aligned to state and WIDA standards
- Presents strategies which are searchable by grade level, subject, literacy domains, and proficiency levels, within a powerful online teacher resource
- Supplies step-by-step directions for implementation and differentiation
- Offers a perfect complement to instructional frameworks such as the SIOP® Model

Visit **www.PearsonELL.com**
for more ELL support.